30/-

11/55
402

Date Due

JUL 28 9

THE
OXFORD ENGINEERING SCIENCE
SERIES

General Editors

E. B. MOULLIN   D. R. PYE   R. V. SOUTHWELL

THE OXFORD ENGINEERING SCIENCE SERIES

General Editors: E. B. MOULLIN, D. R. PYE, R. V. SOUTHWELL

RELAXATION METHODS
IN
THEORETICAL PHYSICS

A Continuation of the Treatise

RELAXATION METHODS
IN ENGINEERING SCIENCE

BY

R. V. SOUTHWELL

M.A., LL.D., F.R.S., For. Ass. U.S. Nat. Acad. Sci.

RECTOR OF THE IMPERIAL COLLEGE
OF SCIENCE AND TECHNOLOGY
HONORARY FELLOW OF BRASENOSE COLLEGE AND
FORMERLY PROFESSOR OF ENGINEERING SCIENCE
IN THE UNIVERSITY OF OXFORD

OXFORD
AT THE CLARENDON PRESS

Oxford University Press, Amen House, London E.C.4

GLASGOW NEW YORK TORONTO MELBOURNE WELLINGTON
BOMBAY CALCUTTA MADRAS CAPE TOWN

Geoffrey Cumberlege, Publisher to the University

FIRST EDITION 1946

Reprinted lithographically in Great Britain
at the UNIVERSITY PRESS, OXFORD, 1949, 1952
from sheets of the first edition

PREFACE

A SENTENCE in the preface to my *Relaxation Methods in Engineering Science* (1940) implied that a cognate treatise might some day follow: '. . . the trend of our most recent work has been towards problems in two dimensions, a field of less concern to engineering than to theoretical physics'. This second treatise is now presented, under a title meant to indicate at once a common standpoint and a shift of focus. Like the first it presumes the mathematical equipment of a graduate in engineering science.

It retains the essential feature of a tentative approach in which attention is fixed not on the wanted quantities but on the data of a problem, and the task of the computer is to bring unaccounted or 'residual' quantities within specified margins of uncertainty. But whereas the earlier book dealt with systems of finite freedom and with equations in one independent variable, this applies the same notions to partial differential equations involving two independent space-variables and to conditions which must be satisfied at a given 'boundary'. It thus concerns a wider class of readers, and I have tried to make it self-contained.

My task is not completed, for in recent papers Relaxation Methods have dealt successfully with problems of greater difficulty than those of which this volume treats. But the papers have still to be released from the restrictions of war-time secrecy, so may not yet be cited: therefore I have been urged to put out this basic material now, and to leave for a further volume such matters as the 'biharmonic equation' (cf. § 2), *eigenwerte* problems in two dimensions (e.g. the vibration of membranes and the stability of flat elastic plates), stresses in solids of revolution, problems in plasticity, and the complete equations of motion for a viscous fluid. When that final volume can be written, one of the chief merits of Relaxation Methods will appear; for then these harder problems (some of them quite intractable by orthodox methods) will be seen to yield to simple and direct extensions of the treatment here described.

My aim has been to present the underlying theory more consecutively, and in fuller detail, than is feasible in a series of discrete papers; to include some description of techniques which have been developed by my collaborators in the light of gained experience; and to indicate the all but revolutionary change of outlook which results when Relaxation Methods are substituted for 'orthodox' mathematics as an ancillary weapon of physical research. Though well aware that I set myself an almost impossible task in thus attempting to combine three separate purposes in a single work, I have not seen how any one can be dispensed with; and the Introduction will perhaps give guidance to readers having special interests.

I could have brought the book to publication sooner, but for wartime preoccupations: I should have incurred still further delay, had I attempted a general and exhaustive treatise. Accordingly *I have cited no book or paper that was not necessary to my argument*; and I emphasize the restriction, because some reviewers of my earlier book have drawn attention to work which it did not notice, notwithstanding that its preface made a like disclaimer. After years spent in developing a particular method I have no trust in my ability to assess other methods impartially; nor do I believe that a normal student, seeking to master a new technique, is helped by irrelevant digressions.

For errors which have escaped detection I am of course solely responsible; but I would acknowledge help received, in the checking of text and diagrams, both from the staff of the University Press and also from that small but zealous team of co-workers to whom is mainly due the rapid extension of Relaxation Methods in the past eight years. To that small band I dedicate a treatise which their labours have enabled me to write. Most have their names recorded in its Name Index: here I would mention specially the contribution of my daughter and secretary, whose accurate typing has greatly simplified my task.

R. V. S.

Rock, Cornwall
April 1945

CONTENTS

Figs. 25, 107, 117 face respectively pp. 74, 208, and 224; Figs. 84 *a*, *b*, *c*, 89–94, 108, 113, 114, and 116 are at the end of the book.

INTRODUCTION AND SUMMARY

THIS book extends to a different class of problems the outlook and methods of an earlier treatise, *Relaxation Methods in Engineering Science*. It has been given another title, partly on account of its different range of interest, but mainly for the sake of easier cross-reference. In it (usually) the earlier treatise will be cited by its abbreviated title *Rel. Meth. E. S.*

There, a method devised for the computation of stresses in frameworks was shown to have application to other problems in engineering science; it was applied to problems both of equilibrium and of vibration, and to systems both of limited and of unrestricted freedom (i.e. continuous solids). But the systems when continuous could be defined in terms of a single independent variable: *partial* differential equations were not considered, excepting some concerned with 'normal' vibrations from which the time-variable can be eliminated. It excluded problems involving two space-variables, such as are confronted in elasticity, hydrodynamics, and other branches of 'field physics'; merely noticing (in its final chapter) a few which had yielded to 'relaxational' attack.

Here, some two-dimensional problems are treated on lines which in detail differ from those of the earlier treatise, but like them are based upon the notion of 'systematic relaxation of constraints'. A technique is devised for solving (approximately) problems in plane-potential theory; then, by simple extensions of that technique, more complex problems are brought within its range. Again the standpoint is adopted that no problem is solved until, in the actual computations, only the first four rules of arithmetic are involved. But the same basic notion of 'systematic relaxation of constraints' leads now to a different procedure: in place of a table of standard operations, special to every joint in a structure or electrical network, one standard operation (normally) is derived from the specified governing equation; constraints are conceived to operate, no longer at specified 'joints', but at nodal points of a chosen lattice or 'net'; and a new feature is the existence of a boundary to the field of computation, which may have any specified shape, and at all points of which a specified boundary condition must be satisfied. Thereby we confront difficulties far greater than those entailed by terminal conditions in problems which involve only one space-variable. In fact, of the problems treated here (and more especially in Chapter VI) some are quite intractable by orthodox analysis.

'Orthodox' compared with Relaxation Methods

The reader will perhaps desire an explanation of what is meant by 'orthodox' analysis and what are held to be the distinctive features of the 'relaxational' alternative. *For both, the point of departure is a physical or engineering problem formulated in mathematical terms.* Such formulation is itself a problem, but it is one with which the computer (as such) has no concern: accepting the formulation, his task (in most of the problems which this book exemplifies†) is to determine a 'wanted function' which must satisfy (i) a specified 'governing equation' at every point within a specified boundary, and (ii) a specified condition at every point on that boundary. The governing equation may be typified by

$$\frac{\partial}{\partial x}\left(\chi\frac{\partial \psi}{\partial x}\right) + \frac{\partial}{\partial y}\left(\chi\frac{\partial \psi}{\partial y}\right) + Z = 0, \tag{1}$$

ψ denoting the 'wanted function' and χ and Z being specified functions of x and y; the 'boundary condition' by

$$\psi = 0, \quad \text{at every point on the boundary.} \tag{2}$$

Faced with this mathematical problem, 'orthodox' analysis applies to it the methods of pure mathematics: methods of wide variety which have this in common, that based as they are on purely abstract reasoning *they take no account of the inescapable uncertainty of physical data.* Their aims are the aims of pure mathematics—general and exact solutions. But the exactitude is illusory when, on account of this uncertainty, a problem cannot be precisely formulated; and they do not in fact achieve the wanted generality, being restricted (usually) to boundaries of simple geometrical shape.

For Relaxation Methods, on the contrary, the boundary shape has small importance: a problem solved for one could be solved for any. A price is paid in theoretical precision, firstly because they substitute for the specified 'governing equation' an approximation in which its differentials are replaced by finite differences, secondly because the approximation is not solved exactly. But the intervals of the finite differences can be made as small as we please (of course, at a cost in additional labour), so the first step need entail no serious error;

† Chapter VI deals with a special class of problem which need not concern us here.

and *the second feature entails no error that has meaning in a physical problem, since it is always possible to account for the data within their estimated margins of uncertainty.* This is the principle which differentiates the relaxational approach: it is implemented by a technique which fixes attention not on the wanted function but on the data of the problem, seeking to leave their unaccounted parts so small as to be comparable with errors of observation.† Given a relation in finite differences, it has to compute the wanted function, not (as in an orthodox treatment) at every point within the specified boundary, but at nodal points of an appropriate lattice or 'net'; and it does so by a systematic sequence of operations, each entailing localized alteration of the wanted function, which steadily reduces the magnitudes of quantities termed 'residuals', thereby accounting for the data more and more completely.

This is the essence of Relaxation Methods—the feature that has no parallel in an 'orthodox' attack. Their use of finite differences is not new, nor their evaluation of the wanted function at nodal points of a regular net. But in concentrating attention on the data, and in recognizing that these are never exact, they subordinate mathematical to physical aspects in a way that can alter drastically the course of a theoretical research. Discarding orthodox for relaxational methods, an investigator finds his outlook quite transformed: full scope remains for ingenuity and special artifice, but *any problem that can be formulated can be solved.* Such, at all events, are the indications of the past eight years; for by now almost all of the standard equations have been attacked, and none without success.

Contents of this volume

This book deals solely with problems governed by equations of the second order and (with certain exceptions treated in Chapter VI) by a single boundary condition. They, however, will suffice to indicate the power of Relaxation Methods, for they include several that hitherto have seemed intractable.

As has been said, the differential governing equation must be replaced by a finite-difference approximation, related with some regular lattice or 'net'. This, a problem in the Calculus of Finite Differences, is the concern of Chapter I, which moreover explains the meaning here attached to functions and to their determination.

† Thus stated, the principle seems to have been first applied in the 'Moment Distribution Method' of Hardy Cross (1924).

It derives standard formulae for approximate differentiation, integration, and interpolation, also finite-difference approximations to the more common operators. It is purely mathematical, and it makes no mention of 'systematic relaxation of constraints'.

That concept makes its first appearance in Chapter II, which starts by exemplifying the process known as 'reduction to non-dimensional form'. (The example is a case of Saint-Venant's torsion problem in which the exact solution is known.) It explains Prandtl's 'membrane analogue' of the governing equation, and it shows that a tensioned net is the corresponding analogue of the finite-difference approximation, therefore (being a mechanical system of finite freedom) permits the introduction of notions (e.g. 'operations' and 'liquidation') which were developed in *Rel. Meth. E. S.* But whereas in that treatise an 'Operations Table' was normally employed, here all 'unit operations' are identical and so can be represented by a single 'relaxation pattern'. The derivation and use of this are explained, and the chapter ends with some account of relaxation from a practical (computational) standpoint.

Chapter III deals with further problems of technique which are confronted normally, though not in the examples of Chapter II. Most of them concern the computer more than the general reader—who should, however, take note of the last part of the chapter, as showing that 'refraction' can be brought within the scope of Relaxation Methods. Its examples include the torsion problem in respect of 'hollow' sections, problems in which the boundary condition imposes values on the gradient of the wanted function, and problems relating to 'magnetic lines' in fields containing iron (where refraction occurs at the iron-air interface).

Using the technique thus far developed, a reader who has worked the set examples should be competent to deal with any ordinary problem in 'plane-potential theory'—that is, with any problem in which the governing equation has the form assumed by (1) *when* $\chi = 1$ *everywhere*. In particular he will have the means of dealing with the problem known to mathematicians as 'conformal transformation'; but this, as having wide importance, is given special notice in Chapter IV. Four standard types of transformation are distinguished, and an example of each is solved. They should be studied not only for their intrinsic interest, but as aids to the solution of harder problems.

When χ as well as Z is a function of position, (1) may be termed a 'quasi-plane-harmonic' equation; it is met in many problems of theoretical physics, some of which are exemplified in Chapter V. There, two classes of problem are distinguished: in the first, χ is specified initially; in the second, χ is additionally related with ψ by some other equation, so must be found along with ψ by computation. The first class presents no special difficulty, being tractable by a slight extension of the technique developed in Chapters II–III. The second (exemplified in Chapter V by problems of lubrication and of the flow of gases) entails a use of patterns that are modified as the solution proceeds. On this account their relaxational treatment entails much labour; but by orthodox methods they are normally intractable, mainly on account of the non-linearity of their governing equations.

Chapter VI deals with problems also intractable by orthodox methods, but of which the difficulty lies in their boundary conditions. They comprise the problem of allowing, in the theory of torsion, for the occurrence of *plastic* straining in a region initially undefined; and a further class of problem in which boundaries are not known initially, viz. 'free surface problems' in hydrodynamic theory. Chapters V and VI should have interest for every reader, since they exemplify the emergence of Relaxation Methods as an indispensable rather than a merely alternative weapon of research.

Throughout the book results are presented not in tables (as in *Rel. Meth. E. S.*) but in diagrams which record 'accepted values'† of the 'wanted function' at nodes of the relaxation net, also exhibit their trend by contours. Such presentation is essential in order that a solution may be put to practical use, and here too Relaxation Methods have an advantage over 'orthodox' methods of attack; for while the latter yield solutions that are formally exact, not uncommonly their practical interpretation is a task entailing no less computational labour than would have yielded solutions *ab initio* by the relaxation process.

Recommendations in regard to reading

Two classes of reader must be contemplated, and to cater for both simultaneously is not an easy task. The first, having already some

† i.e. values of which the errors are deemed to be negligible, having regard to the uncertainty of the physical data.

experience of research, will want such knowledge of Relaxation Methods as is needed in order to apply them to new problems, so must have not only their details but their underlying theory. The second, less well equipped mathematically, will want to apply the methods to other examples of problems already solved: such readers, content to take foundations for granted, will look for clear description of the processes they must employ. All are advised to start by reading the résumés which conclude the book's six chapters and (with the diagrams in which solutions are presented graphically) should afford clear indication of their scope.

Thereafter all should closely study Chapters I–III, for these contain the foundations of everything that follows. One point must be strongly emphasized: for apprehension of a practical technique (and 'relaxation' is a process no less practical than hand-scraping), reading is not enough, trial is essential. As was remarked by a reviewer of *Rel. Meth. E. S.*, a reader who would master Relaxation Methods 'must do the homework'; and only thereby will he come to realize how simple a process relaxation is in fact. Like all techniques that are best learned under supervision, it acquires a false complexity in the printed page; but a reader should find no difficulty in the detailed explanations of Examples I–VIII, and in solving these for himself he will come to see that harder problems, though they will entail more labour, must yield to a like attack.

Having the fundamental concepts, from subsequent chapters he may select for intensive study those parts in which he has particular interest. A diagram shows the nature of each solution, and any one can be checked at will. Though formulation is not the task of the computer, all who work with Relaxation Methods should endeavour to keep physical aspects in view; and on that account every example is preceded by a summary of its underlying theory. For brevity, the shortened title *Elasticity* is used in references to the author's *Introduction to the Theory of Elasticity* (second edition, 1941).

I

PRELIMINARY CONSIDERATIONS

1. IN Physics, thought like a pendulum swings continually between two opposite extremes: the thinking that would ascribe phenomena to the interaction of discrete particles or 'points of force'—e.g. the 'atomic' theories of Democritus and of Dalton, or modern atomic theory in its 'particle aspect'; and the thinking that would ascribe them to occurrences in a structureless *aether* or *continuum*—an outlook characteristic of nineteenth-century physics, and still exemplified in the 'wave-mechanics' of to-day. It is the fact that physicists, in recent years, have agreed to pursue both lines of thought concurrently, so that 'on Mondays, Wednesdays, and Fridays we use the wave theory, on Tuesdays, Thursdays, and Saturdays we think in streams of flying energy quanta or corpuscles';[†] but the fact does not conflict with our assertion that the lines are diametrically opposed.

They represent not so much a clash about fundamentals (for science cannot explain, but can only describe)[‡] as a search conditioned in any period by the intellectual equipment of the time. It is no new thing that both lines of approach should be pursued simultaneously, for in the nineteenth century there existed both a kinetic and a hydrodynamic theory of gases, solids were treated as having structure (by Boscovitch) and as *continua* (in Navier's equations). Finality is not attainable in science.

2. This book is concerned with Field Physics—i.e. with that development of science in which physical phenomena are explained on the basis of an assumed *continuum*; but it will employ what may be termed an 'atomic' treatment, assuming (with Lord Rayleigh in his *Theory of Sound*) that a finite number of coordinates will suffice to define for all practical purposes any configuration that a physical system can assume. Its aim is to bring within the scope of computation problems governed by partial differential equations which involve two independent space-variables.

[†] Sir W. H. Bragg, 23rd Robert Boyle Lecture (11 May 1921), p. 11 (Oxf. Univ. Press). Cf. article by K. Darrow in *Bell System Tech. J.*, July 1941.

[‡] 'For Newton, as for the best of his successors, science was concerned with the question of "How ?"; Descartes, like the ancients, was concerned with the insoluble question of a fundamental "Why ?".' (E. N. da C. Andrade at Newton Tercentenary celebrations, 1942. *Proc. Roy. Soc.* A, **181**, 230.)

It excludes consideration of equations into which time enters as an independent variable: as yet our methods have not been applied to these 'kinematic' problems, except indirectly as a means to the determination of normal modes of free vibration. Its problems call for an evaluation of some 'wanted function' at points within some specified region or 'domain': within that region the function must satisfy a specified 'governing equation', and on one or more closed curves which delimit the region it must satisfy appropriate 'boundary conditions'.

Such problems are confronted in several branches of theoretical physics. In the simplest, the wanted function (ψ, say) is governed by the **two-dimensional Laplace equation**

$$\nabla^2 \psi \equiv \frac{\partial^2 \psi}{\partial x^2} + \frac{\partial^2 \psi}{\partial y^2} = 0, \tag{1}$$

—i.e. computation must determine a **plane-harmonic function** satisfying an appropriate boundary condition. Harder problems entail the determination of **biharmonic functions** governed by equations of the form

$$\nabla^4 \psi = 0, \tag{2}$$

and as variants we have problems in which

$$\nabla^2 \psi + Z = 0 \tag{3}$$

and

$$\nabla^4 \psi = Z \tag{4}$$

replace (1) and (2), Z being a *specified* function of x and y. Other problems will present equations of which (3) is a special case—e.g. such equations as

$$\frac{\partial}{\partial x}\left(\chi \frac{\partial \psi}{\partial x}\right) + \frac{\partial}{\partial y}\left(\chi \frac{\partial \psi}{\partial y}\right) + Z = 0, \tag{5}$$

in which χ as well as Z is specified. Hardest of all are those of which the governing equations are not linear, so that solutions cannot be superposed; e.g. problems where χ, in (5), is additionally related with ψ and/or with its differentials. Biharmonic problems are not discussed in the present volume, which is restricted to the relaxational treatment of (1), (3), and (5).

Definition of a function from (1) the mathematical and (2) the experimental standpoint

3. We say that a quantity z is a function of two independent variables x and y, when with any pair of values x and y (or with any pair of values lying within some definite region or 'domain') there corresponds a definite value (or a definite sequence of values) for z; in other words, when the value of z depends upon the values of x and y. The dependence can be stated either mathematically in the form of an equation, viz.

$$\left.\begin{aligned} z &= F(x,y), \\ &= ax^2 + 2hxy + by^2 \text{ (for example)}, \end{aligned}\right\} \qquad (6)$$

or geometrically, by a surface such that the height of any point P above some datum plane represents z, and the other coordinates of P, namely x and y, are measured along two fixed directions in the datum plane.

The ordinary relief map is a familiar example, 'sea-level' being the datum plane;[†] and it will serve to illustrate a contention which underlies the whole argument of this book, that *nothing in our definition of a function requires the mathematical form of $F(x,y)$, in* (6), *to be known*. Clearly, according to that definition the height above sea-level of a point on a map (e.g.) of England is a function of its east–west and north–south coordinates x and y; but equally it is clear that the function cannot be presented in any concise equation.

When, as in the second of (6), a functional relation can be stated mathematically, then a relief map (or surface) can be constructed to represent it geometrically. (The wooden models used in teaching solid geometry are a familiar example.) But the converse operation is not always feasible: it can be done in some cases, but not in all. The point now emphasized is that from the standpoint of this book its feasibility is a question of no importance.

'Determination' of a function (1) in mathematics, (2) in experiment

4. It will be useful to consider, in this connexion, what operations are entailed in the construction of a 'relief map', whether geographical or intended to exhibit some physical 'law' not known to be representable by a mathematical equation. The first point needing emphasis is that in both instances the data must be obtained by physical measurement, *therefore can be neither exact nor complete.* Exact data are unobtainable, because all measurement is liable to error: complete data would include a measurement for every point in the domain, therefore could not be obtained in finite time.

---

† This statement presumes that the scale of the map is large enough to permit neglect of the Earth's curvature.

                                  B

Both of these statements would be true even though the wanted quantity were a function of a single variable—e.g. the curve of deflexion for a loaded beam, or some 'section' of a geographical relief map; but in two-dimensional problems the points at which measurement is possible are doubly instead of singly infinite in number, so the second limitation is correspondingly stringent. In the construction of two-dimensional relief maps, sketching and 'smoothing' play an indispensable part.

This being so, it is clear that 'determination' of a wanted function has in practical work a meaning very different from what it carries in orthodox mathematics, where a solution determines the wanted function at every point in a domain. From the practical standpoint a function is *sufficiently* determined when its values are known within tolerable margins of uncertainty and at a number of points which is large enough to define the trend of its values elsewhere. Precisely this standpoint is adopted in the gauging of curved surfaces in engineering workshops: we cannot measure the height of every point above the reference plane, but we can and do make measurements at a number of points judged in the light of experience to be sufficient.

The 'Relaxation Net'

5. Throughout this book the practical standpoint will be adopted in respect of purely theoretical computation; i.e. we shall regard our task as completed when the wanted function has been evaluated at a large number of chosen points within the specified domain. To facilitate the computation of contours we arrange these points on a regular lattice or 'net', so that on straight lines drawn in various directions we have series of computed values equally spaced. Every mesh of the net will usually be similar to every other, and special interest will attach to meshes having the shapes of *regular polygons*. Only three shapes satisfy both requirements—namely, the square and the equilateral triangle or hexagon.† These are indicated in Fig. 1, together with the number (N) of meshes which adjoin at any one point, and the number (k) of sides in any one mesh. The mesh-side (i.e. the standard distance between adjacent points) we shall denote by a.

Later, in propounding techniques by which the wanted values may

† The condition requires that $2\pi/N$ shall be the internal angle of a regular polygon: i.e. (Fig. 1) that $N-2 = 4/(k-2)$, where N and k ($\not< 3$) are integral.

be found within known margins of error, we shall view these lattices more realistically, as nets of tensioned strings which sustain transverse forces in virtue of appropriate deflexions from the plane. On that account we shall term them **relaxation nets** and refer to the sides of their hexagonal, square, or triangular meshes as **strings,** the junctions of their strings as **nodal points.** Usually, by converting

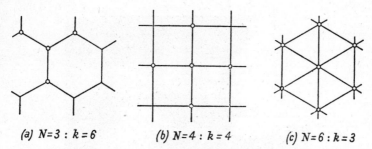

(a) N=3 : k = 6   (b) N=4 : k = 4   (c) N=6 : k = 3

Fig. 1. Types of Relaxation Net.

our governing equations into 'non-dimensional' form we shall make the **mesh-side** a (defined above) representable by a pure number independent of the choice of units. Our techniques will provide for steadily increasing accuracy, attainable at the cost of proportionately increased labour; and to this end they will utilize results obtained on one size of net as a starting assumption in relation to a net of smaller mesh. This device will be termed **advance to a finer net:** its details are explained in §§ 49–53.

6. In practice it matters little whether we regard a solution as giving actual values of the wanted function at the nodal points or as giving its mean values in areas which surround those points. Adopting the second standpoint, we find a parallel in the 'half-tone process' whereby photographs are reproduced in printed papers. Analysed with the aid of a low-power magnifying glass, these are seen to consist of discontinuous dots, lines, and crosses whereby the correct amount of light is reflected from each of a large but limited number of small squares into which the whole area is divided (Fig. 2). Even with the use of coarse 'screens' (i.e. when the squares are fairly large) a surprising amount of detail can thus be reproduced.

Figs. 3 pursue this notion somewhat further. They are due to Mr. A. N. Black, who employed a travelling microscope to analyse part of a half-tone reproduction taken from a newspaper. Each elemental square was viewed in turn, and an estimate made and recorded of that fraction of its area which was 'black' (i.e. inked): then, from the record of these numerical estimates, a diagram was constructed on squared paper to have the same fractions inked of its corresponding squares. No particular convention was adopted— the inked fraction might have any shape or position in its square;

FIG. 2. (Photograph by V. Belfield.)

but viewed from an appropriate distance the resulting diagram (Fig. 3 c) reproduces with fidelity both the details and the general quality of the original photograph. No function wanted in mathematical physics is likely to be more complex.

Subsequently, to reproduce the effects of coarser screens, the estimates were averaged over larger squares comprising successively four and sixteen of the original squares, and in the subsequent reconstruction all of the small squares in any one of these 'unit squares' were 'blacked' to the same fractional amount—namely, the average recorded for that square. Figs. 3, a and b, are typical results: they too, viewed from suitable distances, are recognizable reproductions of the original photograph. (The numbered squares indicate the relative sizes of the squares in the averaging process. The numbers are proportional to the fractions which were blacked.)

Considering all three diagrams, now in the order left to right, we see the nature of the process termed (§ 5) 'advance to a finer net'. Fig. 3 a (the coarsest net) records the main features only of the distribution of light and shade; in Fig. 3 b the salient details of that distribution are exhibited; in Fig. 3 c enough detail has been recaptured to make it hardly profitable to refine further.

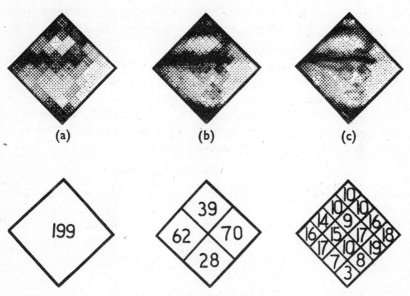

(a)   (b)   (c)

FIGS. 3. (Photograph by V. Belfield.)

Basic assumptions in the Calculus of Finite Differences

7. Reverting to § 5, suppose that we have completed our task and have attached a value to the wanted function at every nodal point in the domain. Then from the standpoint of § 4 the function is *sufficiently* determined, because by interpolation we can find its values elsewhere within narrow margins of uncertainty. But this is on the tacit assumption that the function is 'smooth'. No intermediate value can be excluded positively, as inconsistent with our specification: all that we can say is that 'peak' values are unlikely.

Now it is a familiar difficulty of graphical constructions that uncertainties in regard to the shape of a curve become magnified in relation to its slopes, and are still more serious as regards its higher differentials. On this account numerical methods are obligatory when (as will often happen in the problems to be studied in this book) second or higher differentials of the wanted function must be evaluated. We are faced with one of the basic problems in the Calculus of Finite Differences, and a brief account must now be given of the methods there adopted for its solution.

8. Clearly, in order that a function may be differentiated its values must be known not only at selected points but at all intermediate points in the range with which we are concerned. Wanting this fuller knowledge, we are compelled to make some assumption, and it is reasonable to identify the wanted function with the 'smoothest' function (i.e. the function having fewest higher differentials) which is consistent with the data.

Suppose that y, a function of the independent variable x, is required to have the values $y_0, y_1,..., y_n$ when x has the values 0, a, $2a,..., na$; and consider the functions defined by†

$$F(x) = x(x-a)(x-2a)...(x-na),$$
$$f_0(x) = \frac{F(x)}{x}, \quad f_1(x) = \frac{F(x)}{x-a}, \quad ..., \quad f_k(x) = \frac{F(x)}{x-ka}, \quad ..., \text{ etc.} \quad \right\} (7)$$

When $x = ka$, all of the f's vanish except $f_k(x)$, which has the value

$$a^n \times k(k-1)...2.1.-1.-2....(k-n)$$
$$= (-1)^{n-k}k!\,(n-k)!\,a^n = p_k a^n \quad \text{(say)}. \tag{8}$$

Consequently the function

$$y = \frac{1}{a^n}\left[y_0 \frac{f_0(x)}{p_0} + y_1 \frac{f_1(x)}{p_1} + ... + y_n \frac{f_n(x)}{p_n} \right] \tag{9}$$

satisfies the imposed requirements, and from (7) we see that it is a **polynomial** in x of degree n, i.e. an expression of the form

$$y = c_0 + c_1 x + c_2 x^2/2! + ... + c_n x^n/n! \tag{10}$$

in which each of the $(n+1)$ quantities $c_0, c_1,..., c_n$ is constant.

Differentiating (10) we obtain successively polynomial expressions of degree $n-1$, $n-2,...$, etc., for $\frac{dy}{dx}, \frac{d^2y}{dx^2},...$, etc. Thus all the differentials of (9) are continuous and have finite values (x being finite) in the range considered; the nth differential $d^n y/dx^n$ has a constant value (independent of x), and all higher differentials are zero. We have shown that a polynomial of the nth degree is necessary

† Such functions are termed *factorials*.

when y is required to assume specified values at $n+1$ points: consequently (9) satisfies our requirement (stated above) of the smoothest possible function which is consistent with the data.[†]

Limitations of the Calculus of Finite Differences

9. Representation by polynomials is (Ref. 11, § 8) the most fundamental of the assumptions underlying the Calculus of Finite Differences, which explores its consequences as these relate to interpolation, differentiation, integration, etc. But it should be remarked that y as given by (10), and its differentials of all orders up to the $(n-1)$th, tend to infinity with x. This fact should be a warning against undue reliance on any derived formulae for extrapolation to points outside the range of the specified values, or on formulae of differentiation close to either end of the range.

Any function likely to occur in physical problems will be expressible in a series of positive integral powers of the independent variable (i.e. a Taylor series) *within some finite range of this variable measured from some particular point*; but that range may not embrace the whole range in which we are interested, and in consequence it will often happen that better representation can be attained by waiving the requirement that *all* differentials of the representing function must be continuous. Such complete continuity is rarely predicable on physical grounds: thus the curve assumed by a continuous girder resting on several supports has the feature that all differentials up to the second are continuous (i.e. its ordinate, slope, and curvature), but its third and higher differentials have (in general) discontinuities at the points of support.

By imposing the requirement of complete continuity, the Calculus of Finite Differences obliges us to use a polynomial of order n in order that the representing curve may pass through all of $n+1$ specified points, and it leads to formulae of increasing complexity in taking more and more points into account. For reasons which have been indicated, *these formulae do not necessarily yield results of increasing accuracy*. Thus as a means to computation of the definite integral

$$4 \int_0^1 \frac{dx}{1+x^2} = \pi = 3\cdot14159265\ldots$$

[†] In this argument the points are assumed to be equally spaced. The assumption is not necessary: cf. § 21.

the '4-strip formula' of integration given by Bickley (cf. § 23) is less accurate than the '2-strip formula' (Simpson's rule): the first gives an answer $3 \cdot 14212$, whereas the second, with the range divided only into 4 parts, gives the answer $3 \cdot 14157$ (Ref. 5, § 9).

It is important that a reader should have these limitations in mind when he comes, in later chapters, to applications of the Calculus of Finite Differences: otherwise he may incur heavy labour in attempting an accuracy which in fact is not realizable. For the present, however (that is, for the remainder of this chapter), we shall pursue the logical consequences of the polynomial assumption.

Formulae for approximate differentiation

10. The degree of a polynomial is not altered when x is replaced by $(x+\text{const.})$, so the origin $(x = 0)$ in (10) may be identified with any one of the datum points. Then *at that point* we have

$$y = c_0, \qquad \frac{dy}{dx} = c_1, \quad ..., \quad \frac{d^k y}{dx^k} = c_k, \quad ..., \quad \frac{d^n y}{dx^n} = c_n, \qquad (11)$$

differentials of higher order than the nth being zero as we have seen already. Since (10) is equivalent to (9), by comparison of coefficients we can express each of c_0, c_1,..., c_n in terms of y_0, y_1,..., y_n: therefore at every datum point every differential of y can be expressed in terms of y_0, y_1,..., y_n, and a, with numerical coefficients.

We now state without proof some expressions of this kind which will be wanted later.

Range of 3 points ($n = 2$: i.e. y_0, y_1, y_2 specified):

$$\left. a\left(\frac{dy}{dx}\right)_0 = \frac{1}{2!}(-3y_0+4y_1-y_2), \atop a\left(\frac{dy}{dx}\right)_1 = \frac{1}{2!}(-y_0+y_2), \atop a\left(\frac{dy}{dx}\right)_2 = \frac{1}{2!}(y_0-4y_1+3y_2). \right\} \qquad (12)$$

$$a^2\left(\frac{d^2y}{dx^2}\right)_{0,1,2} = y_0-2y_1+y_2. \qquad (13)$$

(The second of (12) will be recognized as a well-known first approximation, also (13) in relation to the value of d^2y/dx^2 at the central point 1. Since $n = 2$ for a range of only 3 datum points, it was to be expected from the last of (11) that the polynomial approximation would give a constant value to d^2y/dx^2.)

Range of 4 points ($n = 3$: i.e. y_0, y_1, y_2, y_3 specified):

$$a\left(\frac{dy}{dx}\right)_0 = \frac{1}{3!}(-11y_0+18y_1-9y_2+2y_3),$$

$$a\left(\frac{dy}{dx}\right)_1 = \frac{1}{3!}(-2y_0-3y_1+6y_2-y_3),$$

$$a\left(\frac{dy}{dx}\right)_2 = \frac{1}{3!}(y_0-6y_1+3y_2+2y_3),$$

$$a\left(\frac{dy}{dx}\right)_3 = \frac{1}{3!}(-2y_0+9y_1-18y_2+11y_3),$$

(14)

$$a^2\left(\frac{d^2y}{dx^2}\right)_0 = 2y_0-5y_1+4y_2-y_3,$$

$$a^2\left(\frac{d^2y}{dx^2}\right)_1 = y_0-2y_1+y_2,$$

$$a^2\left(\frac{d^2y}{dx^2}\right)_2 = y_1-2y_2+y_3,$$

$$a^2\left(\frac{d^2y}{dx^2}\right)_3 = -y_0+4y_1-5y_2+2y_3,$$

(15)

$$a^3\left(\frac{d^3y}{dx^3}\right)_{0,1,2,3} = -y_0+3y_1-3y_2+y_3.$$

(16)

(The second and third of (15) will be seen to be identical with (13), but d^2y/dx^2 now varies slightly from point to point, and corresponding changes appear in the expressions for dy/dx. These are further consequences of the polynomial assumption.)

Bickley's tables for approximate differentiation

11. These formulae have been abstracted from tables given by W. G. Bickley (Ref. 2) which cover values of n from 2 to 6 (inclusive), also 8 and 10, and which give the 'error' (E) of every formula. E occurs for the reason that a function $y = f(x)$ has been replaced by a polynomial approximation of type (10), and it is normally a multiple of $a^{n+1}\dfrac{d^{n+1}}{dx^{n+1}}f(X)$, where X is some (unspecified) value of x between x_0 and x_n. Bickley uses h, in place of a, for the interval between adjacent datum points: in our notation, his formula for the mth differential of y at the $(p+1)$th datum point (i.e. at a distance pa from the left-hand end of the range) is

$$\frac{a^m}{m!}\left(\frac{d^my}{dx^m}\right)_{x=pa} = \frac{1}{n!}(A_0y_0+A_1y_1+...+A_ny_n)+E,$$

(17)

E and A_0, A_1,..., A_n having values as given in Tables I–VII.†
The reader can easily become conversant with the application of
these tables by using them to check the formulae (12)–(16), § 10.

He can also test their accuracy by means of Maclaurin's series, substituting
for y_1, y_2,..., y_n in (17) from

$$y_k = y_0 + ka\left(\frac{dy}{dx}\right)_0 + \frac{(ka)^2}{2!}\left(\frac{d^2y}{dx^2}\right)_0 + \frac{(ka)^3}{3!}\left(\frac{d^3y}{dx^3}\right)_0 + \dots \text{ etc.,} \qquad \text{(i)}$$

and for $\left(\frac{d^my}{dx^m}\right)_{x=ka}$ its similar expression

$$\left(\frac{d^my}{dx^m}\right)_{x=ka} = \left(\frac{d^my}{dx^m}\right)_0 + ka\left(\frac{d^{m+1}y}{dx^{m+1}}\right)_0 + \frac{(ka)^2}{2!}\left(\frac{d^{m+2}y}{dx^{m+2}}\right)_0 + \dots \text{ etc.} \qquad \text{(ii)}$$

Thus according to (17) and Table III

$$\frac{a^3}{3!}\left(\frac{d^3y}{dx^3}\right)_{x=2a} = \frac{1}{4!}(-2y_0 + 4y_1 - 4y_3 + 2y_4) + \left[E = -\frac{a^5}{24}\left(\frac{d^5y}{dx^5}\right)_{x=X}\right], \qquad \text{(iii)}$$

and we have from (i)

$$4y_1 = 4\left(y_0 + ay_0' + \frac{a^2}{2!}y_0'' + \frac{a^3}{3!}y_0''' + \frac{a^4}{4!}y_0^{iv} + \frac{a^5}{5!}y_0^{v} + \dots\right),$$

$$-4y_3 = -4\left(y_0 + 3ay_0' + 9\frac{a^2}{2!}y_0'' + 27\frac{a^3}{3!}y_0''' + 81\frac{a^4}{4!}y_0^{iv} + 243\frac{a^5}{5!}y_0^{v} + \dots\right), \qquad \text{(iv)}$$

$$2y_4 = 2\left(y_0 + 4ay_0' + 16\frac{a^2}{2!}y_0'' + 64\frac{a^3}{3!}y_0''' + 256\frac{a^4}{4!}y_0^{iv} + 1024\frac{a^5}{5!}y_0^{v} + \dots\right),$$

dashes denoting differentiations with respect to x. Adding $-2y_0$ to (iv), we
find that the first term on the right of (iii)

$$= \frac{a^3}{3!}y_0''' + 8\frac{a^4}{4!}y_0^{iv} + 45\frac{a^5}{5!}y_0^{v} + \dots, \text{ etc.,} \qquad \text{(v)}$$

and according to (ii)

$$\left(\frac{d^3y}{dx^3}\right)_2 = y_0''' + 2ay_0^{iv} + \frac{(2a)^2}{2!}y_0^{v} + \dots, \text{ etc.} \qquad \text{(vi)}$$

So (iii) is verified, E being shown to have the expression

$$-\frac{a^5}{24}y_0^{v}\dots, \text{ etc.}$$

Finite-difference approximations to some common operators

12. We have now dealt with the problem, propounded in § 7, of
computing differentials of the wanted function. Finite-difference
formulae for interpolation and for integration will be given later.

The accuracy with which (assuming y to be represented by a poly-

† Tables I–VII, being of general application, are placed at the end of this book:
they have been abstracted by permission (with slight changes of notation as explained
above) from Ref. 2. Table V is identical with Table XXXIX of *Rel. Meth. E. S.*
In a later paper (*Phil. Mag.* 33 (1942), 1–14) Bickley and Miller have given 'ended
formulae' which permit more accurate estimation of derivatives near the extremities
of a range.

nomial) we can estimate dy/dx, d^2y/dx^2, etc., depends upon the number of points in the range of x at which y is specified: two points are sufficient for an estimation of dy/dx, three for an estimation of

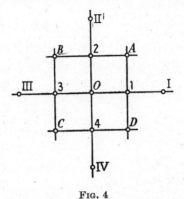

FIG. 4

d^2y/dx^2, and so on. Referring to Fig. 4, we have from (12)–(16) and Table III, as the simplest formula which is available in each instance,

$$\left(\frac{\partial w}{\partial x}\right)_0 \approx \frac{1}{2a}(w_1-w_3),$$

$$\left(\frac{\partial^2 w}{\partial x^2}\right)_0 \approx \frac{1}{a^2}(w_1+w_3-2w_0),$$

$$\left(\frac{\partial^3 w}{\partial x^3}\right)_0 \approx \frac{1}{2a^3}(-w_{III}+2w_3-2w_1+w_I),$$

$$\left(\frac{\partial^4 w}{\partial x^4}\right)_0 \approx \frac{1}{a^4}(w_{III}-4w_3+6w_0-4w_1+w_I).$$

$$(18)$$

We have replaced the ordinary differentials in (12)–(16) by partial derivatives in (18), because we want now to extend our results to functions of two variables. Corresponding with (18) we have (again in relation to Fig. 4)

$$\left(\frac{\partial w}{\partial y}\right)_0 \approx \frac{1}{2a}(w_2-w_4),$$

$$\left(\frac{\partial^2 w}{\partial y^2}\right)_0 \approx \frac{1}{a^2}(w_2+w_4-2w_0),$$

$$\left(\frac{\partial^3 w}{\partial y^3}\right)_0 \approx \frac{1}{2a^3}(w_{II}-2w_2+2w_4-w_{IV}),$$

$$\left(\frac{\partial^4 w}{\partial y^4}\right)_0 \approx \frac{1}{a^4}(w_{II}-4w_2+6w_0-4w_4+w_{IV}).$$

$$(19)$$

13. Equations (18) and (19) give the simplest finite-difference approximations to some common operators. From them other approximations can be deduced: thus according to the first of (18) we have (replacing w by $\partial w/\partial y$)

$$2a\left(\frac{\partial^2 w}{\partial x \partial y}\right)_0 = \left(\frac{\partial w}{\partial y}\right)_1 - \left(\frac{\partial w}{\partial y}\right)_3, \tag{i}$$

and from Fig. 4 we have, by analogy with the first of (19),

$$\left.\begin{aligned} 2a\left(\frac{\partial w}{\partial y}\right)_1 &= w_A - w_D, \\ 2a\left(\frac{\partial w}{\partial y}\right)_3 &= w_B - w_C; \end{aligned}\right\} \tag{ii}$$

then from (i) and (ii) we have

$$4a^2\left(\frac{\partial^2 w}{\partial x \partial y}\right)_0 = w_A - w_B + w_C - w_D, \tag{20}$$

when the positions of A, B, C, D, relative to O, are as shown in Fig. 4.

The Laplacian operator ∇^2

14. A finite-difference approximation to the operator

$$\nabla^2 \equiv \frac{\partial^2}{\partial x^2} + \frac{\partial^2}{\partial y^2}, \tag{21}$$

which governs the wanted function in Laplace's equation (1), § 2, can be deduced from the second of (18) and of (19). These yield

$$a^2(\nabla^2\psi)_0 \equiv a^2\left\{\left(\frac{\partial^2\psi}{\partial x^2}\right)_0 + \left(\frac{\partial^2\psi}{\partial y^2}\right)_0\right\} \approx \psi_1 + \psi_2 + \psi_3 + \psi_4 - 4\psi_0 \tag{22}$$

as a suitable approximation for use with a net of square mesh ($N = 4$, § 5).

15. The same result can be attained by a somewhat different approach, and can, moreover, be generalized so as to be applicable to nets of hexagonal or triangular mesh ($N = 3$ or 6, § 5). We saw in § 8 that a polynomial function of x can be formulated to have specified values at any number of selected or datum points, equally spaced: in § 21 this result is generalized, and it is shown that a polynomial function of x and y can be formulated to have specified values at any number of points (not necessarily separated by equal distances) in a specified domain. As before a polynomial, being an essentially 'smooth' function, may be accepted as the wanted function (**w**, say); i.e. we may identify $\mathbf{w} \equiv f(x, y)$ with w, a polynomial function of x and y.

Now expressing x and y in polar coordinates r, θ, we can apply known trigonometrical relations to obtain

$$w = A_0(r) + \sum_n [A_n(r)\cos n\theta + B_n(r)\sin n\theta], \tag{23}$$

in which n (in general) has all integral values; and because the original polynomial contained no negative powers of x and y, it will follow that $A_n(r)$ and $B_n(r)$ involve no power of r lower than the nth. Each, in fact, has the form

$$r^n \times (\text{polynomial in } r^2). \tag{24}$$

16. Expressed in polar coordinates, the operator†

$$\nabla^2 \equiv \frac{\partial^2}{\partial r^2} + \frac{1}{r}\frac{\partial}{\partial r} + \frac{1}{r^2}\frac{\partial^2}{\partial \theta^2}: \tag{25}$$

consequently we have according to (23)

$$\nabla^2 w = A_0'' + \frac{A_0'}{r} + \sum_n \left[\left(A_n'' + \frac{1}{r}A_n' - \frac{n^2}{r^2}A_n \right)\cos n\theta + \right.$$
$$\left. + \left(B_n'' + \frac{1}{r}B_n' - \frac{n^2}{r^2}B_n \right)\sin n\theta \right], \tag{26}$$

dashes denoting differentiations with respect to r. Now let $\sum_{a,N} (w)$ stand for the sum of the values assumed by w at N points equally spaced on the circle $r = a$, so as to have angular positions β, $\beta + \alpha$, $\beta + 2\alpha, ..., \beta + (N-1)\alpha$, where $\alpha = 2\pi/N$. Then according to (23)

$$\sum_{a,N} (w) = NA_0(a) + \sum_n [\{A_n(a)\cos n\beta + B_n(a)\sin n\beta\} \times$$
$$\times \{1 + \cos n\alpha + ... + \cos(N-1)n\alpha\} +$$
$$+ \{B_n(a)\cos n\beta - A_n(a)\sin n\beta\}\{0 + \sin n\alpha + ... + \sin(N-1)n\alpha\}]$$
$$= NA_0(a) + \sum_n \left[\frac{\sin \frac{1}{2}Nn\alpha}{\sin \frac{1}{2}n\alpha}\{\cos \frac{1}{2}(N-1)n\alpha[A_n(a)\cos n\beta + B_n(a)\sin n\beta] + \right.$$
$$\left. + \sin \frac{1}{2}(N-1)n\alpha[B_n(a)\cos n\beta - A_n(a)\sin n\beta]\} \right], \tag{27}$$

by known formulae in trigonometry. Since $N\alpha = 2\pi$ and n is integral, the quantity in the summation will be zero unless $\sin \frac{1}{2}n\alpha$ vanishes,—that is, unless $n\alpha$ is some integral multiple of 2π: in that

† Cf. (e.g.) *Elasticity*, § 240.

event n is an integral multiple of N, and the quantity takes the value $N\{A_n(a)\cos n\beta + B_n(a)\sin n\beta\}$. Consequently

$$\frac{1}{N}\sum_{a,N}(w) = A_0(a) + A_N(a)\cos N\beta + A_{2N}(a)\cos 2N\beta + ... + \\ + B_N(a)\sin N\beta + B_{2N}(a)\sin 2NB + ..., \quad \text{etc.,} \quad (28)$$

N being the number of points at which values of w are taken. In particular, if $\beta = 0$ then

$$\frac{1}{N}\sum_{a,N}(w) = A_0(a) + A_N(a) + A_{2N}(a) + ..., \quad \text{etc.,} \quad (29)$$

and if $\beta = \frac{1}{2}\alpha$, so that $N\beta = \pi$, then

$$\frac{1}{N}\sum_{a,N}(w) = A_0(a) - A_N(a) + A_{2N}(a) - ..., \quad \text{etc.} \quad (30)$$

We have seen that $A_N(a)$ is a polynomial in a of degree not less than N. Consequently the neglected terms will be of order a^N at least if we replace (29) by the approximate equation

$$\frac{1}{N}\sum_{a,N}(w) = A_0(a). \quad (31)$$

17. Now consider the expression (26). As stated in (24), the terms of lowest order in $A_n(r)$, $B_n(r)$ involve r^n and r^{n+2}. Also

$$\left[\frac{d^2}{dr^2} + \frac{1}{r}\frac{d}{dr} - \frac{n^2}{r^2}\right]r^n = 0,$$

$$\left[\frac{d^2}{dr^2} + \frac{1}{r}\frac{d}{dr} - \frac{n^2}{r^2}\right]r^{n+2} = 4(n+1)r^n$$

$$= 0 \text{ when } r = 0, \text{ if } n > 0,$$

and according to (24) we may write

$$A_0(r) = c_0 + c_2 r^2 + c_4 r^4 + ..., \quad (32)$$

in which c_0, c_2,..., etc., have constant values. Consequently when $r = 0$ we have

$$\nabla^2 w = A_0'' + \frac{A_0'}{r} = 4c_2, \quad (33)$$

and a similar argument will show (since all of $\nabla^2 w$, $\nabla^4 w$,..., etc., have polynomial expressions in x and y) that at the origin

$$\left.\begin{array}{l} \nabla^4 w = 4.16.c_4, \\ \nabla^6 w = 2^2.4^2.6^2.c_6, \\ ..., \quad \text{etc.} \end{array}\right\} \quad (34)$$

Finally, at the origin we have from (23), (24), and (32)

$$w = c_0. \tag{35}$$

Substituting these values for c_0, c_2,..., etc. in (32) we find that

$$A_0(r) = w_0 + \frac{r^2}{4}(\nabla^2 w)_0 + \frac{r^4}{64}(\nabla^4 w)_0 + \frac{r^6}{2^2.4^2.6^2}(\nabla^6 w)_0 + ..., \text{ etc.,}$$

and it follows that the approximate relation (31) may be replaced by

$$\frac{1}{N}\sum_{a,N}(w) - w_0 = \frac{a^2}{4}(\nabla^2 w)_0 + \frac{a^4}{64}(\nabla^4 w)_0 + \frac{a^6}{2^2.4^2.6^2}(\nabla^6 w)_0 + ..., \text{ etc. } \tag{36}$$

18. Already, in substituting (31) for (30), we have (cf. §16) neglected terms of order a^N: therefore it is useless to retain terms of this or higher order on the right-hand side of (36), but within this restriction we can proceed to find expressions for $(\nabla^2 w)_0$,..., etc.

As explained in § 5, in our investigations the selected points will lie on some regular lattice, or 'net', such that the summation $\sum_{a,N}$ can be effected at each and all; and by similar reasoning we can derive relations similar to (36), viz.

$$\left. \begin{aligned} \frac{1}{N}\sum_{a,N}(\nabla^2 w) - (\nabla^2 w)_0 &= \frac{a^2}{4}(\nabla^4 w)_0 + \frac{a^4}{64}(\nabla^6 w)_0 + ..., \\ \frac{1}{N}\sum_{a,N}(\nabla^4 w) - (\nabla^4 w)_0 &= \frac{a^2}{4}(\nabla^6 w)_0 + \frac{a^4}{64}(\nabla^8 w)_0 + ..., \\ ...,\ \text{etc.} & \end{aligned} \right\} \tag{37}$$

N may have any of the values 3, 4, or 6, but higher values are not admissible (cf. § 5): therefore it is useless to retain in (36) terms which involve a^6 or higher powers of a. But with an error of order a^N (at worst) in each case we have, from (36) combined with (37),

for $N = 3$ or 4:
$$\frac{1}{N}\sum_{a,N}(w) - w = \frac{a^2}{4}(\nabla^2 w); \tag{38}$$

for $N = 6$:
$$\frac{1}{N}\sum_{a,N}(w) - w = \frac{a^2}{4}\left[\nabla^2 w + \frac{1}{4}\left\{\frac{1}{N}\sum_{a,N}(\nabla^2 w) - \nabla^2 w\right\}\right]$$
$$= \frac{a^2}{16}\left[3\nabla^2 w + \frac{1}{N}\sum_{a,N}(\nabla^2 w)\right]. \tag{39}$$

Suffixes have been deleted as no longer necessary.

Having regard to the meaning of $\sum_{a,N}$ (§ 16), we see that when $N = 4$ (i.e. for a net of square mesh) equation (38) is equivalent to

$$a^2(\nabla^2 w)_0 = w_1 + w_2 + w_3 + w_4 - 4w_0, \tag{40}$$

when the relative positions of 0, 1, 2, 3, 4 are as given in Fig. 4. We have thus arrived by different reasoning at a result identical with (22) of §14; and we also have, in (38) and (39), corresponding approximations for use with hexagonal and with triangular nets ($N = 3$ and 6). The formula (39), in which the error is of order a^6 at least, has closer approximation than (38), in which the error is of order a^3 (for a hexagonal) or a^4 (for a square-mesh net).

Initial correction of Z in the governing equation $\nabla^2 w + Z = 0$

19. Laplace's equation (1), § 2, may be regarded as a special case ($Z = 0$) of **Poisson's equation**

$$\nabla^2 w + Z = 0, \tag{41}$$

in which Z is a specified function of x and y. In this book the same technique will be applied to both equations. It will entail, first, replacement of (41) by an approximation involving finite differences, secondly, satisfaction of this substituted equation, *approximately*, by a relaxation process. The first step is the concern of the present chapter.

Working on some regular 'net' as described in § 5, we can compute the value of Z for every nodal point. Then, if the net is hexagonal or square, we have to satisfy at all interior points the relation

$$\frac{1}{N} \sum_{a,N} (w) - w + \frac{a^2}{4} Z = 0, \tag{42}$$

which comes from (38) and (41). If, on the other hand, we would take full advantage of the closer approximation shown (§ 18) to be a characteristic of triangular nets ($N = 6$), then the relation to be satisfied is either

$$\sum_{a,6} (w) - 6w + 6\left[\frac{a^2}{4} Z + \frac{a^4}{64} (\nabla^2 Z)\right] = 0, \tag{43}$$

which comes (with an error of order a^6 at least) from (36) and (41), or

$$\sum_{a,6} (w) - 6w + \frac{a^2}{16}[18Z + \sum_{a,6} (Z)] = 0, \tag{44}$$

which comes from (39) and (41), and has a like approximation.

20. The introduction of $\nabla^2 Z$ in (43), and the parallel introduction of $\sum\limits_{a,6} (Z)$ in (44), recall the device described in *Elasticity*, § 191, and there termed **initial modification of the specified loading**. The relation between the ('non-dimensional') loading $W(z)$ and the consequent bending-moment $\mu(z)$ in a straight beam having the direction z—namely,

$$\frac{d^2}{dz^2}\mu(z) = -W(z) \tag{i}$$

—may be replaced for the purpose of approximate numerical computation by

$$\mu_1 - 2\mu_0 + \mu_3 = -h^2 W_0, \tag{ii}$$

when the relative positions of the sections numbered 1, 0, 3 are as in Fig. 4, and when h (instead of a as used in this chapter) denotes the distance between 1 and 0 and between 0 and 3. But the left-hand side of (ii) is in fact equivalent to the value of

$$2\left[\frac{h^2}{2!}\mu''(z) + \frac{h^4}{4!}\mu^{\mathrm{iv}}(z) + \frac{h^6}{6!}\mu^{\mathrm{vi}}(z) + ..., \text{ etc.}\right] \tag{iii}$$

at the section 0, dashes denoting differentiations with respect to z; consequently in satisfying (ii) we are in fact satisfying the equation

$$-W(z) = \mu''(z) + \frac{2h^2}{4!}\mu^{\mathrm{iv}}(z) + \frac{2h^4}{6!}\mu^{\mathrm{vi}}(z) + ..., \text{ etc.}$$

which is equivalent to

$$-W(z) = -\left[W(z) + \frac{2h^2}{4!}W''(z) + \frac{2h^2}{6!}W^{\mathrm{iv}}(z) + ..., \text{ etc.}\right]$$

$$= -\mathbf{W}(z), \text{ say,}$$

when $\mu(z)$ is an exact solution of (i).

Thus (ii) as it stands will not yield an exact solution. If on the other hand $W(z)$ in (ii) is replaced by $\mathbf{W}(z)$ *at the outset*, then our computed values of $\mu(z)$ will be exact. In (43) and (44) we have introduced a similar modification of Z.

Generalization of the theorem (§ 8) regarding polynomial representation

21. In § 8 we showed that a polynomial function of x can be formulated to have specified values at any number of selected or datum points, equally spaced. We now consider the corresponding theorem in two dimensions, and when the datum points have *any* distribution within some bounded area. Its truth has been assumed in the argument of §§ 15–18. *In the argument which follows N and n have different significances from what they have carried in preceding sections.*

Let lines be drawn parallel with the x-axis to pass through every one of the specified points, and suppose that there are N of these lines, defined by the equations

$$y = y_1, \quad ..., \quad y = y_n, \quad ..., \quad y = y_N. \tag{i}$$

Then, if

and if

$$\left.\begin{array}{l} \Phi(y) = (y-y_1)(y-y_2)...(y-y_N) \\ \Phi_n(y) = \Phi(y)/(y-y_n), \end{array}\right\} \tag{ii}$$

it is clear that $\Phi_n(y)$ vanishes on all of the lines (i) except the line $(y = y_n)$. Therefore the polynomial function

$$F(x,y) = X_1\Phi_1(y)+X_2\Phi_2(y)+...+X_n\Phi_n(y)+...+X_N\Phi_N(y) \tag{iii}$$

(in which $X_1, X_2,..., X_n$ are functions of x as yet unspecified) will be given on the line $y = y_n$ by

$$F(x, y_n) = X_n\Phi_n(y_n). \tag{iv}$$

Suppose that x has the values $a_n, b_n,..., k_n$ at those specified points which lie on the line $(y = y_n)$, and that the specified values of the polynomial function at these points are $Q_{a,n}, Q_{b,n},..., Q_{k,n}$. Then, if

and if

$$\left.\begin{array}{l} F_n(x) = (x-a_n)(x-b_n)...(x-k_n) \\ f_{a,n}(x) = F_n(x)/(x-a_n), \end{array}\right\} \tag{v}$$

it is clear that $f_{a,n}(x)$ vanishes at all of the points $(x = b_n),..., (x = k_n)$, but that at the point $(x = a_n)$ it has a finite value

$$f_{a,n}(a_n) = (a_n-b_n)...(a_n-k_n). \tag{vi}$$

Therefore the polynomial function of x given by

$$X_n = \frac{1}{\Phi_n(y_n)}[Q_{a,n}f_{a,n}(x)/f_{a,n}(a_n)+...+Q_{k,n}f_{k,n}(x)/f_{k,n}(k_n)] \tag{vii}$$

will assume the values

$$\frac{1}{\Phi_n(y_n)}[Q_{a,n},..., Q_{k,n}] \tag{viii}$$

at the points $(x = a_n),..., (x = k_n)$ on the line $y = y_n$; and it follows from (iv) that if we substitute the value (vii) for X_n in (iii), then $F(x,y)$ will assume the specified values at these specified points.

Deriving expressions of the type of (vii) for all of $X_1, X_2,..., X_N$ in (iii), we shall have an expression for $F(x,y)$, polynomial both in x and y, which takes the specified value at every one of the specified points.

Other applications of the Calculus of Finite Differences†

22. Our formulae for approximate differentiation (§ 10) were based on the assumption that the wanted function, attaining specified values y_0, y_1,..., y_n at $(n+1)$ datum points equally spaced, can be replaced by a certain polynomial having the same values at those points. On the same assumption we can integrate the polynomial over this range (na) of the variable x, thus obtaining formulae for approximate integration; and we can also calculate its value at a point lying between two consecutive datum points, thus obtaining formulae of interpolation.

Formulae for approximate integration

23. These formulae may be exemplified by 'Simpson's rule', which in effect assumes that over any two contiguous portions of the range (i.e. over a length $2a$) the integrand y can be replaced by a quadratic function of x, so in fact is the formula appropriate to the value $n = 2$. But corresponding formulae can be constructed in which n has higher values. The formulae (45)–(47) which follow are representative of a more complete list which in Table VIII is reproduced (by permission, and with slight changes of notation) from a paper by W. G. Bickley (Ref. 1).‡

Two-strip formula $(n = 2)$:

$$I_2 = \frac{a}{3}(y_0 + 4y_1 + y_2) \qquad [E_2 = -y^{\text{iv}}a^5/90]. \tag{45}$$

(Simpson's first, or 'one-third', rule.)

Four-strip formula $(n = 4)$:

$$I_4 = \frac{2a}{45}\{7(y_0 + y_4) + 32(y_1 + y_3) + 12y_2\} \qquad [E_4 = -8y^{\text{vi}}a^7/945]. \tag{46}$$

Six-strip formula $(n = 6)$:

$$I_6 = \frac{a}{140}\{41(y_0 + y_6) + 216(y_1 + y_5) + 27(y_2 + y_4) + 272y_3\}$$
$$[E_6 = -9y^{\text{viii}}a^9/1400]. \tag{47}$$

In these formulae a ($= l/n$) stands as in § 11 for the interval between adjacent points of subdivision of the whole range l of

---

† §§ 22–31 are included in this chapter for future reference. At a first reading the reader may pass to § 32.

‡ Table VIII, as having general application, is placed at the end of this book.

integration; the integrand is y, and it has known values $y_0, y_1, ..., y_n$ at the points of subdivision. I stands for $\int_0^l y\, dx$, so that (for example) the formula (47) is equivalent to

$$\frac{1}{l}\int_0^l y\, dx = \frac{1}{840}\{41(y_0+y_6)+216(y_1+y_5)+27(y_2+y_4)+272y_3\},$$

(48)

since $a = l/6$. The error E is the amount by which, in each case, the expression on the right-hand side exceeds I_n: in it a as before stands for l/n, and y^m for $f^m(X)$ or $\dfrac{d^m}{dx^m}f(X)$, where X is some (unspecified) value of x between 0 and x_n (cf. §11).

24. To explain the use of the formulae we shall take and apply the 'six-strip formula' (48).† Suppose that we want an approximation to the exact value of

$$\int_0^1 x\sin^2\pi x\, dx \quad (y = x\sin^2\pi x),$$

which is easily shown to be 0·25. Then we have

$x =$	0	1/6	2/6	3/6	4/6	5/6	6/6
$\sin \pi x =$	0	1/2	$\sqrt{3}/2$	1	$\sqrt{3}/2$	1/2	0
$\sin^2\pi x =$	0	0·25	0·75	1·0	0·75	0·25	0
$x\sin^2\pi x =$	0	1/24	6/24	12/24	12/24	5/24	0

and accordingly the approximation given by (48) is

$$\int_0^1 x\sin^2\pi x\, dx = \frac{41\times 0+216\times(1+5)+27\times(6+12)+272\times 12}{140\times 6\times 24}$$

$$= 0{\cdot}250298.$$

Thus the error entailed by (48) in this instance is about 0·12 per cent.

25. Our formulae for approximate integration have an obvious extension to approximate surface-integration; and the formulae for approximate differentiation and integration can, moreover, be used in combination. Thus suppose that we want to compute approximately the definite integral

$$\int_0^1 xy'^2\, dx$$

† For the material of §§ 24–5, as of Tables I–VIII, I am indebted to Dr. W. G. Bickley.

for the case in which $y = \sin \pi x$. (It is easy to show that the exact value is $\pi^2/4$.)† As a first step we proceed to calculate y' $(= dy/dx)$ by means of (17) and Table V *without recourse to the orthodox process of differentiation* (which of course can be applied without difficulty to $\sin \pi x$).

For the calculation of $\left(\dfrac{dy}{dx}\right)$ at the end $r = 0$ we have

$x =$	0	1/6	2/6	3/6	4/6	5/6	6/6
$y = \sin \pi x =$	0	1/2	$\sqrt3/2$	1	$\sqrt3/2$	1/2	0
A from Table V $=$	-1764	4320	-5400	4800	-2700	864	-120
$Ay =$	0	2160	$-2700\sqrt3$	4800	$-1350\sqrt3$	432	0

Therefore $\sum(Ay) = 377{\cdot}1942 = 5!\left(\dfrac{dy}{dx}\right)_0$, according to (17), since here $a = 1/6$.

So our approximate formula gives the estimate $\left(\dfrac{dy}{dx}\right)_0 = 3{\cdot}14329$, which agrees well with the correct value (π).

Proceeding in the same way for other values of r, we obtain the second line of the table which follows. The third line is self-explanatory.

$x =$	0	1/6	2/6	3/6	4/6	5/6	6/6
$y' = \dfrac{dy}{dx} =$	3·14329	2·72051	1·57083	0	$-1{\cdot}57083$	$-2{\cdot}72051$	$-3{\cdot}14329$
$xy'^2 =$	0	1·23353	0·82251	0	1·64501	6·16764	9·88024

Finally, using (48) in the manner of § 24, we obtain the approximation

$$\int_0^1 xy'^2\,dx\ (y = \sin\pi x) \approx \frac{2070{\cdot}3656}{840} = 2{\cdot}46472\ldots.$$

The correct value $\pi^2/4 = 2{\cdot}46740\ldots$, so the error entailed by (17) and (48) in this instance is $-0{\cdot}11$ per cent.

Approximate integration round a closed contour or boundary

26. Proceeding in the manner of these examples, we can integrate the wanted function, or its differentials, along any straight line containing a row of nodal points (§ 5).

In another kind of integration which we shall require later, the integrand is to be regarded as a function of s, i.e. of distance measured from some datum point along a closed boundary or contour. Usually the range of integration is one complete circuit of the closed curve, and in that event the integral is known as a **contour integral**. The integrals $\displaystyle\int_1^2 \Psi\,ds$ and $\displaystyle\int_1^2 \frac{\partial\phi}{\partial\nu}\,ds$ will serve as examples, ν denoting

---

† This example was given in *Rel. Meth. E. S.*, § 199.

(Fig. 5) the normal to the contour drawn outward from the contained area, and 1, 2 defining the limits of integration.† The corresponding contour integrals will be denoted by $\oint \Psi \, ds, \oint \dfrac{\partial \phi}{\partial \nu} \, ds$.

Clearly, in order to evaluate $\oint \Psi \, ds$ in the manner of §§ 23–5 we

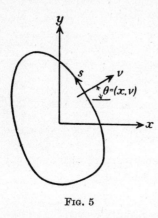

shall require to know the values of Ψ at a number of points dividing the whole range of s into n equal parts. Usually this information is not available, first, because no large number of nodal points fall exactly on the specified contour, and secondly, because such points as do fall on the contour do not divide s into equal parts. Both difficulties must be met by interpolation and/or extrapolation (§ 28), employed first to obtain a series of related values of Ψ and s, secondly to deduce values of Ψ for points spaced evenly in the range of s.

Fig. 5

27. The treatment of $\oint \dfrac{\partial \phi}{\partial \nu} \, ds$ is similar but (in general) more laborious. Occasionally the problem *for a complete contour integral* is made simpler by the fact that the result does not depend upon the particular path of integration. Thus we know from Green's theorem that

$$\oint \frac{\partial \phi}{\partial \nu} \, ds = \iint \nabla^2 \phi \, dx dy, \left. \right\}$$
$$= 0 \text{ when } \phi \text{ is plane-harmonic,} \qquad (49)$$

∇^2 having the same significance as in § 14, and the surface-integral extending to the whole area contained within the contour. When (49) is applied to the region enclosed between two boundaries (Fig. 6), both boundaries must be included within the contour integral: then an equivalent statement is

$$\oint_1 \frac{\partial \phi}{\partial \nu_1} \, ds + \oint_2 \frac{\partial \phi}{\partial \nu_2} \, ds = 0, \qquad (50)$$

† When ν and s have directions as shown in Fig. 5, then
$$\frac{\partial}{\partial \nu} \equiv \cos(x, \nu) \frac{\partial}{\partial x} + \sin(x, \nu) \frac{\partial}{\partial y}, \qquad \frac{\partial}{\partial s} \equiv \cos(x, \nu) \frac{\partial}{\partial y} - \sin(x, \nu) \frac{\partial}{\partial x}.$$

suffixes 1 and 2 denoting the outer and inner contour, and ν_1, ν_2 having senses as shown. This again may be written as

$$\oint_1 \frac{\partial \phi}{\partial \nu}\, ds = \oint_2 \frac{\partial \phi}{\partial \nu}\, ds = I \quad \text{(say)}, \tag{51}$$

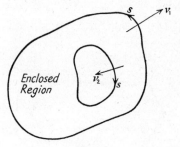

FIG. 6

ν *now standing (as in § 26) for the normal to either contour drawn out-ward from the area which that contour encloses.* From (51) we deduce that if ϕ is plane-harmonic, then $\oint \frac{\partial \phi}{\partial \nu}\, ds$ has a value independent of the path of integration.

It follows that in these circumstances we are free to choose any convenient contour in evaluating I, and evidently, when we have values of ϕ at nodal points of a regular net (§ 5), a convenient con-tour will be one consisting either (as in Fig. 7 a) of a series of 'strings' or (when the net is square) of a series of mesh-diagonals. Then, for a first approximation, we have only to replace

$$\oint \frac{\partial \phi}{\partial \nu}\, ds \quad \text{by} \quad \sum \left[\frac{\phi_S - \phi_R}{RS} \cdot PQ \right], \tag{i}$$

—this being equivalent to the assumption that along PQ (Fig. 7 b or 7 c) the normal gradient has a constant value given by $(\phi_S - \phi_R)/RS$. The ratio PQ/RS will have a constant value depending on the mesh-shape: when this is square and PQ is a mesh-diagonal (Fig. 7 b), i.e.

$$\text{when } N = 4, \quad \text{then } PQ/RS = 1; \tag{ii}$$

when it is triangular and PQ is a 'string' (Fig. 7 c), i.e.

$$\text{when } N = 6, \quad \text{then } PQ/RS = 1/\sqrt{3}. \tag{iii}$$

Hexagonal nets ($N = 3$) are not convenient for contour integration.

Combining (i)–(iii), we have as **formulae for approximate contour integration**

$$\oint \frac{\partial \phi}{\partial \nu}\, ds = \sum (\phi_S - \phi_R) \quad \text{when } N = 4,$$
$$= \frac{1}{\sqrt{3}} \sum (\phi_S - \phi_R) \quad \text{when } N = 6,$$

$$\left.\begin{array}{c} \\ \\ \end{array}\right\} \quad (52)$$

R typifying a point just inside, and S a point just outside, the contour of integration.

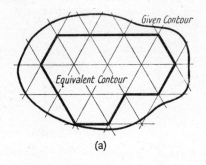

(a)

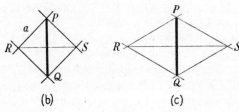

(b)   (c)

FIG. 7

Interpolation and extrapolation

28. It remains to discuss the problem, noticed in § 26, of computing the value of the wanted function Ψ at a point lying between two datum points at which Ψ is known. *It should be remarked at the outset that very often a graphical method, which is obvious and easy to apply, will be quite sufficiently accurate and accordingly preferable.*†

Using Maclaurin's series

$$y \equiv f(x) = f(0) + x \cdot f'(0) + \frac{x^2}{2!} \cdot f''(0) + ..., \text{ etc.}, \qquad (53)$$

we can compute $f(x)$ for any value of x, given $f(0), f'(0), f''(0), ...,$ etc. We have moreover given (§ 10) rules whereby these first and higher

† More especially when the datum points are not equally spaced (cf. § 26). On this account no mention is made here of 'divided differences' (Ref. 11, Chap. II).

differentials of x at 0 may be computed. Therefore in a sense we have solved our problem already; but the procedure that we have indicated would be very laborious in practice, and it is better to employ the Gregory-Newton formula of interpolation, which we now proceed to describe.

Difference tables

29. In the first place we must explain the construction of a table of finite differences (Ref. 11, § 2). As in § 8, let y have the values $y_0, y_1,..., y_n$ when x has the values 0, a, $2a$,..., na, and now let

$$\Delta f(x) \text{ stand for the quantity } f(x+a)-f(x),$$
$$\Delta^2 f(x) \quad ,, \qquad ,, \qquad ,, \quad \{\Delta f(x+a)-\Delta f(x)\}, \qquad (54)$$
$$..., \text{ and so on.}$$

Clearly, given $y_0, y_1,..., y_n$ we can compute n values of Δy (namely, $\Delta y_0 = y_1-y_0$, $\Delta y_1 = y_2-y_1$,..., $\Delta y_{n-1} = y_n-y_{n-1}$), $(n-1)$ values of $\Delta^2 y$ (namely, $\Delta^2 y_0 = \Delta y_1-\Delta y_0$,..., $\Delta^2 y_{n-2} = \Delta y_{n-1}-\Delta y_{n-2}$), $(n-2)$ values of $\Delta^3 y$, and so on. Arranging these in a **difference table** as under (*in practice all entries will be numerical*), we see that every line contains one term less than the line preceding it; so the table ends at the $(n+1)$th line, and this contains only one term.

y_0	y_1	y_2	$\cdots$	y_{n-2}	y_{n-1}	y_n
Δy_0	Δy_1	Δy_2	$\cdots$	Δy_{n-2}	Δy_{n-1}	
$\Delta^2 y_0$	$\Delta^2 y_1$	$\Delta^2 y_2$	$\cdots$	$\Delta^2 y_{n-2}$		
$\cdot$	$\cdot$	$\cdot$	$\cdot$	$\cdot$		
$\cdot$	$\cdot$	$\cdot$				
$\Delta^{n-2} y_0$	$\Delta^{n-2} y_1$	$\Delta^{n-2} y_2$				
$\Delta^{n-1} y_0$	$\Delta^{n-1} y_1$					
$\Delta^n y_0$						

The Gregory-Newton formula for interpolation

30. The Gregory–Newton formula corresponds with (53), § 28, but the finite differences Δy_0, $\Delta^2 y_0$,..., $\Delta^n y_0$ appear in place of the true differentials y_0', y_0'',..., $y_0^{(n)}$. It is (Ref. 11, § 8)

$$y_{xa} = f(xa)$$
$$= y_0 + x\,\Delta y_0 + \frac{x(x-1)}{2!}\,\Delta^2 y_0 + ... + \frac{x(x-1)...(x-n+1)}{n!}\,\Delta^n y_0, \qquad (55)$$

and it enables $f(xa)$ to be calculated (approximately) when Δy_0,

$\Delta^2 y_0,..., \Delta^n y_0$ have been calculated by the construction of a difference table. Evidently it gives

$$y \equiv f(xa) = y_0, \text{ when } x = 0,$$
$$= y_0 + \Delta y_0 = y_1 \text{ according to § 29, when } x = 1,$$
$$= y_0 + 2\Delta y_0 + \Delta^2 y_0$$
$$= y_0 + \Delta y_0 + \Delta y_1 = y_1 + \Delta y_1$$
$$= y_2 \text{ according to § 29, when } x = 2,$$

..., and so on.

31. To illustrate the application of §§ 29–30 we shall deal with the following example (Ref. 11, § 8): *Values of y are given, in the second column of the appended table, for values of X (in the first column) ranging from 20 to 30 by intervals (a) of 2. It is required to estimate the value of y which corresponds with X = 21.*

X	y	Δy	$\Delta^2 y$	$\Delta^3 y$	$\Delta^4 y$
20	0·229314955248	701747247	602297	−1944	4
22	0·230016702495	702349544	600353	−1940	3
24	0·230719052039	702949897	598413	−1937	
26	0·231422001936	703548310	596476		
28	0·232125550246	704144786			
30	0·232829695032				

Except that rows and columns are interchanged, this is a difference table of precisely the kind discussed in § 29, and it calls for no remark except that decimal points, and the zeros which follow them, have been omitted to save space. In (55) if we replace y_0, $\Delta y_0,...,$ etc., by y_{20}, $\Delta y_{20},...,$ etc., then to obtain the wanted value (corresponding with $X = 21 = 20 + \frac{1}{2}a$) we have only to make $x = \frac{1}{2}$. Thereby we obtain

$$y_{21} =$$
$$y_{20} + \tfrac{1}{2}\Delta y_{20} + \frac{\tfrac{1}{2} \cdot -\tfrac{1}{2}}{2!}\Delta^2 y_{20} + \frac{\tfrac{1}{2} \cdot -\tfrac{1}{2} \cdot -\tfrac{3}{2}}{3!}\Delta^3 y_{20} + \frac{\tfrac{1}{2} \cdot -\tfrac{1}{2} \cdot -\tfrac{3}{2} \cdot -\tfrac{5}{2}}{4!}\Delta^4 y_{20}$$

$$= 10^{-12} \times [229314955248 + \tfrac{1}{2}(701747247) - \tfrac{1}{8}(602297) +$$
$$+ \tfrac{1}{16}(-1944) - \tfrac{5}{128}(4)]$$

$$= 0·229665753463.$$

RÉSUMÉ

32. This chapter has laid foundations for the initial stage in our treatment of partial differential equations—namely, their replacement by approximate relations involving finite differences. No use has been made, as yet, of notions peculiar to Relaxation Methods:

it has merely been anticipated (§ 5) that our aim will be to evaluate the wanted function at nodal points of some regular 'net'.

For every differential of the wanted function there can be sub-stituted a finite-difference approximation, based on the assumption (§ 8) that *with an accuracy sufficient for practical purposes* the function can be identified with a polynomial function of the independent variables. The approximation involves the interval a between the points at which the function is to be determined, and its accuracy can be improved (always on the basis of the assumption stated) by an inclusion in it of more terms (of higher order in a). For partial differentials the simplest approximations are those given in (18)–(20), §§ 12–13, as relating to the points in Fig. 4. These yield the approxi-mation (22) for the Laplacian operator ∇^2, in relation to nodal points of a *square-mesh* net.

In §§ 15–18 we have generalized this result, showing that the finite-difference expression

$$\frac{1}{N}\sum_{a,N}(w)-w = \frac{a^2}{4}(\nabla^2 w) \quad \text{when } N = 3 \text{ or } 4, \qquad\qquad (38)\,bis$$

with neglect of a^4 and higher powers of a,

$$= \frac{a^2}{16}\left[3\nabla^2 w + \frac{1}{N}\sum_{a,N}(\nabla^2 w)\right] \quad \text{when } N = 6, \qquad (39)\,bis$$

with neglect of a^6 and higher powers of a; and in § 19 we have illustrated the use of these approximations by transforming Poisson's differential equation (41) into a relation in-volving finite differences. This last relation (namely (42) when $N = 3$ or 4, (43) or (44) when $N = 6$) will be used in place of (41) for pur-poses of numerical computation. *We shall transform each problem studied from one in which an exact (differential) equation has to be satisfied everywhere into one in which an approximate (finite-difference) relation has to be satisfied at a finite number of lattice-points;* thereby converting each problem into one which calls for the solution of a system of simultaneous equations, and as such comes within the scope of Relaxation Methods.

In Chapter II we shall start our description of the relaxational technique.

Historical survey

33. The notion of finite-difference approximations to differential operators is of very long standing,—in all probability it is as old as the infinitesimal calculus itself. It was systematized by W. F. Sheppard (Ref. 10), whose conventions and notation have been widely adopted (Ref. 11, Chap. III). As has been shown, it permits the transformation of a differential equation into a system of simultaneous equations. Notable examples are to be found in papers by L. F. Richardson (Refs. 7–9).

Since the number of the simultaneous equations is large, though formally soluble these in practice still present a problem. Some investigators (Refs. 3, 6, 7) have replaced them by equivalent geometrical relations and have sought to obtain solutions by freehand sketching improved successively either by eye or by the imposition of analytical checks. Richardson, who has considerably developed this line of attack (Ref. 9), has also sought to develop numerical methods for solving the simultaneous equations, and has (Ref. 8) propounded a very ingenious device whereby approximate solutions may be improved. This, in future investigations, may be found to have application in a relaxational approach: hitherto, Relaxation Methods have developed along quite separate lines.

Those lines have still to be described. In this chapter the only point of novelty is the demonstration whereby (§§ 15–18) the finite-difference approximation to ∇^2 has been generalized so as to permit the use not only of square but also of hexagonal or triangular mesh. Our argument reproduces, with slight modifications, that given in Ref. 4, §§ 4–8.

Triangular nets $(N = 6)$ do not appear to have been used by previous investigators. They have the advantage (as will appear in subsequent chapters) that in many problems they increase the number of the 'boundary points', thus giving closer definition to the wanted function. Hexagonal nets have not been found to have utility (cf. § 52).

REFERENCES

1. BICKLEY, W. G. 1939. 'Formulae for Numerical Integration'. *Math. Gazette*, **23**, 352–9.
2. BICKLEY, W. G. 1941. 'Formulae for Numerical Differentiation'. Ibid., **25**, 19–27.
3. CASAGRANDE, A. 1937. *Journal New England Water Works Association*, **51**, 131–72.
4. CHRISTOPHERSON, D. G., and SOUTHWELL, R. V. 1938. *Proc. Roy. Soc. A*, **168**, 317–50.

5. KARMAN, Th., and BIOT, M. A. 1940. *Mathematical Methods in Engineering.* McGraw Hill Co.

6. PORITSKY, H., SNIVELY, H. D., and WYLIE, C. R. 1939. *Journ. Appl. Mech.,* **6,** A–63–6.

7. RICHARDSON, L. F. 1908. *Proc. Roy. Dublin Soc.,* **11,** 295–316.

8. RICHARDSON, L. F. 1910. *Phil. Trans. Roy. Soc.* A, **210,** 307–57.

9. RICHARDSON, L. F. 1911. *Proc. Phys. Soc.,* **23,** 75–85.

10. SHEPPARD, W. F. 1899. *Proc. Lond. Math. Soc.,* **31,** 449–88.

11. WHITTAKER, E. T., and ROBINSON, G. *The Calculus of Observations.* (2nd ed. 1926.) Blackie & Son.

II

RELAXATION METHODS APPLIED TO PLANE-POTENTIAL PROBLEMS. I

The plane-harmonic equation, and its finite-difference approximation

34. CHAPTER I laid foundations for a relaxational treatment of partial differential equations, showing how these can be replaced by approximate (finite-difference) relations imposed at nodal points (finite in number) of a chosen lattice or 'net'. We now explain the treatment in relation both to the 'two-dimensional Laplace equation'

$$\nabla^2\psi \equiv \frac{\partial^2\psi}{\partial x^2} + \frac{\partial^2\psi}{\partial y^2} = 0 \tag{1}$$

and to the more general ('Poisson') equation

$$\nabla^2 w + Z(x, y) = 0, \tag{2}$$

in which w denotes the wanted function, $Z(x, y)$ denotes some *specified* function of x and y.

In § 2 we described a function governed by (1) as 'plane-harmonic', and in conformity with that description (1) might be termed a plane-harmonic equation. But for Relaxation Methods, as we shall see, (2) presents an exactly similar problem; and on that account, since a name has already been given to (1), we shall say that **plane-harmonic equations** are typified by the more general equation (2).

35. Equation (2) is identical in form with (41) of § 19, and the argument of that section shows that its finite-difference approximation is

$$\frac{1}{N}\sum_{a,N}(w) - w_0 + \frac{a^2}{4}Z_0 = 0 \tag{3}$$

when $N = 3$ or 4 (i.e. when the 'net' is hexagonal or square), or

$$\frac{1}{N}\sum_{a,N}(w) - w_0 + \left[\frac{a^2}{4}Z_0 + \frac{a^4}{64}(\nabla^2 Z)_0\right] = 0 \tag{4}$$

when the net is triangular ($N = 6$). The notation was explained in § 16; the suffix 0 defines the nodal point.

Later we shall show by examples (cf. § 37) that a governing equation, though expressed in 'dimensional' terms, can always be thrown into 'non-dimensional' (i.e. purely numerical) form. *This is an essential preliminary to computation*, which (in the nature of the case) can only deal with numerical quantities. We assume it to have been done for (1) and (2)—i.e. that x, y, Z, ψ, w, in those equations, are purely numerical: then, in (3) or (4), a, w, Z, and $\nabla^2 Z$ are similarly numerical.

Prandtl's 'membrane analogue' of the plane-harmonic equation

36. For solving (1) or (2) as relating to certain problems in Elasticity, extensive use has been made of an analogue due to Prandtl (*Elasticity*, §§ 386–7) which gives them a mechanical interpretation. Consider a continuous membrane (e.g. a soap film) which at every point, and in every direction, has uniform tension T per unit length.† Let it be pictured as weightless and initially flat, and let w (a function of x and y) denote its transverse displacement from this flat configuration due to an applied transverse pressure p (also a function of x and y). Then, on account of w, at any point of a chosen contour the membrane will exert a transverse force having line-intensity $T \sin\{\tan^{-1}(\partial w/\partial v)\}$,—i.e., when w is infinitesimal, $T(\partial w/\partial v)$. Here (cf. Fig. 5, § 26) v denotes the outward-drawn normal to the contour, so $\partial w/\partial v$ measures the normal gradient of w.

For equilibrium, the total force exerted on that part of the membrane which lies within the contour (i) by the applied pressure p and (ii) by the outer parts of the membrane must (since the membrane is weightless) be zero. The first part (i) is measured by $\iint p\, dxdy$, the second (in view of what has been said above) by $\oint T\dfrac{\partial w}{\partial v}\, ds$: consequently ($T$ being constant) we have

$$\iint p\, dxdy + T \oint \frac{\partial w}{\partial v}\, ds = 0,$$

and applying Green's transformation to the contour integral we deduce that

$$\iint (p + T\nabla^2 w)\, dxdy = 0$$

when the surface-integration extends to the whole of the area within the contour. But no restriction has been imposed upon the size and shape of this contour: therefore the equation

$$\nabla^2 w + p/T = 0 \tag{5}$$

must hold at every point in the membrane,—i.e. it governs this mechanical system. In form it is identical with (2).

† In the soap-film T comes from the surface-tension on *both* faces.

37. Writing $\qquad x = D \cdot x', \qquad y = D \cdot y',$ (6)

we can convert equation (5) to

$$\nabla'^2 w \equiv \frac{\partial^2 w}{\partial x'^2} + \frac{\partial^2 w}{\partial y'^2} = -\frac{pD^2}{T},$$

or to $\qquad\qquad \nabla'^2 w' = -\frac{pD}{T} = -Z' \quad \text{(say)}$ (7)

if in addition we write $\qquad w = w' \cdot D,$ (8)

so that w', like x' and y', is purely numerical. D denotes some representative dimension fixing the size as contrasted with the shape of the boundary. Since $p \cdot D^2$ and $T \cdot D$ both have the dimensions of a force, Z' is also numerical and so (7) involves only numerical quantities. With suppression of the dashes (i.e. when x, y, w, Z have purely numerical significance) it again becomes identical with (2).

A corresponding 'net analogue' of the finite-difference approximation †

38. Thus (2) can be interpreted as governing the small transverse displacement (w) of a transversely loaded membrane, whether x, y, w, Z stand for 'dimensional' or for purely numerical quantities. We now interpret (3) and (4) similarly, as governing the small transverse displacement of a transversely loaded net.

Suppose that Figs. 1 (§ 5) represent real nets of mesh-side a in which every string exerts a tension $\mathbf{T}$ and so (by symmetry) every node is in equilibrium when the net is flat; and let w stand for the transverse displacement from this flat configuration which occurs as the result of transverse loading. Then, in the deflected net, the string joining nodal points 0 and 1 (say) will exert on 0 a transverse force $\mathbf{T} \sin\left\{ \tan^{-1}\left(\frac{w_1 - w_0}{a} \right) \right\}$,—i.e., when the w's are infinitesimal, $\frac{\mathbf{T}}{a}(w_1 - w_0)$; and it follows from the definition of $\sum\limits_{a,N}(w)$ in § 16 that

$$F_0 = \frac{\mathbf{T}}{a}\left[\sum_{a,N}(w) - N w_0 \right] \qquad (9)$$

measures the total force exerted on 0 by the N strings which radiate from it.

If now we denote by $\mathbf{F}_0$ the external (transverse) load applied at 0, then

$$\mathbf{F}_0 = F_0 + F_0 = 0 \qquad (10)$$

† §§ 38–41 are based on §§ 7–10 of Ref. 13.

is the condition for transverse equilibrium of 0, i.e. it is one condition of equilibrium for the loaded net; and its form can be identified
with (3) or (4) provided that

$$\mathbf{F_0} = \frac{\mathbf{T}}{a} N \frac{a^2}{4} Z_0 \quad \text{when } N = 3 \text{ or } 4,$$

$$\left. = \frac{\mathbf{T}}{a} N \left[\frac{a^2}{4} Z_0 + \frac{a^4}{64} (\nabla^2 Z)_0 \right], \quad \text{when } N = 6. \right\} \tag{11}$$

This is the more realistic picture of 'relaxation nets' which was
forecast in § 5. Just as, in § 36, equation (2) was shown to govern the
small transverse displacements imposed on a membrane of tension
T by a transverse pressure

$$p = T \cdot Z(x, y), \tag{12}$$

so (3) or (4), multiplied through by $N\mathbf{T}/a$, have now been shown to
govern the small transverse displacements imposed on a net of string-
tension $\mathbf{T}$ by transverse forces applied at the nodal points and given
at a typical node 0 by (11). The membrane is not amenable to computation, which can only deal with systems of finite 'freedom': the
net provides such a system, and it will, if chosen to 'correspond',
closely reproduce the deflexions of the membrane.

We proceed to examine the conditions of such 'correspondence'—
i.e. to relate the string tension $\mathbf{T}$ with the tension T of the corresponding membrane. Thereby we shall explain the different forms
assumed by the expression (11) for $\mathbf{F_0}$, according as $N = 4$ or 6.

39. Clearly, if a distributed loading is to be brought to bear upon
a net of finite mesh, and in such a way that every string connecting
two adjacent nodes will remain straight when the net is deflected,
some mechanism must be envisaged for effecting the distribution,
e.g. a light rigid plate having the shape of the mesh and suspended
from its nodal corners by inextensible ties.† Suppose in the first
place that the mesh is triangular ($N = 6$) and that a concentrated
force Z acts vertically through the point P of the rigid plate OAB
(Fig. 8). Then the part of Z which on statical principles has to
be sustained by O is $Z \cdot \dfrac{PM}{ON}$, i.e. it is $Z\left(1 - \dfrac{x}{d}\right)$, where $d = \frac{1}{2}a\sqrt{3}$.
Dealing in this manner with the pressure-intensity $T \cdot Z$ over the

† Or furnished with feet which bear upon the nodal points.

whole of OAB, we see that the total contribution of the pressures on this triangle to the force at O is

$$T \iint Z\left(1-\frac{x}{d}\right) dxdy, \text{ for the whole triangle } OAB; \qquad \text{(i)}$$

and if in the manner of §15 (Chap. I) we now assume Z to be representable by a polynomial function of x and y, so that

$$Z = Z_0 + \tfrac{1}{4}(\nabla^2 Z)_0(x^2+y^2) + Ax + By + F(x^2-y^2) + 2Gxy +$$
$$+ \dots \text{(terms of higher order in } x, y), \quad \text{(ii)}$$

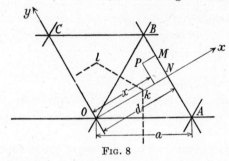

FIG. 8

then, to the order of the terms retained in (ii), we have in (i)

$$\iint \left(1-\frac{x}{d}\right) Z\, dxdy = (\text{area } OAB) \times$$
$$\times [\tfrac{1}{3}Z_0 + \tfrac{1}{6}Ad + \tfrac{1}{10}Fd^2(1-\tfrac{1}{9}) + \tfrac{1}{40}(\nabla^2 Z)_0\, d^2(1+\tfrac{1}{9})]. \quad \text{(iii)}$$

For axes Ox', Oy' inclined at θ to Ox, Oy, so that

$$x = x' \cos\theta - y' \sin\theta, \qquad y = x' \sin\theta + y' \cos\theta,$$

the expression (ii) becomes

$$Z = Z_0 + \tfrac{1}{4}(\nabla^2 Z)_0(x'^2+y'^2) +$$
$$+ (A \cos\theta + B \sin\theta)x' + (B \cos\theta - A \sin\theta)y' +$$
$$+ (F \cos 2\theta + G \sin 2\theta)(x'^2-y'^2) +$$
$$+ 2(G \cos 2\theta - F \sin 2\theta)x'y' +$$
$$+ \dots \text{(terms of higher order in } x' \text{ and } y');$$

so for the triangular mesh OBC adjacent to OAB in Fig. 8 (i.e. a triangle like OAB but rotated through $\pi/3$) the expression corresponding with (iii) is

$$(\text{area } OAB) \times \left[\frac{1}{3}Z_0 + \frac{1}{6}\left(A \cos\frac{\pi}{3} + B \sin\frac{\pi}{3}\right)d +\right.$$
$$\left. + \frac{8}{90}\left(F \cos\frac{2\pi}{3} + G \sin\frac{2\pi}{3}\right)d^2 + \frac{1}{36}(\nabla^2 Z)_0\, d^2\right].$$

The other four triangles surrounding O can be treated similarly. Summing the contributions of all six triangles, we find that the terms involving A, B, F, G sum to zero, leaving

$$T \times (\text{area } OAB) \times 2[Z_0 + \tfrac{1}{12}(\nabla^2 Z)_0 d^2] \qquad \text{(iv)}$$

as the total force which, according to (i), comes on the nodal point O.

Since $4d^2 = 3a^2$, and since the area $OAB = \dfrac{\sqrt{3}}{4}a^2$, the expression (iv) may be written as

$$\mathsf{F}_0 = T\frac{\sqrt{3}a^2}{2}\Big[Z_0 + \frac{a^2}{16}(\nabla^2 Z)_0\Big], \qquad \text{(v)}$$

and this (for $N = 6$) agrees with F_0 as given by the second of (11), provided that
$$\mathbf{T} = aT/\sqrt{3}$$
$$= aT\tan \pi/N, \qquad \text{(13)}$$

—i.e. *provided that we concentrate in the string OB (Fig. 8) the whole force which in the membrane was exerted by the tension T acting across the line $kl = (OB)\tan \pi/N$.* (On our assumption (12) of a transverse pressure proportional to the membrane tension T, it was evident that the magnitude of T would be immaterial.)

40. We saw in § 38 that (10), when (9) and the second of (11) are satisfied, becomes identical with (4) and expresses the condition of equilibrium for any node O of a loaded triangular net: now, we have found the conditions for correspondence of this net with the 'Prandtl membrane' which (§ 36) provides a mechanical analogue of our starting (and exact) equation (2). Correspondence is attained when

(i) every string tension $\mathbf{T}$ has a value equivalent to the resultant pull of the membrane tension T across a side ($a \tan \pi/N$) of the hexagon surrounding that point,

(ii) the transverse pressure ($T . Z$) is concentrated at nodal points in accordance with the principles of Statics.

But when the mesh is square or hexagonal ($N = 4$ or 3), statical principles no longer suffice to determine the partition of the transverse pressure between adjacent nodal points, and the best that we can do is to concentrate at O (Fig. 9) the whole of the pressure acting on the surrounding polygon $abc...a$. On that understanding the total pressure force at O is

$$\mathsf{F}_0 = TZ_0 \times (\text{area } abc...a) = TZ_0 \times N\Big(\frac{a}{2} \times \frac{a}{2}\tan\frac{\pi}{N}\Big) = \tfrac{1}{4}NZ_0\,Ta^2\tan\frac{\pi}{N}.$$
$$\text{(i)}$$

If, moreover, (as before) we concentrate in each string the total force exerted by the membrane tension T acting across a side of the polygon $abc...a$, then we have

$$\mathbf{T} = aT \tan \pi/N, \qquad (13)\,bis$$

as in § 39, and equation (i) becomes identical with the first of (11), —i.e., the square or hexagonal net is made (like the triangular) to correspond with the Prandtl membrane.

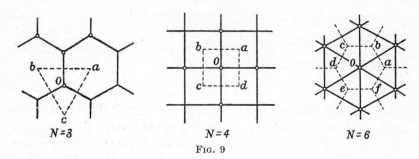

$$N=3 \qquad\qquad N=4 \qquad\qquad N=6$$

Fig. 9

41. The factor $\mathbf{T}/a$, in (9) and (11), cancels out from (10) and accordingly is immaterial. For simplicity we may make it unity, and then we have as the final form of our condition of equilibrium

$$\mathbf{F}_0 = \mathsf{F}_0 + F_0 = 0, \qquad (10)\,bis$$

where $\quad \mathsf{F}_0$, the externally applied load,

$$\left. \begin{aligned} &= N\frac{a^2}{4}Z_0, \text{ when } N = 3 \text{ or } 4, \\[2mm] &= N\left[\frac{a^2}{4}Z_0 + \frac{a^4}{64}(\nabla^2 Z)_0\right], \text{ when } N = 6, \end{aligned} \right\} \qquad (14)$$

and where F_0, the force due to the displacements w,

$$= \sum_{a,N}(w) - Nw_0, \qquad (15)$$

whether $N = 3$ or 4 or 6. Our simplifying assumption

$$\left. \begin{aligned} \mathbf{T} &= a \\[2mm] T &= \cot \pi/N \end{aligned} \right\} \qquad (16)$$

requires, according to (13), that

in the membrane analogue. We shall need this result when we come (§ 70) to consider that case of the plane-potential problem in which boundary *gradients* are specified.

Introduction of the concepts of the Relaxation Method

42. Having this mechanical picture of the finite-difference relations (3) and (4), we can visualize our problem as that of determining the behaviour of a chosen net under specified transverse loading and with specified conditions imposed at the boundary. We have transformed our problem into one of the kind for which Relaxation Methods were first devised, and on that account we can utilize immediately many of the arguments and results of *Rel. Meth. E. S.*

Thus we can at once predict that computations effected by the relaxation method will converge, because we know that *the net when in equilibrium assumes a configuration of minimum total potential energy.* We can utilize the devices of 'block' and of 'group relaxation' (*Rel. Meth. E. S.*, Chap. IV) to speed the 'liquidation' process. Intuitively we can estimate the accuracy with which a net of finite mesh will reproduce the behaviour of a continuous membrane, and the extent to which that accuracy can be improved by 'advance to a finer net' (§ 5). This last device we visualize as a use of additional strings (making for reduced mesh-size) either throughout the net or in a region where the displacements alter sharply.

43. We take over *en bloc* from *Rel. Meth. E. S.* its nomenclature, typographic symbolism, and general picture of the liquidation process. What follows is part of *Rel. Meth. E. S.*, §§ 2–4, altered so as to apply to a loaded net instead of a loaded framework.

'We follow in computation a physical procedure which could (at least in imagination) be applied to an actual net. . . . The ordinary "screw-jack" (e.g. for automobiles) is a means whereby a controlled displacement may be imposed at any desired point: it is easy to imagine devices whereby the displacement may be recorded, together with the load sustained at any instant; also to visualize an arrangement in which every nodal point of the net which would normally be free to move is provided with a jack of this kind (hereafter termed a *constraint*), arranged so as to control its displacement. . . . Suppose that initially the nodal points are fixed in positions such that the net is not deflected: then, when the concentrated external loads are applied, these will be taken wholly by constraints. Suppose that subsequently one constraint is relaxed so that one nodal point is permitted to travel slowly† through a specified distance . . .: then force will be transferred from that constraint to adjacent constraints and to the net, and strain-energy will be stored in the latter in virtue of the tensions in its strings. If the initial force on the relaxed constraint had a component in the direction of the travel, that constraint will be relieved, and strain-energy will be stored at the expense of the potential energy of the

† So that equilibrium is maintained, and vibrations are not excited.

external forces. All nodal points but the one being fixed, a simple calculation will tell us how much force is transferred as a result of any specified displacement; therefore we can so adjust the displacement that the constraint is relieved either entirely or to any desired extent.[†]

44. Equation (10), § 41, expresses the concept mathematically, F_0 standing for the force which comes upon the constraint at O. We know the external forces (of type F_0), and we seek by altering the displacements (w) to bring all of the F's to zero. *It is the essence of Relaxation Methods that they focus attention not on the wanted quantities (i.e. the displacements) but on the datum quantities (i.e. the loads)*:[‡] they do so by accounting for the F's, which we term **residual forces** since they measure the loads not yet accounted for.

From (15) we can determine, once for all, the effects of a 'unit operation'—in this instance the imposition of a unit displacement at a single nodal point; then by a sequence of such operations—in some degree arbitrary, but guided by certain basic principles—we can liquidate the residual forces, i.e. bring them (sensibly) to zero. Any initial values can be attached to the displacements, and the corresponding residual forces can be calculated from (10), (14), and (15). The better the starting assumption, the less will be the labour of their subsequent liquidation.

The 'relaxation pattern'

45. According to (15), for all values of N the effect on F_0 of a unit increase in w_0 is an increment

$$\Delta F_0 = \Delta F_0 \quad (F_0 \text{ being specified and therefore invariant})$$
$$= -N, \tag{i}$$

[†] Alternatively the relaxational procedure can be interpreted geometrically, as in papers by G. Temple (Ref. 11), R. E. Gaskell (Ref. 3), and J. L. Synge (Ref. 10). In a valley devoid of friction the place at which a ball will come to rest is its lowest point: that point is the 'wanted configuration' in a system defined by two variables— x (east and west) and y (north and south). Proceeding in accordance with Relaxation Methods, we start from anywhere and proceed by 'stages': sometimes east and west, sometimes north and south; but always proceeding downhill, and in every stage continuing until our path is level. (Slope is here the analogue of 'residual force'; friction will give a 'margin of uncertainty'.) Clearly we shall tend always towards our goal unless the valley contains other 'stationary points' at which all paths are level; but this would mean that more than one point exists at which a ball can come to rest, and that possibility (in mechanical systems) can usually be excluded by a theorem of 'uniqueness of solution'.

No restriction other than this is imposed on the shape of the valley; i.e. the argument does not postulate that the total potential energy is a quadratic function of the displacements. Consequently it is *not* restricted to linear equations,—all that it requires is that the wanted configuration shall be unique.

[‡] Cf. *Rel. Meth. E. S.*, § 266.

and from the same equation, applied to any of the points immediately surrounding O, we see that it also results in increments

$$\Delta F_1 = \Delta F_2 = \Delta F_3 = \ldots = 1. \tag{ii}$$

Each string, in effect, transfers a unit force from O to its other end point, as the result of a unit increment made to w at O.

Thus the 'unit operation' for a net is very simple: by imposing unit displacement at O, we alter the residual forces at O and at surrounding points by amounts which are exhibited in Fig. 10 for

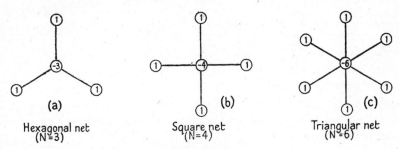

(a) Hexagonal net ($N = 3$)
(b) Square net ($N = 4$)
(c) Triangular net ($N = 6$)

Fig. 10. Relaxation Patterns.

$N = 3$, 4, or 6. Such diagrams are termed **relaxation patterns**. They replace the 'Operations Tables' of *Rel. Meth. E. S.*

Using the 'pattern' appropriate to the chosen net, *and working not with a 'Relaxation Table' but on the net itself*, by a sequence of unit operations combined with suitable multipliers we can bring successively (and temporarily) to zero the largest 'residual forces' (of type F_0). In the first and simplest class of plane-potential problem (which alone is exemplified in this chapter) w is specified on the boundary, therefore must not there be altered; *but residual forces are permitted at the boundary, so our task will be ended when all residuals have been brought (sensibly) to zero at internal points.*

Details will be best explained in relation to a particular example.

The torsion problem of Saint-Venant

46. An equation of type (2) is presented in de Saint-Venant's well-known theory of the stresses induced by twisting couples in straight bars of non-circular cross-section. There (cf., e.g., *Elasticity*, § 386) the shearing stresses acting on cross-sections are expressed in terms of a 'stress-function' Ψ which has a constant value on the boundary (or on each closed boundary, in the case of 'multiply-connected' sections), and which satisfies the condition

$$\nabla^2\Psi \equiv \frac{\partial^2\Psi}{\partial x^2} + \frac{\partial^2\Psi}{\partial y^2} = -2 \tag{17}$$

at every internal point. Comparing (17) with (2), § 34, we see that it is a special case of that equation in which $Z(x,y)$ is independent of x and y.

z being directed along the axis of the twisting couples, the stress-components X_x, Y_y, Z_z, X_y are zero everywhere, and

$$Y_z = -\mu\tau\frac{\partial\Psi}{\partial x}, \qquad X_z = \mu\tau\frac{\partial\Psi}{\partial y}, \tag{18}$$

τ denoting the angle of twist per unit length—a quantity of dimensions $[L]^{-1}$. μ denotes the modulus of rigidity—a quantity of the same dimensions as Y_z, Z_x: consequently Ψ has the dimensions $[L]^2$, so that by using D to denote some representative length in the cross-section (e.g. when this is *square*, the length of a side), and by writing

$$\Psi = D^2 . \chi,$$

we make χ purely numerical. Writing also

$$x = D.x', \qquad y = D.y', \tag{19}$$

so that x', y' are also numerical, we may substitute in (17) to obtain

$$\nabla'^2\chi \equiv \frac{\partial^2\chi}{\partial x'^2} + \frac{\partial^2\chi}{\partial y'^2} = -2, \tag{20}$$

—an equation similar in form, but involving only numerical quantities.

This treatment exemplifies the remark made in § 35, that it is always possible *initially* to reduce the governing equation to 'non-dimensional' form. As explained in *Elasticity*, § 189, it has the advantage that solutions of the reduced equation will apply without restriction on the size (as distinct from the *shape*) of the twisted bar.

In § 41, equation (2) was replaced by finite-difference relations stated in (10), (14), and (15). Here, χ replaces w, and $Z(x,y)$ has a uniform value 2; so (14) reduces to

$$\mathsf{F}_0 = N\frac{a^2}{4}Z_0 = \tfrac{1}{2}Na^2, \tag{21}$$

whether $N = 3$ *or* 4 *or* 6 (i.e. in relation either to hexagonal, square, or triangular nets). In (21), a is a 'non-dimensional', like x' and y'.

Example I: The torsion problem for an equilateral triangle†

47. To make the problem definite, χ must have specified values at all points on the boundary. In the torsion problem for a solid section (cf. § 46), χ must have a constant value along the boundary, and it can be shown (*Elasticity*, § 390) that no generality is lost by making this value zero. In illustration of Relaxation Methods we

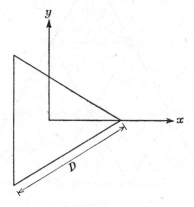

Fig. 11

now attack, on the basis of the approximate relation (4), the torsion problem for a section having the form of an equilateral triangle.

This form is chosen, first, as entailing computations less complicated by detail than is usual, and secondly, as having a known (exact) solution by which our results may be judged. Clearly the function

$$\chi = \tfrac{1}{18}(2\sqrt{3}x'+1)(\sqrt{3}x'-3y'-1)(\sqrt{3}x'+3y'-1)$$

satisfies (20) and vanishes when either

$$x = Dx' = -\frac{D}{2\sqrt{3}}$$

$$(22)$$

or

$$x\pm y\sqrt{3} = D(x'\pm y'\sqrt{3}) = \frac{D}{\sqrt{3}},$$

—i.e. on every side (of length D) of the equilateral triangle in Fig. 11.

48. The shape of the boundary suggests the use in this instance of a triangular net ($N = 6$) and the taking of D to denote the length

† §§ 47–51 are based on Section II (§§ 14–18) of Ref. 2.

of a side. In the coarsest net which is convenient a has the value $\frac{1}{3}$ (Fig. 12); consequently
$$\mathbf{F}_0 = \tfrac{1}{3} \tag{i}$$
according to (21), and the appropriate relaxation pattern is that shown in Fig. 10 c.

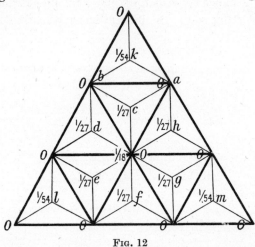

FIG. 12

There is only one internal node, namely the centre O; and it is only at internal nodes that (10) must be satisfied. Clearly, we can liquidate $\mathbf{F}_0$ by imposing on O a displacement
$$\chi_0 = \tfrac{1}{6}\mathbf{F}_0 = \tfrac{1}{18} \text{ according to (i),} \tag{23}$$
and comparing with (22) we see that this computed value for the point $(0,0)$ is *exact*. The reason of this exceptional result is explained in § 51.

'Advance to a finer net'

49. If we would determine χ at other points in the section, we must have recourse to the device (§ 5) of 'advance to a finer net'.

Consider the triangular mesh Oab in Fig. 12, and let its centroid be designated by c. Since O, a, b are grouped symmetrically round c at a distance
$$\frac{1}{\sqrt{3}}Oa = \frac{D}{3\sqrt{3}},$$
the formulae of § 41, with $N = 3$, $a = 1/(3\sqrt{3})$, will give a value for the residual force at c. We have from (21)
$$\mathbf{F}_c = \frac{3a^2}{2} = \frac{1}{18},$$

and from (15)

$$F_c = \chi_0 + \chi_a + \chi_b - 3\chi_c = \tfrac{1}{18} + 0 + 0 - 3\chi_c.$$

Therefore $\qquad\qquad \mathbf{F}_c = \tfrac{1}{18}(2 - 54\chi_c),$

and will vanish if $\qquad\qquad \chi_c = \tfrac{1}{27}.$ $\hfill$ (24)

From considerations of symmetry we see that χ must have the same value at $d, e, f, g,$ and h, Fig. 12; and by similar reasoning we deduce that

$$\chi_k = \chi_l = \chi_m = \tfrac{1}{54}. \hfill (25)$$

Consequently we have values of χ which may be used as starting assumptions in relation to a triangular net of mesh-side $a = 1/(3\sqrt{3})$. From (21), with N given (when this is possible) the value 6, we can deduce initial values of the residual forces; and these we can proceed to liquidate as before.

50. Alternatively, since for d, f, h, k, l, m, Fig. 12, the data do not permit us to relax with $N = 6$ (because there are not six surrounding nodes at which χ is known), we may there postpone liquidation until—by a repetition of the foregoing process—trial values have been deduced for a third and still finer net in which a has the value $1/9$. The reader will have no difficulty in verifying that the trial values of χ, and the consequent residuals, are *correctly* given by the figures to left and right, respectively, of nodal points in Fig. 13 a.† Regarded as a deduction from Fig. 12, that diagram illustrates what may be termed **two-stage advance to a finer net.**

Example I (concluded)

51. In Fig. 13 b these trial displacements and residuals, multiplied by 486 to avoid fractions, are shown to left and right of nodal points, and the process of final liquidation is recorded. Thus an imposed displacement -2 at a brings the residual (-12) at that point to zero and makes an addition -2 to the residual at every surrounding point: we are not concerned with residuals at the boundary, so the only change recorded is a change of the residual at b from 0 to -2. The imposition of a displacement $+2$ at c brings the residual there to zero, also the (altered) residual (-2) at b; and it adds $+2$ to the residuals at d and e. These, together with the residual -12 at f, are all brought to zero simultaneously by imposition of a displacement -2 at f.

† N has been taken as 3 in the deduction of trial values, as 6 in the calculation of residuals.

The system here adopted in recording residuals (namely, insertion of the altered above the original value) is standard practice also exemplified in Fig. 20. Usually (as in that diagram) several displacements have to be imposed and recorded to the left of nodal points: *their summation is left until liquidation is deemed complete.*

The final (summed) displacements of Fig. 13 b, divided by the multiplying factor (486) which was introduced above, are recorded

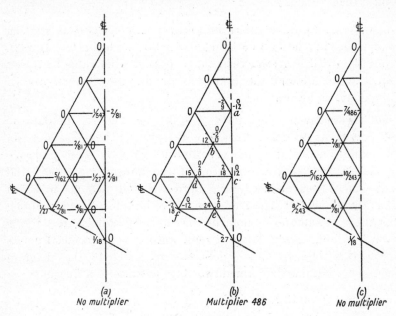

(a)
No multiplier

(b)
Multiplier 486

(c)
No multiplier

FIG. 13

in Fig. 13 c. They agree exactly with (22) of § 47. This (cf. § 48) is an unusual circumstance: normally we must be content to reduce the residual forces to some small fraction (e.g. 1 per cent.) of the greatest of their starting values, and even when they can be completely liquidated the displacements, *on account of errors implicit in the finite-difference approximations*, are not correct.

The reason why a correct result has been obtained in this instance is that the exact solution (22) is in fact a polynomial of the third degree. Consequently n, in (23) of § 15, has no value greater than 3; and hence on the right of (29), § 16, all terms vanish when $N = 6$ except $A_0(a)$, which has the form $c_0 + c_2 r^2$. This means that when $N = 6$ all terms except the first vanish on the right of (36), § 17, and (39) accordingly is exact. When $N = 3$, (38) is in error on account of our neglect of $A_N(a)$ in (29).†

General discussion of 'advance to a finer net'

52. Reverting to § 50, where 'two-stage advance' was found convenient in relation to nets of triangular mesh, we now consider the same device in relation to hexagonal or square nets ($N = 3$ or 4).

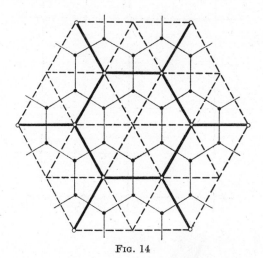

FIG. 14

For $N = 3$, having determined the wanted function at nodal points of the net depicted by bold lines in Fig. 14, we may use (14) and (15) in association with (10), with $N = 6$, to determine it at the centre of each hexagon. Adding the 'strings' depicted by broken lines in Fig. 14, we have a value of the wanted function at every nodal point of a triangular net of the same mesh-side a as before, and the residual forces are zero at the centres of the original hexagons. Again using the same relations, we can calculate the residual forces at the corners of the hexagons (open circles in Fig. 14); and these we can then proceed to liquidate *on the triangular net*.

Alternatively we can make a 'two-stage advance' by using (14) and (15), with $N = 3$, to compute the wanted function at the points indicated by black dots in Fig. 14. These can be joined, as shown

† The expression (22), § 47, is equivalent to
$$\chi = \tfrac{1}{18}\{1 - 9r^2 + 6\sqrt{3}r^3 \cos 3\theta\}$$
when $x' = r\cos\theta,\ y' = r\sin\theta$. Thus $A_3(a) \neq 0$.

by fine lines, to form a second hexagonal net in which a has been reduced (compared with the first) in the ratio $1 : \sqrt{3}$. By this procedure we continue to work with $N = 3$; but its slight advantage in respect of simplification is offset by the disadvantages (i) that the two nets have no common nodal point, (ii) that the residual forces (not yet computed) will not, in general, vanish at any node initially.

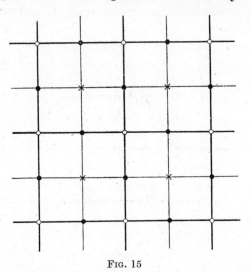

Fig. 15

Hexagonal nets have been considered here as a theoretical possibility: they have not as yet been utilized in published researches.

53. Square nets, on the other hand, have advantages which in some cases outweigh the less close approximation of which they are capable, compared with triangular nets ($N = 6$). We shall meet examples later.

Having values of the wanted function at nodal points of the net depicted by bold lines in Fig. 15, we can use (14) and (15) with $N = 4$ and a reduced in the ratio $1 : \sqrt{2}$, first to find its values at mesh-centres as indicated by crosses in Fig. 15, and then (with a again reduced in the same ratio as before—i.e. to $\frac{1}{2}$) to determine values at the centres of the mesh-sides. Thereby we arrive by a 'two-stage advance' at values for all nodal points of a second square twice as fine as the original; and for some nodes (viz. those indicated by black dots in Fig. 15) the initial values of the residual forces will be zero. *We work throughout with $N = 4$.*

'Block relaxation'

54. In Example I the basic operation (entailing use of the 'relaxation pattern' of Fig. 10c) led quickly to complete liquidation of residual forces: normally the convergence of the computations, though demonstrable mathematically (§ 42), is much less rapid and may be too slow to have practical value. Accordingly we now examine the possibility of 'block relaxation' on the lines of *Rel. Meth. E. S.*, Chapter IV.

Suppose that we connect a group of nodes, arbitrarily chosen, to a flat and rigid plate, of negligible weight, *which constrains them all to undergo the same deflexion* **w**. Then, except at points outside the plate, the net remains flat and in consequence the residuals are not altered. If, moreover, (by constraints of normal type) we prevent displacement of points outside the plate, then the only strings of which the ends undergo differential displacements are those strings (indicated by bold lines in Figs. 16) which connect these fixed points to edge points of the plate. For unit deflexion, according to § 45, each string exerts a force $+1$ at its fixed end and a force -1 at its end which is moved.

It is thus an easy matter to investigate the effect of a unit block-displacement ($\mathbf{w} = 1$) of the type considered, and so to liquidate the *resultant* of the residual forces on the plate. We have only to count the strings which join fixed and moving points; for if the number of these is **n**, then a unit block-displacement will transfer a resultant force **n** away from the plate. Every nodal point which is attached to the plate (e.g. those falling within the shaded areas in Figs. 16) will undergo the unit displacement, and every connecting (bold line) string will alter the resultant force on the plate by an amount -1. Choosing **w** so that the resultant is completely liquidated, we shall leave (in the region of the plate) residual forces which are *self-equilibrating* and as such lend themselves more readily to liquidation effected by point-relaxations of the normal kind.

Fig. 16a relates to a square, Fig. 16b to a triangular net. The numerals in circles show the increments to the residuals which result from unit block-displacement of the shaded area.

55. We can choose the shaded area in any way we like, and we can alternate sequences of block-displacement with sequences of point-relaxation. Thus in Fig. 17a we can move successively the

shaded areas which are denoted by I and II. For I, the initial value
of the resultant residual force is 89·4 and n (§ 54) = 28, consequently
an appropriate value for **w** is 89·4/28 = 3·19; for II, the resultant
residual force is 8·8 and **n** = 16, consequently an appropriate value

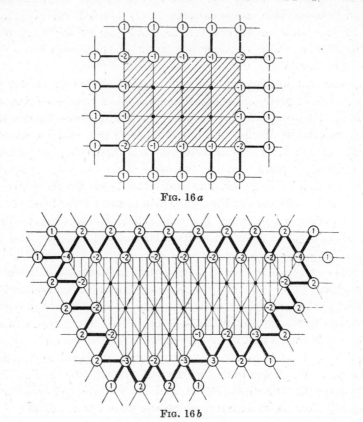

Fig. 16 *a*

Fig. 16 *b*

for **w** is 8·8/16 = 0·55: accordingly we move I by 3·19 and II by
3·74 (= 3·19+0·55). When these two block-relaxations have been
effected, the residual forces at points in the shaded areas are as
shown in Fig. 17 *b*. By further point-relaxations based on § 45, followed
by further block-relaxations determined as above, they are brought to
the negligible values shown (to the right of the nodal points) in Fig.
17 *c*.† The final displacements are shown to left of the nodal points.

    † The complete sequence of operations is not recorded, because it is of great
importance that the reader should convince himself of his ability to liquidate
residuals by standard processes *applied in any sequence which his own judgement
deems to be appropriate.*

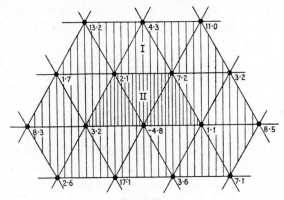

Fig. 17a

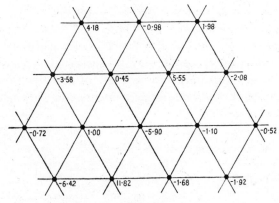

Fig. 17b

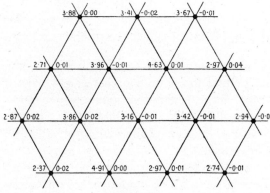

Fig. 17c

Diagrams of the kind of Fig. 17 c replace, in this book, the tabular records (Relaxation Tables) of *Rel. Meth. E. S.* Usually their final entries entail some 'residuals', therefore are not exact solutions even of the finite-difference relations. They are solutions judged to be *sufficiently* exact, and as such will be termed **accepted solutions.**

'Group relaxation'

56. The rigid plate of § 54 need not (as there) be assumed to move perpendicularly to its own plane, so as to undergo the same displacement **w** at every point: we can equally imagine it to execute a **block rotation** (*Rel. Meth. E. S.*, § 78) whereby some of its points move with, others against, the direction *Oz*. Whatever the nature of its rigid-body displacement, when this is given we can deduce the displacement of every nodal point and hence (cf. § 54) the forces exerted by each string which joins a moved nodal point with a fixed; so we can liquidate not only the resultant force sustained by the rigid plate, but the resultant moment about any line of nodal points. Clearly, three independent rigid-body displacements can be imposed upon the shaded areas of Figs. 16.

In fact, as in *Rel. Meth. E. S.* (§ 84) we can discard the notion of a rigid connexion between the points which are moved, and impose a **group displacement** in which *arbitrary* values are assigned to the relative displacements of some chosen set of nodal points, with consequences that can be calculated from the basic formulae. '. . . We often know intuitively . . . the main features of the distortion which we are seeking to determine, and usually it will be worth while to capitalize this knowledge in the form of new operations . . .' Examples will appear in subsequent chapters.

57. Again, it can happen in an 'advance to a finer net' that although the residual forces on the coarser net were insignificant, those on the finer net (calculated initially in the manner of §§ 49–50) not only have sensible values individually, but a sensible *resultant*. In such cases it may be worth while to multiply all of the calculated (starting) displacements by some constant factor, chosen so as to liquidate the resultant force on the new (i.e. finer) net. The multiplication amounts, in effect, to the imposition of a group-displacement based on previous computation.

Example II: the torsion problem for a bar of solid rectangular cross-section

58. Fig. 18 records a solution (by Miss G. Vaisey) of the torsion problem for a rectangular boundary. The reader may work this as an example: a square net ($N = 4$) is appropriate, and computation

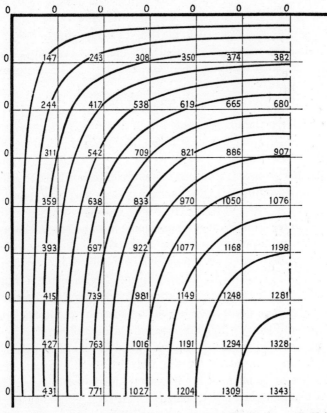

Fig. 18.   The torsion problem solved for a rectangular section. (G. Vaisey)

should be done *ab initio* in accordance with the directions of this chapter, block or group relaxations being used as may seem desirable. The recorded numbers are values of χ (§ 46) multiplied by 7200, where D (§ 37) denotes the length of the shorter side, so that $a = 1/12$. The curves are contours of constant χ—i.e. of constant Ψ: it can be shown to follow from (18) of § 46 that they have at every point the direction of the resultant shear stress due to torsion, and that the closeness of their spacing is a measure of its intensity.

Example III: the torsion problem for a hollow square section

Fig. 19 records, similarly, χ-values for a hollow square computed by Mr. F. S. Shaw (Ref. 9). This example too may be worked by the reader in accordance with the directions of this chapter if, disregarding the radius at the inner corner, he assumes χ to be specified on *two* square boundaries. (On the outer boundary $\chi = 0$, and on the inner boundary $\chi = 1210$: disregarding the radius, he should accept the values 1149, 1033 at the resulting sharp corner.) In Fig. 19, a has the value $1/20$, and all χ-values have been multiplied by 800. The curves are contours of constant shear-intensity—i.e. on each S has a constant value, where

$$S^2 = Y_z^2 + Z_x^2, \tag{26}$$

and Y_z, Z_x have the expressions (18), § 46.

RÉSUMÉ

59. In this chapter, starting from the finite-difference relations which were developed in Chapter I, we have described some parts of a technique whereby those relations (constituting an extensive system of linear simultaneous equations) can be solved as exactly as practical requirements may demand. Our illustrative examples have been taken from de Saint-Venant's theory of torsion: they are generally representative of the simplest type of plane-potential problem, in which Poisson's equation (2) (including Laplace's equation as a special case) has to be satisfied in combination with boundary conditions which impose values on the wanted function (not on its gradient, as in examples which will be confronted later); but they are unrepresentative in that (when the net is suitably chosen) lines of nodal points fall exactly on the boundary. Usually we shall be concerned with 'irregular stars'—a complicating factor which will receive attention in Chapter III.

The essence of our discussion is a mechanical ('net') analogy which permits the introduction of ideas developed previously—i.e. the basic notions of the Relaxation Method.† Instead of attacking by orthodox methods a set of simultaneous equations expressed in terms of the wanted quantities (i.e. displacements), we study the effects of standard 'operations' upon 'residual forces' which, since they

---

† Other analogies can be developed, e.g. transmission of heat or electricity through a network of uniform conductors. Cf. (e.g.) H. W. Emmons, *Quart. J. App. Math.*, **2** (1944), 173–95.

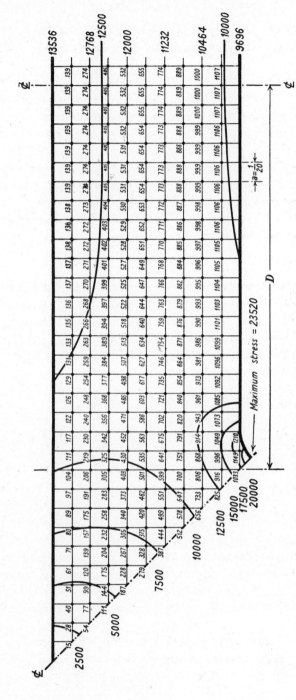

Fig. 19. The torsion problem solved for a hollow square section. (F. S. Shaw)

constitute errors, have to be brought to zero, or 'liquidated'. This transformation of the problem is the essence of Relaxation Methods, and the basis of every solution described in later chapters. Other investigators have either dealt directly with simultaneous equations formulated explicitly (Refs. 3, 6, 12), or have replaced these by equivalent geometrical relations which they proceed to satisfy by freehand sketching improved successively either 'by eye' or by a use of some analytical criterion (Refs. 1, 4, 5, 7).

Thom has come nearest to employing a relaxation method. In his paper (Ref. 12) dealing with Laplace's equation ($Z = 0$), he begins by attaching plausible values to the wanted function w at nodal points of his (square-mesh) net, and thereafter systematically modifies these values so as to satisfy the equation

$$w = \tfrac{1}{4} \sum_{a,4} (w) \tag{27}$$

at every point in turn: in time the modifications become inappreciable, and then the process is stopped. Equation (27) being identical with (3) when $Z = 0$, $N = 4$, his iterative process may be regarded as an application of Relaxation Methods whereby at every step he (temporarily) relieves some particular constraint of the residual force which it previously sustained.

Practical aspects of the liquidation process

60. Our aim has been to present the relaxation technique in a way which will convince the reader of its *logical* validity. But assurance of its validity *in practice* can come only by actual trial, which should be made before extensions are considered: therefore some account will be appropriate here of experience gained in actual computation. What follows is based on notes supplied by three research students who have applied the technique to numerous problems and have contributed largely to its development.† It should be studied before the examples are attempted, notwithstanding that in some respects (e.g. in its reference to 'irregular stars') it goes beyond the scope of this chapter; and it should again be studied after subsequent chapters have been assimilated, when the significance of its details will be more apparent.

(i) First, full advantage should be taken of the net analogy (§ 38), whereby the main features of the wanted solution can be foreseen

---

† Messrs. L. Fox, J. R. Green, and F. S. Shaw.

intuitively. *Any* assumption will serve at starting, because the relaxation technique will in time eliminate any error; but a close
assumption will greatly reduce the labour of subsequent correction,
so time spent in preliminary thinking is seldom wasted. It should
be remembered that a 'net', however fine, will blur the finer detail
of the 'membrane deflexion': one of the first questions for decision
is the fineness of the **ultimate net**—i.e. that net beyond which no
further advance will be attempted.

(ii) When this fineness has been decided, the boundary should be
drawn on tracing-paper to a size such that the ultimate meshes have
sides of about 1 inch:† thereby sufficient space will be left on the
finest net for numerical computations which háve to be recorded
near each node, and more space on the coarser (preliminary) nets,
where usually the computations will be more lengthy. Whether a
square or triangular net is more suitable depends, *inter alia*, upon
the shape of the boundary. Coarser (preliminary) nets can be constructed as required, on other sheets laid over the original tracing:
on them it will be sufficient to sketch the boundary roughly,—much
more important is a fairly accurate measurement of the arms of their
'irregular stars' (§ 62), and in this the original (and accurate) drawing
of the boundary will be helpful. For each successive net, at starting,
initial values of the residual forces should be computed *accurately*
(cf. § 41).

(iii) It has become customary to record displacements just to the
left of nodal points, residual forces just to the right. Fig. 20 shows
the progress of a typical computation on a triangular net. The largest
initial 'residual' (namely, 253 at *a*) suggested the imposition of a
'displacement' +42 (namely, 253/6 to the nearest whole number)
which is recorded on the left of *a*, and this 'point-relaxation' entails
additions of 42 to each of the six residuals surrounding *a*, also an
addition −252 to the residual force at *a*. These changes are recorded
to the right of the points affected, *not as increments but as revised
values of the residuals* (the old values have been struck out‡).

(iv) Since decimal points entail a possibility of error, at starting
the residuals may with advantage be multiplied by a numerical
factor so chosen that any fraction of unity (in residuals so multiplied)

---

† The 'net' and the boundary (which must not be erased) should be drawn either
in ink or on the reverse of the tracing paper.
‡ This is not normal practice.

denotes a quantity deemed to be negligible.† Further multiplication
may be effected at each advance to a finer net, when the residuals
have been reduced in magnitude and so smaller quantities remain to
be liquidated. Since neglected quantities may accumulate (and to

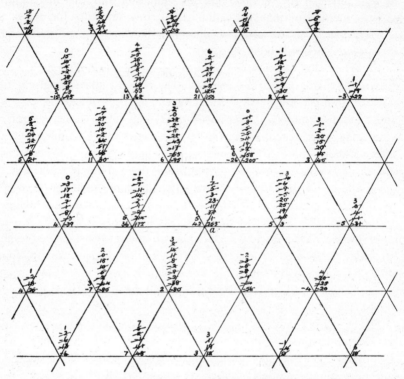

FIG. 20. Progress of a typical computation.

eliminate possible errors of computation), it will be prudent at each
advance to calculate residuals afresh, and accurately, from the recorded *total* 'displacements'. To this end a calculating machine (e.g.
'Facit' or 'Brunsviga 15' or '20') is desirable.

The accuracy required in any problem should be decided by physical considerations—i.e. by the reliability of the data. Later we shall
consider problems in which *differentials* of the wanted function give
the required solution: then a higher standard of accuracy is demanded
(e.g. if second differentials are required to have an accuracy of 1 per
cent., four-figure accuracy may be necessary in the 'displacements').

† Such multiplication has been exemplified in § 58.

(v) To explain every detail of a practical technique is to risk an appearance of complexity and difficulty which may repel the reader:† only by actual trial will he come to realize that this process is *not* difficult and that the return for a morning's work is a sense of high satisfaction. A beginner is advised to work some simple problem *twice*,—first by systematic advance from coarse to finer nets, secondly by starting on the finest net, with frequent use of 'block relaxation'. Thereby he will learn that two alternative lines of attack are open: the second appeals more strongly as experience accumulates. In both, when any displacement greater than $\frac{1}{2}$ would make some residual greater, liquidation may be deemed complete.

This standpoint has been adopted in the treatment of examples such as those described in § 58, and the reader should accordingly disregard errors that are numerically less than unity when verifying the solutions (e.g.) of Figs. 18 and 19. That is to say, he should accept the recorded χ-values as a solution of the finite-difference approximation to (20), if changes numerically less than unity would make them satisfy that relation exactly.

(vi) In point-relaxation, attention should be paid first to residuals which are surrounded by residuals of opposite sign: there, liquidation is immediate. When, on the other hand, surrounding values have the same sign, experience shows the desirability of **over-relaxation,** i.e. the imposition of exaggerated displacements to allow for the effects of relaxing these subsequently. Over-relaxation is in fact an alternative to group-relaxation, similarly aimed at quick results.

(vii) Complete liquidation on each successive net has the advantage that the computer can observe the convergence of his calculated displacements to their final values, and so obtain an indication as to whether further advance is necessary: when displacements are unchanged as between one net and the next, clearly there is no point in advancing farther. Sometimes farther advance may be desirable in a localized region.

Relaxation methods are still in process of development, and their technique cannot yet be standardized. But one general maxim can be offered confidently:—Use intuition to the full, and any device (such as graphical interpolation) which seems likely to shorten labour. The method detects all errors, so the computer will not be 'let down'.

† Thus (as remarked by J. R. Green) a verbal description of the tying of a 'reef knot' would make that simple operation appear quite formidable.

REFERENCES

1. CASAGRANDE, A. 1937. *Journal New England Water Works Association,* **51**, 131–72.

2. CHRISTOPHERSON, D. G., and SOUTHWELL, R. V. 1938. *Proc. Roy. Soc.* A, **168**, 317–50.

3. GASKELL, R. E. 1943. *Quarterly J. App. Math.,* **1**, 237–49.

4. PORITSKY, H., SNIVELY, H. D., and WYLIE, C. R. 1939. *J. Appl. Mech.,* **6**, A–63–6.

5. RICHARDSON, L. F. 1908. *Proc. Roy. Dublin Soc.,* **11** (N.S.), 295–316.

6. RICHARDSON, L. F. 1910. *Phil. Trans. Roy. Soc.* A, **210**, 307–57.

7. RICHARDSON, L. F. 1911. *Proc. Phys. Soc.,* **23**, 75–85.

8. RICHARDSON, L. F. 1925. *Math. Gazette,* XII, 415–21.

9. SHAW, F. S. 1944. *C.S.I.R. (Australia) Aero. Div. Report SM.* 36.

10. SYNGE, J. L. 1944. *Quarterly J. App. Math.,* **2**, 87–9.

11. TEMPLE, G. 1939. *Proc. Roy. Soc.* A, **169**, 476–500.

12. THOM, A. 1928. *Aero. Res. Comm. Rep. and Mem.,* No. 1194.

13. VAISEY, G., and SOUTHWELL, R. V. 1943. *Proc. Roy. Soc.* A, **182**, 129–51.

RELAXATION METHODS APPLIED TO PLANE-POTENTIAL PROBLEMS. II

61. DISREGARDING practical details (discussed in § 60) we may summarize as follows our attack in Chapter II on the plane-potential problem:—First (§§ 34–5) we replaced the differential equation (1) or (2) by its finite-difference approximation (3) or (4); then, having introduced the net analogue (§§ 38–41), we stated this approximation in the terminology of 'residual forces on constraints', making (10) with (14) and (15), § 41, the condition of equilibrium for a node of the chosen net. F_0, the residual force which has to be 'liquidated',† is the resultant of an external force $\mathbf{F}_0$ and of a force F_0 due to the 'displacements' w: $\mathbf{F}_0$ is given by (14), F_0 by (15). *We did not use (15) directly, but we based on it (§ 45) standard 'relaxation patterns' which are shown in Figs.* 10. These patterns provide the means of liquidation: they may be generalized in the statement that *unit deflexion, imposed at one end of any string, entails a transfer of 1 unit of 'residual force' from the end which is moved to the end which is fixed.*

Adhering to these principles, in the present chapter we shall cope with difficulties which are presented normally, though not in the three examples of Chapter II.‡

The treatment of 'irregular stars'

62. First, it will not usually happen that many nodal points fall exactly on the boundary, therefore close to the boundary it will sometimes not be possible to employ (15) of § 41, for the reason that surrounding points at which w is known do not all lie at the same distance from O. Thus from A, close to the triangular boundary in Fig. 21, there run five strings of standard length, but the sixth string (connecting A with the boundary) is only half as long. B close to the internal (circular) boundary, is connected with it by one still shorter string.

We thus have need of a generalization whereby the formula (15), § 41, can be applied to 'stars' of unequal strings. This is a problem

---

† i.e. brought within an agreed 'margin of uncertainty'.
‡ That these are not entirely representative was remarked in § 59.

in interpolation, of which an elaborate treatment would not be worth while in a method whereby periodically (at each advance to a finer net) we calculate the errors of a trial solution and (in effect) start afresh. Therefore we now propose a simple modification of the formula, logically consistent with our concept of an actual net in which (§ 61) a force is transmitted by each several string.

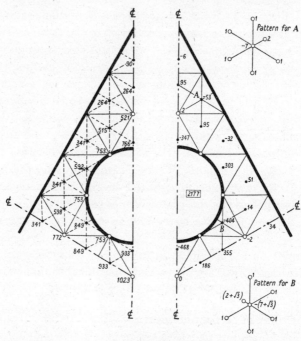

Fig. 21

63. In the tensioned net which was envisaged in § 38, the force exerted by any string is its tension **T** multiplied by the slope resulting from the displacements of its ends and so, for given displacements, is inversely proportional to its length. Therefore in place of (i) and (ii), § 45, if the N strings radiating from a displaced node O have lengths $x_1 a, x_2 a, ..., x_N a$, we have

$$\Delta \mathbf{F} = -\left(\frac{1}{x_1} + \frac{1}{x_2} + ... + \frac{1}{x_N}\right) \text{ at the node } O \text{ which is moved,}$$

$$- + \frac{1}{x_1}, + \frac{1}{x_2}, ... + \frac{1}{x_N}, \text{ at each of the } N \text{ surrounding nodes,} \Bigg\} \quad (1)$$

and the 'relaxation pattern' (Fig. 10) is modified accordingly.† In place of (10) and (15), § 41, we have

$$\mathbf{F_0} = \mathbf{F_0} + \left\{ \sum_N \left(\frac{w}{x}\right) - w_0 \sum_N \left(\frac{1}{x}\right) \right\}. \tag{2}$$

The formulae (1) and (2) cannot be justified by an argument on the lines of §§ 15–18, because the quantity within twisted brackets on the right of (2) has the expression

$$\sum_N \left[\frac{1}{x}\{A_0(xa) - w_0\} + \frac{1}{x}\{A_1(xa)\cos\theta + B_1(xa)\sin\theta\} + \right.$$
$$\left. + \frac{1}{x}\{A_2(xa)\cos 2\theta + B_2(xa)\sin 2\theta\} + ..., \text{ etc. } \right],$$

in which (§ 15) $A_n(r)$, $B_n(r)$ have the form $r^n \times$ (polynomial in r^2) and *the x's have different values for different strings of the 'star'.* On this account the trigonometrical series associated with A_n and B_n no longer sum to zero when $0 < n < N$, and hence we can no longer count on attaining closer approximation by a use of triangular nets. All that such argument yields is an indication (calling for further examination) that (14) and (15), § 41, ought now to be replaced by

$$\mathbf{F_0} \text{ (the applied external load)} = \frac{a^2}{4} Z_0 \sum_N (x) \tag{3}$$

and by

$$F_0 \text{ (the force due to the displacements } w) = \sum_N \left(\frac{w}{x}\right) - w_0 \sum_N \left(\frac{1}{x}\right), \tag{4}$$

whether $N = 3$ or 4 or 6. The condition of equilibrium for O is still

$$\mathbf{F_0} = \mathbf{F_0} + F_0 = 0, \tag{5}$$

$\mathbf{F_0}$ and F_0 having the expressions (3) and (4) unless all strings which radiate from O have the same length a, so that every $x = 1$: in that event (3) and (4) are replaced by

$$\mathbf{F_0} = N\frac{a^2}{4} Z_0, \quad \text{when } N = 3 \text{ or } 4,$$
$$= N\left[\frac{a^2}{4} Z_0 + \frac{a^4}{64}(\nabla^2 Z)_0\right], \quad \text{when } N = 6, \tag{6}$$

and $\qquad F_0 = \sum_{a,N} (w) - N w_0, \tag{7}$

—which are (14) and (15) of § 41.

† Cf. § 64.

Example IV: The torsion problem for a pierced triangular shaft

64. At A in Fig. 21, $N = 6$ and all the x's are unity except one which is 0.5. The mesh-side $a = 1/9\sqrt{3}$ and $Z = 2$; so by (3) the contribution of Z to the initial force at A is $\dfrac{5.5}{2 \times 243}$, and according to (1) a unit displacement at A will change the residual force:

by -7 at A,

by $+1$ at the five equidistant nodes,

by $+2$ at the near point of the boundary (where, of course, the residual force is not required to vanish).

The standard 'relaxation pattern' for $N = 6$ (Fig. 10c) is thus replaced at A and B by special patterns (shown in Fig. 21) which are not symmetrical. They are deduced exactly as before.

Fig. 21 relates to an example of the torsion problem (§ 34) which was solved in Ref. 3, §§ 19–27, by a method differing slightly from that which we now describe. The cross-section is an equilateral triangle pierced by three circular holes symmetrically situated (Fig. 22), and in order to estimate stresses we must determine the stress-function Ψ,—i.e. we must compute the numerical function χ of § 46. As stated there, Ψ and therefore χ must have a constant value along each internal boundary, and in this instance considerations of symmetry show that χ has the same constant value on all three. It can moreover be shown (*Elasticity*, § 392) that in Prandtl's membrane analogue (§ 36) the membrane is held fixed ($\chi = 0$) at the outer boundary and at the internal boundaries is attached to light plates which remain throughout parallel with the plane ($\chi = 0$), but subject to this condition are free to 'float'. As in § 46, the 'non-dimensional' governing equation is†

$$\nabla^2\chi + 2 = 0. \tag{8}$$

We retain these boundary conditions in replacing the membrane by a net, and we observe that the plates which they envisage are exactly like those which entered into our account (§ 54) of the device of 'block-relaxation'. That is to say, residual forces need not be brought to zero at every node, severally, within any one plate, but the resultant for all such points must vanish. The symmetry in this

† As in § 48, the side of the equilateral triangle has been identified with D in the reduction of the governing equation to 'non-dimensional' form.

particular example permits us (in effect) to confine attention to one-sixth of the whole cross-section, since every median of the triangle is a line of symmetry.†

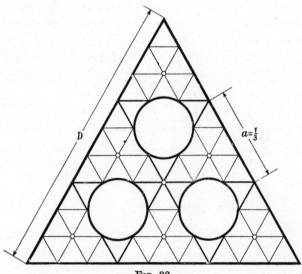

FIG. 22

65. On account of the internal (circular) boundaries we need not start from the coarse net ($a = 1/3$) shown by bold lines in Fig. 22, but can proceed at once to the smaller mesh shown by fine lines ($a = 1/9$). Each internal boundary passes through six nodal points of this finer net. Near to each corner, and to the middle point of each side of the triangle, is a node surrounded by six others at the same distance a, and the same is true of the central point. Consequently at all of these seven nodes (distinguished by open circles in Fig. 22) we can employ the standard relaxation pattern of Fig. 10c.

On this understanding, figures on the left of Fig. 21 give starting values of 'displacements', figures on the right give corresponding values of the initial forces in an advance (§§ 6, 49) to the finer net which is drawn in broken line. The full-line net is the finer net $a = 1/9$ of Fig. 22, and values of χ at its mesh-centroids (the black circles) have been calculated from (5)–(7) with $N = 3$, $a = 1/9\sqrt{3}$. To avoid decimals in the subsequent computations all figures have

† This is the significance of the ⌢ symbol in Fig. 21.

been multiplied by 43740 (= 60 × 27²), and allowance for this multiplication will have to be made in the solution ultimately accepted.

66. Now, in the process of liquidation, 'irregular stars' are confronted—e.g. at A, Fig. 21. The special 'patterns' needed in such cases can be calculated in the manner of § 63, and thereafter the procedure is along standard lines. Accordingly the reader may be left to verify the solution (for $a = 1/27$) which is given in Fig. 23.

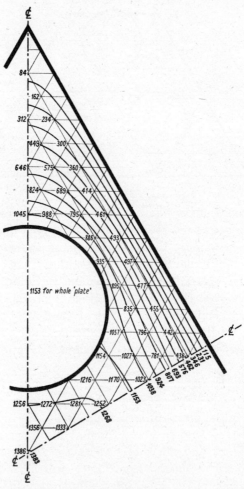

FIG. 23. The torsion problem solved for a pierced triangular shaft.
(O. C. Zienkiewicz)

The contours (obtained by cross-plotting) show the direction and
(by the closeness of their spacing) the intensity of the resultant shear
stress (cf. § 58).

The treatment of 'irregular stars' (continued). 'Fictitious nodes'

67. We have said (§ 63) that the formulae (1)–(4) are not defensible
by strict mathematical argument although (§ 62) they are a logical

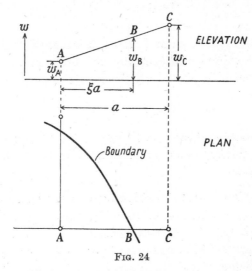

FIG. 24

implication of our replacement of the membrane by a net of finite
mesh. More approximate formulae have been propounded, but these
being more elaborate entail greater labour. As remarked in § 62,
simplicity may be deemed a decisive merit in formulae which in any
event will be replaced by others in each advance to a finer net.

By concentrating the loading Z at nodal points (§ 38), in effect we
ensure that every string remains straight when its ends are deflected,
and our formulae (1)–(4) are deductions from that fact. Another way
of looking at the problem is to imagine the strings continued past
the boundary (so as all to have the standard length a) and attached
to 'fictitious nodes' outside the region with which we are concerned.
Consider a string AB which is connected with a nodal point at A
and with a boundary at B; let it have length ξa, and let it be
prolonged beyond the boundary to a fictitious node at C. Then
(Fig. 24), since $AB = \xi a$, $AC = a$, and since the deflexions w_A, w_B,

w_C must be such as leave the string still straight, we have

$$\frac{w_B - w_A}{w_C - w_A} = \frac{AB}{AC} = \xi,$$

i.e. $$(1-\xi)w_A - w_B + \xi w_C = 0. \tag{9}$$

Consequently when w_B is known we can relate w_C with w_A.

68. If w_B is specified and accordingly invariant, then according to (9) we have
$$(1-\xi)\Delta w_A + \xi \Delta w_C = 0,$$

i.e. $$(\Delta w_C - \Delta w_A)\xi = -\Delta w_A.$$

Increments to w_A, w_C must satisfy this relation. Thus when w_A is increased by unity the contribution of the string AB to the quantity $\sum_{a,N} (w) - Nw_A$ is

$$\Delta w_C - \Delta w_A = -\frac{1}{\xi}\Delta w_A = -\frac{1}{\xi},$$

—a result consistent with (1) of § 63, and so leading to the same conclusion (namely, to special 'relaxation patterns' for nodes just inside a boundary).

Example V: The torsion problem for a splined circular shaft

69. Fig. 25 records solutions (by F. S. Shaw: Ref. 7) of the torsion problem for a splined shaft either 'solid' (a) or hollow (b). These are left to the reader as examples suited to triangular nets and entailing 'irregular stars'. In treating the hollow shaft he should proceed in the manner of § 64, and verify that χ *must* have the value 2374 on the inner, when $\chi = 0$ on the outer boundary. (In Fig. 25, the mesh-size $a = D/9\sqrt{3}$ when D is identified with R, and a multiplying factor 5000 has been introduced in order to eliminate decimals.)

Other types of boundary condition. (1) Normal gradients specified

70. 'Fictitious nodes' have other applications,—notably in problems which involve refraction at an interface between two different media (e.g. in Optics or Electricity). In this chapter we shall bring such problems within range of the methods summarized in § 61. First, however, we consider that other standard case of the plane-potential problem which is governed as before by the equation

$$\nabla^2 w + Z(x,y) = 0, \tag{10}$$

but in which the *normal gradient of w* (instead of *w* itself) has to take specified values at the boundary.

What follows is a treatment given in Ref. 8 (and there termed 'Method 1'†), slightly modified in accordance with Ref. 1, §§ 24–5. It adopts the physical standpoint of §§ 38–41: that is to say, it interprets (10) as the condition of transverse equilibrium for a uniformly tensioned membrane, and its finite-difference approximation as the corresponding condition for a uniformly tensioned net.

71. Seen from this standpoint, specified values of $\partial w/\partial v$ are specified values of $T\partial w/\partial v$, T denoting the membrane tension; i.e. they are line-intensities of transverse loading applied to the membrane at its edge. Introducing the 'net approximation', we concentrate this distributed loading on the strings which cross the boundary, and are thereby left with a problem suited to computation by Relaxation Methods, in which strings which cross the boundary have not there to undergo specified displacements (as in Chap. II), but to sustain specified transverse forces.

It was remarked in § 41 that the magnitude of T is not important in cases where boundary values of w are specified: *it matters now, since it determines the transverse loading*. Equations (3)–(7), § 63, rest on the assumption (cf. § 41) that the string tension $\mathbf{T}$ has a value a; and this requires that the membrane tension T be given by

$$\left.\begin{aligned} T &= \cot \pi/N, \\ &= 1 \text{ for a square net } (N = 4), \\ &= \sqrt{3} \text{ for a triangular net } (N = 6). \end{aligned}\right\} \qquad (11)$$

72. An element of boundary intercepted between two strings carries a total loading

$$\int T\frac{\partial w}{\partial v}\,ds = \cot(\pi/N)\int \frac{\partial w}{\partial v}\,ds, \quad \text{according to (11),} \qquad (12)$$

and this must be divided between its two end points. Strictly, the partition should be effected in accordance with the rules of Statics, and with due regard to the shape of the element; but small errors will not make the problem intractable, and it will entail no sensible error to treat all elements as straight. Two adjacent elements, of course, contribute to the force on any one string.

† An alternative technique ('Method 2' of Ref. 8) is explained in §§ 126–30 (Chap. IV).

One condition, however, must be satisfied. In relation to the membrane we have

$$T \oint \frac{\partial w}{\partial \nu}\, ds + \iint T Z(x,y)\, dx dy$$

$$= T \iint \{\nabla^2 w + Z(x,y)\}\, dx dy, \quad \text{by Green's transformation,}$$

$$= 0, \quad \text{in virtue of (10),}$$

showing that the total of the edge-loading must be in equilibrium with the total transverse pressure. We must ensure a corresponding equilibrium of the net, adjusting the computed values of the forces (12) so that their total neutralizes exactly the sum of the nodal forces of type $\mathbf{F}_0$. Since T has a value such that $\mathbf{T} = a$ (§ 71), these last are calculable from (6).

73. Concentrating the edge-loading in this way, without affecting the equilibrium we may imagine every loaded string to be prolonged beyond the boundary and its load to be transferred to its outer end. If moreover it has the standard length, that end will be a 'fictitious node' outside the boundary. The question is then presented, whether the fictitious nodes should or should not be assumed to have strings connecting them. The answer is, that in some circumstances strings having *half* the standard tension $\mathbf{T}$ should connect fictitious nodes, in other circumstances fictitious nodes should *not* be connected.

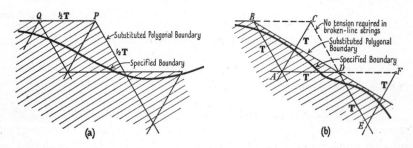

Fig. 26

The argument for the answer is as follows:[†] The fictitious nodes, if we join them, define a polygonal boundary A which lies either on or outside the specified boundary B (cf. Fig. 26); so a membrane of plan-form B (the 'Prandtl analogue' of our problem) is replaced, in this treatment, by a slightly larger net which represents (approxi-

† An alternative proof was given in Ref. 1, §§ 19–22.

mately) a slightly larger polygonal membrane A. Let A have
the form indicated by shading in Fig. 26 a: then the tension in a
fictitious string like PQ replaces the tension in a membrane-element
of which half lies inside, half outside the boundary; the outer half
has no real existence, so the string must have tension $\frac{1}{2}T$. But

the substituted (polygonal) membrane
should be no larger than is necessary,
and sometimes this consideration suggests the replacement indicated in Fig.
26 b, where the shaded area indicates
a membrane larger than B but lying
within the polygon (indicated by broken
lines) which would be obtained by joining fictitious nodes in the manner of
Fig. 26 a. Replacing this shaded membrane by a net, we shall account for all
of its tension in giving the standard
tension $\mathbf{T}$ to each of the strings (of type
AB, EF) which join 'fictitious nodes' to
nodes inside the boundary. *No membrane element calls for strings to connect
BC, CD, DF*, which accordingly are
shown in broken line. (BD is not a
string of the substituted net.)

Fig. 26 relates to triangular nets, but
square-mesh nets can be treated similarly. It now remains to deal with the
loaded strings.

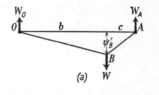

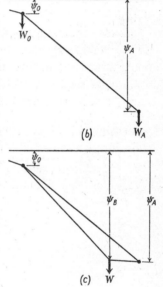

Fig. 27

74. Let OBA, Fig. 27, be a string
loaded at B by a known concentrated
force W, and assume in the first place that its ends O, A (which are
nodal points) do not deflect (Fig. 27 a). Then, in the notation of the
diagram, forces

$$W_O = \frac{c}{a}W, \qquad W_A = \frac{b}{a}W \quad (b+c = a)$$

are required, for equilibrium, at O and A respectively; so the deflexion of B is

$$bcW/a\mathbf{T} = \psi'_B, \quad \text{say}, \tag{13}$$

$\mathbf{T}$ denoting the tension in the string OA. Now let forces equal and opposite to W_O, W_A act at O and A, and let ψ_O, ψ_A (Fig. 27 b) be the displacements (determinable by Relaxation Methods) which result from these and corresponding forces at other mesh-points. The consequent displacement of B is

$$\psi_B'' = (c\psi_O + b\psi_A)/a, \tag{14}$$

and if, finally, we superpose the two solutions (13) and (14) *so as to neutralize the forces at O and A*, the resultant displacement of B will be (Fig. 27 c)

$$\psi_B = \psi_B' + \psi_B'' = \frac{c}{a}\left(\psi_O + \frac{bW}{\mathbf{T}}\right) + \frac{b}{a}\psi_A. \tag{15}$$

From (15), having determined ψ_O and ψ_A, we can compute the wanted boundary displacements of type ψ_B, thus completing the solution.

Because the integral relation of § 72 must hold in respect of B, it will also hold in respect of A (§ 73) if we assume that no force acts upon the added membrane (between B and A).† Complete liquidation will thus be possible (theoretically), leaving no residual force at any nodal point whether inside or on the specified boundary.

Example VI: Normal gradients specified for a circular boundary

75. In Ref. 8, which first set out these methods (cf. § 70), Miss G. Vaisey applied them to a problem specially chosen (i) as having

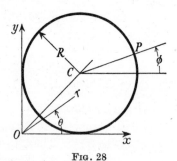

Fig. 28

a known solution, simple to compute, and (ii) as entailing rapid variations of $\partial w/\partial \nu$ in some part of the boundary.

The function $w = \theta = \tan^{-1}\dfrac{y}{x}$ (16)

---

† This added membrane may be termed the 'selvedge'. (Ref. 1, § 23.)

is plane-harmonic and can be evaluated for any point (x, y) from a table of inverse tangents; and on a circular boundary touching the axes of coordinates, viz.

$$x^2 + y^2 - 2R(x+y) + R^2 = 0, \tag{17}$$

its normal gradient

$$\frac{\partial w}{\partial \nu} = \left(\frac{\partial w}{\partial r}\right)_{r=R}, \quad \text{where } r^2 = (x-R)^2 + (y-R)^2,$$

$$= \left[\frac{\partial}{\partial r} \tan^{-1}\left(\frac{R+r\sin\phi}{R+r\cos\phi}\right)\right]_{r=R}$$

$$= \frac{1}{R}\frac{\sin\phi - \cos\phi}{3 + 2\sin\phi + 2\cos\phi}, \quad \text{where } \tan\phi = \frac{y-R}{x-R}. \tag{18}$$

Fig. 28 explains the significance of θ, R, ϕ.

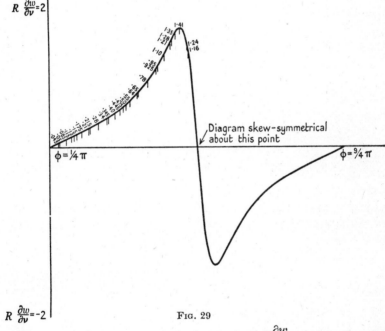

FIG. 29

Fig. 29 exhibits the variation with ϕ of $R\dfrac{\partial w}{\partial \nu}$ as given by (18).

The variation is rapid in the neighbourhood of $\phi = \frac{5}{4}\pi$; consequently by setting ourselves to determine a plane-harmonic function w which on the circular boundary (17) has normal gradients given by (18), we impose a severe test on our computational methods, notwithstanding that the wanted function is in fact simple (its contours being straight lines through the origin).

The test, moreover, is fair, because the data (i.e. the forces to be

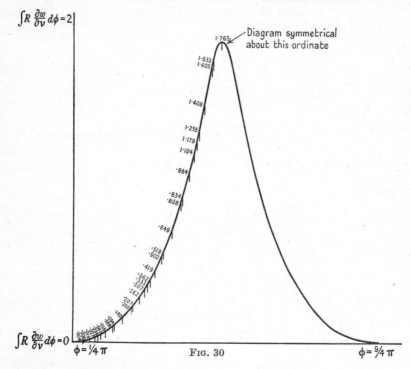

$$\int R \frac{\partial w}{\partial v}\,d\phi = 2$$

1·763

Diagram symmetrical about this ordinate

1·633
1·605

1·408

1·255
1·179
1·104

·984

·834
·808

·649

·519
·502

·419

·362
·333
·307
·262

·207
·200

$$\int R \frac{\partial w}{\partial v}\,d\phi = 0$$

$\phi = \frac{1}{4}\pi$ Fig. 30 $\phi = \frac{9}{4}\pi$

concentrated on the several strings) can be calculated and so are not subject to inaccuracies resulting from faulty estimation of normals. According to (18)

$$\int \frac{\partial w}{\partial v}\,ds = R \int \frac{\partial w}{\partial v}\,d\phi = \int \frac{\sin\phi - \cos\phi}{3 + 2\sin\phi + 2\cos\phi}\,d\phi$$
$$= -\tfrac{1}{2}\log(3 + 2\sin\phi + 2\cos\phi), \qquad (19)$$

the lower limit of integration being arbitrary; so $\oint \dfrac{\partial w}{\partial v}\,ds = 0$, as required in § 72. Fig. 30 exhibits $\displaystyle\int \frac{\partial w}{\partial v}\,ds$ as a function of ϕ, with the lower limit taken at $\phi = \tfrac{1}{4}\pi$.

76. In Fig. 30 values of $\displaystyle\int \frac{\partial w}{\partial v}\,ds$ are recorded for estimated cutting points which are shown. The difference of any two adjacent values, multiplied by $\cot \pi/6$ ($= \sqrt{3}$) in accordance with (12), gives the total load on the corresponding element of boundary; and the proportion to be concentrated at each end point can be estimated in accordance with statical principles (§ 72). Thereby we ensure that errors of estimation leave forces summing to zero (§ 72) and—on a fine net—departing so little from exact statical equipollence with the specified edge-loading as to entail no sensible error in the result.

Fig. 31 shows, for three successive nets, the computed deflexions and (Figs. *b* and *c*)† contours for comparison with straight lines representing the exact solutions. (These last, for clarity, are not drawn in the diagrams, but their directions are shown on circular arcs. All, of course, pass through the origin of coordinates.) To save space the plotted quantity is not w as given by (16), but w as given by

$$w = \theta - \tfrac{1}{4}\pi, \tag{20}$$

which makes the wanted function skew-symmetrical with respect to OC in Fig. 28, therefore makes that line a contour ($w = 0$). (It is evident that any constant value may be added to w without violating the boundary gradients.) In all three diagrams broken lines indicate strings (through fictitious nodes) which were assumed to exert 'half-tensions' (§ 73), chain lines with open circles indicate strings which were given no tension—i.e. were suppressed.

77. The correspondence of the computed contours with the (correct) straight lines through the origin gives an indication of the over-all accuracy which can be achieved by the methods of §§ 72–4. For comparison Fig. 32 exhibits corresponding solutions, obtained by the methods of Chapter II, to the problem of determining w when boundary *values* are specified. There is not much difference in the accuracy attainable (with a net of given mesh-size) by the two techniques, and the errors, though appreciable, are not of an order likely to matter seriously in physical applications.

Other types of boundary condition. (2) 'Mixed' boundary conditions

78. We have now dealt with cases of the plane-potential problem in which either (i) the wanted function, or (ii) its normal gradient has to take specified values at the boundary. A third class may be

---

† In Fig. 31 *a* the net is too coarse to permit construction of contours.

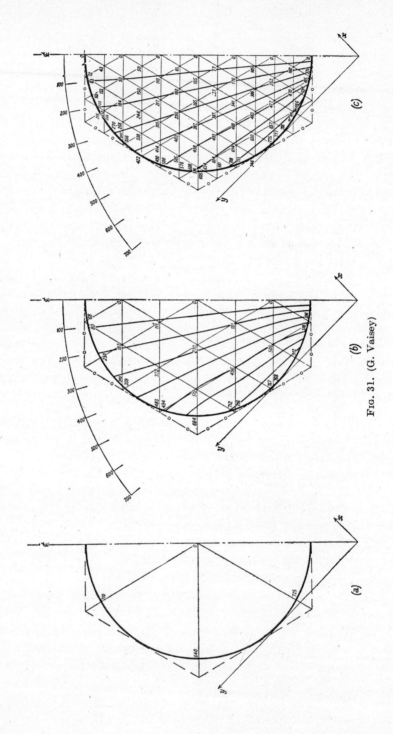

Fig. 31. (G. Vaisey)

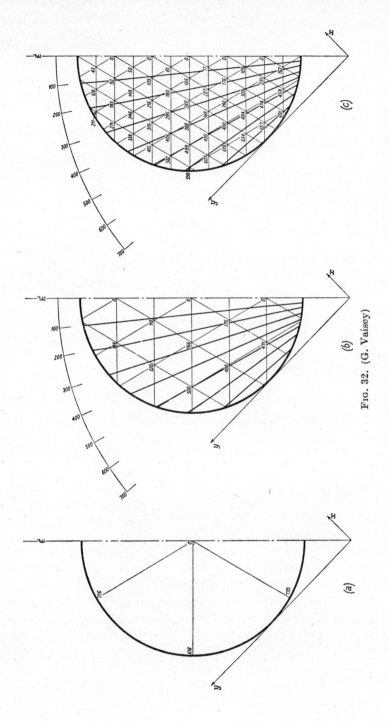

Fig. 32. (G. Vaisey)

presented, in which the wanted function is specified at some parts of the boundary, its normal gradient at others.

This class presents no difficulty, being tractable by a combination of the methods developed in this and in the preceding chapter. An example in the theory of elasticity, permitting easy verification of computed values, is provided by Saint-Venant's 'torsion-function' ϕ for an elliptical shaft. The plane-harmonic function

$$\phi = -\frac{a^2-b^2}{a^2+b^2}xy \tag{21}$$

satisfies the condition

$$\frac{\partial\phi}{\partial\nu} = y\cos(x,\nu)-x\cos(y,\nu) \tag{22}$$

at every point of a boundary represented by

$$\frac{x^2}{a^2}+\frac{y^2}{b^2} = 1, \tag{23}$$

and vanishes on the axis of coordinates; so its determination for a single quadrant ($x \geqslant 0$, $y \geqslant 0$, say) is a problem involving mixed boundary conditions. This example was treated by Miss G. Vaisey in Ref. 8, §§ 17–18.

Example VII: The torsion problem for an elliptical shaft

79. We here consider the case in which $a/b = \frac{5}{3}$, so that the required solution (21) is

$$\phi = -\tfrac{8}{17}xy. \tag{24}$$

According to (12) and (22), the total load on an element of boundary is

$$\cot(\pi/N) \int \frac{\partial\phi}{\partial\nu}\,ds = \cot(\pi/N) \int (y\,dy + x\,dx)$$

$$= \tfrac{1}{2}(x^2+y^2)\cot(\pi/N), \tag{25}$$

computed for the appropriate limits; so on a single quadrant the total load is $\pm\tfrac{1}{2}(a^2-b^2)\cot(\pi/N)$. From (25), having estimated the coordinates of points where strings cut the boundary, we can compute the load on each element of boundary, then concentrate this in accordance with statical principles. As remarked in § 72, slight errors in partition entail—on a fine net—no sensible error in the result.

Fig. 33 presents solutions, obtained on a coarse and on a fairly fine net, to this example of mixed boundary conditions. The correct contours (rectangular hyperbolas) are indicated in fine lines for comparison.

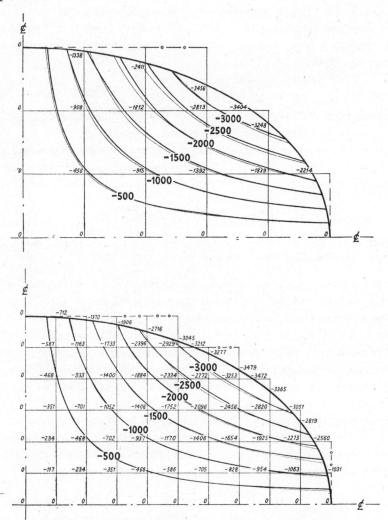

FIG. 33. The torsion problem solved for an elliptical shaft. (G. Vaisey)

Other types of boundary condition. (3) 'Refraction' at an interface

80. We are now prepared to deal with cases of refraction (§ 70), and we shall take examples from the theory of 'magnetic lines' in fields containing iron. Here, if the permeability both of air and iron be taken as constant (i.e. independent of the 'flux-intensity'), the wanted function is plane-harmonic in the region occupied by either medium; but special considerations are presented at an interface (i.e. common boundary of two different media). There, if ν denotes the direction of the normal, the wanted function has to satisfy a condition of the form

$$\lambda_{\mathrm{I}}\left(\frac{\partial w}{\partial \nu}\right)_{\mathrm{I}} = \lambda_{\mathrm{II}}\left(\frac{\partial w}{\partial \nu}\right)_{\mathrm{II}}, \tag{26}$$

in which the suffixes I and II relate to the adjoining media, and λ_{I}, λ_{II} have constant *but different* values.

Later, in discussing problems of percolation through porous media such as sand or peat (§§ 199–201), we shall meet an interface condition which may be regarded as a generalization of (26),—namely,

$$\lambda_{\mathrm{I}}\left(\frac{\partial w}{\partial \nu}\right)_{\mathrm{I}} = \lambda_{\mathrm{II}}\left(\frac{\partial w}{\partial \nu}\right)_{\mathrm{II}} + k, \tag{27}$$

where k is specified. The treatment now to be described applies equally to (26) and (27).

81. In either medium, if the wanted function is plane-harmonic it may be interpreted as the transverse displacement of a uniformly tensioned membrane, to be replaced in computation by a uniformly tensioned net; but if (27), like the governing equation (10) of § 70, is to be interpreted as a condition of transverse equilibrium, then *the membrane tensions must be different in the different media.* For the line-intensity of the transverse force which (at the interface) acts on medium I is measured, as in § 71, by $T_{\mathrm{I}}(\partial w/\partial \nu)_{\mathrm{I}}$; for medium II the corresponding line-intensity is measured by $T_{\mathrm{II}}(\partial w/\partial \nu)_{\mathrm{II}}$ and acts (when ν has the same direction in either medium) in the opposite sense: consequently, if $\mathbf{Z}$ denotes the line-intensity of the external loading at the interface, and if ν is directed outwards from medium II, then

$$\mathbf{Z} + T_{\mathrm{II}}\left(\frac{\partial w}{\partial \nu}\right)_{\mathrm{II}} - T_{\mathrm{I}}\left(\frac{\partial w}{\partial \nu}\right)_{\mathrm{I}} = 0 \tag{28}$$

is the condition for transverse equilibrium of a point on the junction of the two media (i.e. on the interface). Equation (28) may be identified with (27) provided that

$$\mathbf{Z}/k = T_{\mathrm{I}}/\lambda_{\mathrm{I}} = T_{\mathrm{II}}/\lambda_{\mathrm{II}}. \tag{29}$$

(The notion of two membranes differently tensioned, yet joined to one another at the interface, is not incompatible with equilibrium provided that suitable forces act at the interface in directions parallel with the x-y plane. These having no component along Oz will not affect the question of equilibrium in a *transverse* direction,—i.e. they will not enter into the condition (28).)

82. Now replacing the membrane by its 'net approximation', we have according to (13) of § 39 (Chap. II) to concentrate in any one string a tension

$$\mathbf{T} = aT\tan\pi/N, \tag{30}$$
$$= a \text{ if, } but \text{ only } if, \ T = \cot\pi/N. \tag{31}$$

When (31) is satisfied, then (cf. § 61) a unit deflexion, imposed at one end of any 'string', entails a transfer of 1 unit of residual force from the end which is moved to the end which is held fixed. But if T and therefore $\mathbf{T}$ has a different value, then the force transferred will be altered correspondingly.

Reverting to § 81, according to (29) we can give the value (31) either to T_I or to T_II, *but not to both*. If we say that

$$\left. \begin{array}{ll} \qquad T_\mathrm{I} = \cot\pi/N, & \text{so that } \ \mathbf{T}_\mathrm{I} = a, \\[2mm] \text{then} \qquad T_\mathrm{II} = \dfrac{\lambda_\mathrm{II}}{\lambda_\mathrm{I}}\cot\pi/N, & \text{,,} \quad \mathbf{T}_\mathrm{II} = a\dfrac{\lambda_\mathrm{II}}{\lambda_\mathrm{I}}, \\[2mm] \text{and} \qquad \mathbf{Z} = \dfrac{k}{\lambda_\mathrm{I}}\cot\pi/N. & \end{array} \right\} \tag{32}$$

The force transferred per string for unit displacement will be 1 in medium I, $\lambda_\mathrm{II}/\lambda_\mathrm{I}$ in medium II.

Equations (3)–(7), § 63, still hold at nodal points *within* either medium, since they were obtained (§ 41) on the assumption of a transverse loading measured by $T.Z(x,y)$, and thus the magnitude of T was made irrelevant.

83. The external loading $\mathbf{Z}$, in (32), entails a total loading $\int \mathbf{Z}\,ds$, on any element of boundary, which may be concentrated on adjacent strings in the manner of § 72. (In the examples treated in this chapter, k and therefore $\mathbf{Z}$ are zero everywhere.) Allowance must now be made for the change in $\mathbf{T}$ at a point where a string cuts the interface. (As in § 81, such change is not incompatible with equilibrium if suitable forces are postulated as operating in directions parallel with the x-y plane, and these will not affect the question of *transverse* equilibrium.)

Adopting the values (32), suppose (Fig. 34) that a string OA of length a lies as to a part $(\alpha_I a)$ of its length in medium I and as to the remainder $(\alpha_{II} a)$ of its length in medium II. If its deflexions are

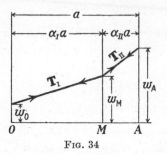

Fig. 34

w_O, w_M, w_A at O, M, and A respectively, the condition for equilibrium at M is

$$\frac{T_{II}(w_A - w_M)}{\alpha_{II} a} = \frac{T_I(w_M - w_O)}{\alpha_I a}, \qquad (i)$$

and serves to determine w_M in terms of w_O and w_A. We deduce that the force at O is

$$\frac{T_I(w_M - w_O)}{\alpha_I a} = \frac{1}{a} T_I T_{II}(w_A - w_O)/(T_I \alpha_{II} + T_{II} \alpha_I), \qquad (ii)$$

and that the force at A has equal magnitude but opposite sign.

Thus in either medium the force exerted by a string in consequence of a relative displacement of its two ends is proportional, as usual, to that relative displacement and to its tension; but in medium I the effective tension (T_I) is increased in the ratio

$$T_{II}/(T_I \alpha_{II} + T_{II} \alpha_I), \qquad (iii)$$

and in medium II the effective tension (T_{II}) is increased in the ratio

$$T_I/(T_I \alpha_{II} + T_{II} \alpha_I). \qquad (iv)$$

When $T_I = T_{II}$, both of these expressions reduce to 1 (as clearly they should) since $\alpha_I + \alpha_{II} = 1$. When $T_{II}/T_I = \infty$ (so that $w_M = w_A$ in Fig. 34) the first expression reduces to $1/\alpha_I$,—consistently with (1) of § 63, since α_I is then identical with the quantity there denoted by x. As they stand, (iii) and (iv) may be expressed in the statement that the equivalent lengths of string in medium I and II are respectively $x_I a$ and $x_{II} a$, where

$$x_I = \alpha_I + \frac{T_I}{T_{II}} \alpha_{II}, \qquad x_{II} = \alpha_{II} + \frac{T_{II}}{T_I} \alpha_I. \qquad (33)$$

On this understanding the formulae (3)–(5) of § 63 can be utilized, in combination with (32), to derive special 'patterns' whereby the computer can deal with 'irregular stars' near a surface of refraction.

84. There remains for discussion the case in which a string lies wholly in the interface. Here we have recourse to the argument of § 73, from which it was concluded that a 'half-tension' ($\frac{1}{2}\mathbf{T}$) should be postulated in any string which lies along the boundary: the same reasoning shows that when a string is a boundary of both media, then its tension should be

$$\tfrac{1}{2}(\mathbf{T}_\mathrm{I}+\mathbf{T}_\mathrm{II}) = \tfrac{1}{2}a\left(1+\frac{\lambda_\mathrm{II}}{\lambda_\mathrm{I}}\right),$$

if the values (32) are adopted.

We now have all the principles required for a relaxational treatment of refraction. Details will be grasped most easily from a study of particular examples.

Lines of magnetic force in a field containing iron

85. A magnetic field can be specified by the distribution of Ω, a function termed the **magnetic potential** (Ref. 5, § 408). In regions occupied by non-magnetic material (such as air) the components of 'magnetic force' are

$$\alpha = -\frac{\partial\Omega}{\partial x}, \qquad \beta = -\frac{\partial\Omega}{\partial y}, \qquad \gamma = -\frac{\partial\Omega}{\partial z}, \tag{34}$$

and in regions occupied by magnetic material of 'permeability' μ the components of 'magnetic induction' are

$$a = -\mu\frac{\partial\Omega}{\partial x}, \qquad b = -\mu\frac{\partial\Omega}{\partial y}, \qquad c = -\mu\frac{\partial\Omega}{\partial z}. \tag{35}$$

At every point within the field Ω must be continuous and must satisfy the equation

$$\frac{\partial}{\partial x}\left(\mu\frac{\partial\Omega}{\partial x}\right)+\frac{\partial}{\partial y}\left(\mu\frac{\partial\Omega}{\partial y}\right)+\frac{\partial}{\partial z}\left(\mu\frac{\partial\Omega}{\partial z}\right) = 0, \tag{36}$$

which reduces to Laplace's equation when μ is uniform; and at every point in an interface where the value of μ alters from μ_1 to μ_2 it must satisfy

$$\mu_1\frac{\partial\Omega}{\partial v_1}+\mu_2\frac{\partial\Omega}{\partial v_2} = 0, \tag{37}$$

v_1 and v_2 denoting normals to the surface drawn *into* the two media (Ref. 5, §§ 432, 461, 466–7).

86. When Ω is two-dimensional (so that $\partial\Omega/\partial z = 0$), (36) permits us to introduce a conjugate function ψ defined by

$$\mu\frac{\partial\Omega}{\partial x} = \frac{\partial\psi}{\partial y}, \qquad \mu\frac{\partial\Omega}{\partial y} = -\frac{\partial\psi}{\partial x}, \tag{38}$$

and then on eliminating Ω we find that ψ (like Ω, two-dimensional) is governed by the equation

$$\frac{\partial}{\partial x}\left(\mu^{-1}\frac{\partial\psi}{\partial x}\right) + \frac{\partial}{\partial y}\left(\mu^{-1}\frac{\partial\psi}{\partial y}\right) = 0, \tag{39}$$

so that ψ is plane-harmonic in any region where μ is uniform. Because, according to (38) and Fig. 5 (cf. footnote to § 26),

$$\mu\frac{\partial\Omega}{\partial\nu} = \mu\cos(x,\nu)\frac{\partial\Omega}{\partial x} + \mu\sin(x,\nu)\frac{\partial\Omega}{\partial y}$$
$$= \cos(x,\nu)\frac{\partial\psi}{\partial y} - \sin(x,\nu)\frac{\partial\psi}{\partial x} = \frac{\partial\psi}{\partial s}, \tag{40}$$

the boundary condition (37) will be satisfied provided that no discontinuity occurs in the value of ψ as we pass from the material of permeability μ_1 into the material of permeability μ_2; but the gradient of ψ in a direction normal to the interface must (Ω being continuous) change its value abruptly in the same ratio as μ, since we have similarly, from (38) and Fig. 5,

$$\mu_1^{-1}\left(\frac{\partial\psi}{\partial\nu}\right)_1 = -\frac{\partial\Omega}{\partial s} = \mu_2^{-1}\left(\frac{\partial\psi}{\partial\nu}\right)_2. \tag{41}$$

This, like (37), has the form of (26), § 80.

Lines of constant ψ will thus change direction abruptly where they cross an interface, but ψ will be continuous. We have not changed the nature of the problem in replacing Ω by ψ—which is a quantity having greater physical interest, for the reason that lines of constant ψ are 'magnetic lines'. We term ψ the **magnetic flux-function.**

Example VIII: Magnetic lines through a triangular prism of iron

87. By orthodox methods the calculation of ψ is difficult, and few solutions have been found. Hele-Shaw and Hay (Ref. 4) devised an experimental technique depending on an approximate analogy between this problem and that of viscous fluid motion between nearly flat and parallel plates (changes in μ being reproduced by changes in the distance between the plates). Their paper contains many beautiful photographs of results. We now discuss the problem shown in their Fig. 29, here reproduced as Fig. 35: namely, the effect on

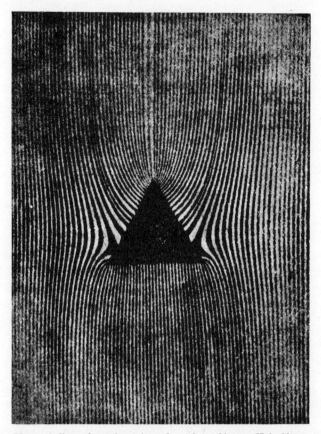

FIG. 35. Magnetic lines through a triangular prism of iron. (Hele-Shaw and Hay)

an otherwise uniform field of inserting a triangular prism of iron (permeability 100).

In the interior of either medium μ is uniform and ψ is accordingly plane-harmonic, so the methods of §§ 80–4 are applicable, λ_{I}, λ_{II} being identified with μ_1^{-1}, μ_2^{-1} in (41), and k being zero. That is to say, giving to $\mathbf{T}_1$ the standard value a, we have $\mathbf{T}_2 = a\mu_1/\mu_2$ in medium 2; and if 1 refers to air, 2 to iron, then in our example the string tension is a in the region occupied by air, $0.01a$ in the region occupied by iron, $0.505a$ (§ 84) in a string which lies along an interface. For a string of length a which is intersected by an interface so as to have a part $\alpha_1 a$ of its length in air and a part $\alpha_2 a$ in iron, the effective lengths are $x_1 a$ and $x_2 a$ respectively, where

$$x_1 = \alpha_1 + 100\alpha_2, \qquad x_2 = \alpha_2 + \alpha_1/100, \tag{42}$$

according to (33).

88. We are concerned to trace the effect of iron on a field which otherwise would be uniform and so represented by

$$\psi \propto x \tag{43}$$

when the axes are as shown in Fig. 36. We choose an outer boundary large in comparison with the extent of the iron, and we assume (43) to hold on this boundary. In Fig. 36 (prepared by Miss G. Vaisey to amplify an earlier diagram by D. G. Christopherson, Ref. 3) the shape of this outer boundary was chosen to accord with the experiment of Hele-Shaw and Hay. Nothing in the method of solution calls for special description here: the standard 'plane-harmonic pattern' (Fig. 10c) holds in respect of any point from which the radiating strings lie wholly in one medium (whether iron or air), and for other points it was a simple matter to determine appropriate patterns, from (4) with a use of (42) to calculate the effective lengths of strings which cut an interface. The subsequent liquidation process (using these patterns) follows on the standard lines of Chapter II, and the derivation of contours calls for no explanation. Fig. 35, a photographic reproduction of Fig. 29 of the paper by Hele-Shaw and Hay, shows how closely their results have been reproduced. The solution in Fig. 36 can either be checked or worked from first principles by the reader.

Example IX: Pole flux in an electric generator

89. A problem of the same kind, but entailing more labour and of greater practical interest, has been worked by Miss G. Vaisey with results which are recorded in Fig. 37. These too can either be verified by the reader, or obtained *ab initio*, without further explanation except in regard to the device by which the use of a *rectangular* net was rendered possible, notwithstanding that the nature of the problem would suggest a use of *polar* coordinates r, θ (one of which has a constant value over any of the concentric circles). The permeability of the iron was taken as 2000.

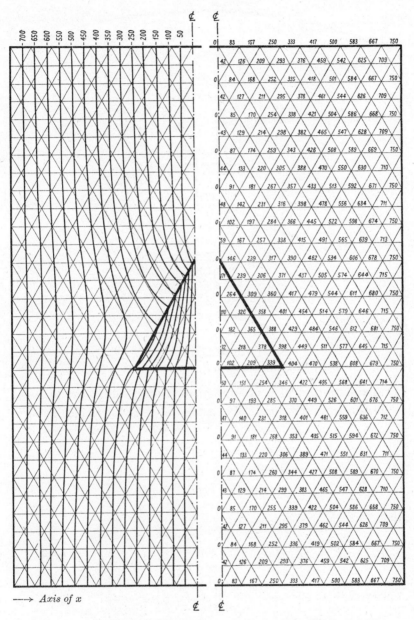

FIG. 36. Relaxational solution for comparison with Fig. 35. (G. Vaisey)

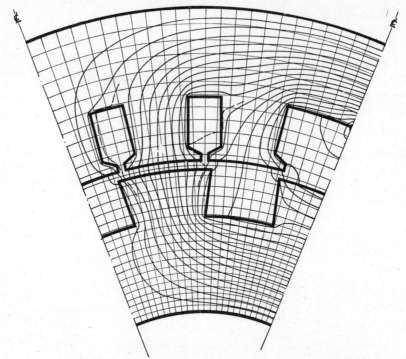

FIG. 37. Flux distribution in an electric generator. (G. Vaisey)

Transformation by a change of the independent variables

90. Expressed in terms of r and θ, the plane-harmonic operator

$$\frac{\partial^2}{\partial x^2}+\frac{\partial^2}{\partial y^2} \equiv \nabla^2 \equiv \frac{\partial^2}{\partial r^2}+\frac{1}{r}\frac{\partial}{\partial r}+\frac{1}{r^2}\frac{\partial^2}{\partial \theta^2} \tag{44}$$

(cf., e.g., *Elasticity*, § 240). Now if

$$\left. \begin{array}{l} \quad\quad \xi \text{ stands for } \log r, \quad\quad \eta \text{ for } \theta, \\[6pt] \text{then} \quad\quad \dfrac{\partial}{\partial r} \equiv \dfrac{d\xi}{dr}\dfrac{\partial}{\partial \xi} \equiv \dfrac{1}{r}\dfrac{\partial}{\partial \xi}, \\[10pt] \text{and so} \quad\quad \dfrac{\partial^2}{\partial r^2}+\dfrac{1}{r}\dfrac{\partial}{\partial r} \equiv \dfrac{1}{r}\dfrac{\partial}{\partial r}\left(r\dfrac{\partial}{\partial r}\right)=\dfrac{1}{r^2}\dfrac{\partial^2}{\partial \xi^2}. \\[10pt] \text{Consequently} \quad\quad \nabla^2 \equiv \dfrac{1}{r^2}\left[\dfrac{\partial^2}{\partial \xi^2}+\dfrac{\partial^2}{\partial \eta^2}\right], \end{array} \right\} \tag{45}$$

and thus in either medium, since $\nabla^2\psi = 0$ and r is finite, we have

$$\nabla^2_{\xi,\eta}(\psi) \equiv \frac{\partial^2\psi}{\partial \xi^2}+\frac{\partial^2\psi}{\partial \eta^2} = 0. \tag{46}$$

This means that ψ, regarded as a function of ξ and η, satisfies the standard plane-harmonic equation, and accordingly may be sought by the normal technique.

A boundary condition which imposes specified values on ψ is clearly unaffected by such change of variables, and the condition on a radial line of symmetry (e.g. the right-hand boundary in Fig. 37) will be

$$0 = \frac{\partial \psi}{\partial \theta} = \frac{\partial \psi}{\partial \eta}. \tag{47}$$

Equally the condition (41) at an interface will be unaffected. For the operator

$$\frac{\partial}{\partial \nu} \equiv \cos(\nu, r) \frac{\partial}{\partial r} - \sin(\nu, r) \frac{1}{r} \frac{\partial}{\partial \theta},$$

$$\equiv \frac{1}{r} \left[\cos(\nu, r) \frac{\partial}{\partial \xi} - \sin(\nu, r) \frac{\partial}{\partial \eta} \right], \quad \text{by (45),} \tag{i}$$

ν denoting the direction of the normal in the (r, θ) plane. Now

$$\tan(\nu, r) = \frac{1}{r} \frac{dr}{d\theta} = \frac{d}{d\theta}(\log r) = \frac{d\xi}{d\eta}, \quad \text{according to (45),} \tag{ii}$$

when the transformed boundary is defined by $\xi = F(\eta)$. This shows that (ν, r) is the angle between the transformed boundary and the η-axis, therefore also the angle between its normal (ν') and the ξ-axis. Consequently (i) shows that

$$\frac{\partial}{\partial \nu} = \frac{1}{r} \left[\cos(\nu', \xi) \frac{\partial}{\partial \xi} - \sin(\nu', \xi) \frac{\partial}{\partial \eta} \right] = \frac{1}{r} \frac{\partial}{\partial \nu'}, \tag{48}$$

and it follows that (41) transforms into an equation of identical form.

Fig. 38 exhibits the problem of Example IX (§ 89) transformed in this manner to permit computation on a square (ξ, η) net. The ψ-values shown were transferred to Fig. 37 as a preliminary to the construction of ψ-contours (i.e. lines of magnetic flux).

The treatment of 'unequal stars' (concluded). Graphical devices for improved approximation

91. The assumption underlying §§ 62–3 and 67–8 (namely, that every 'string' remains straight in the deflected net) is a logical implication of the 'net analogue' and has the great merit of practical simplicity. But a solution started on this basis can be improved, if necessary, in the course of its development, and sometimes it will happen that such improvement has advantages over the alternative of 'advance to a finer net'. We now develop the necessary formulae.

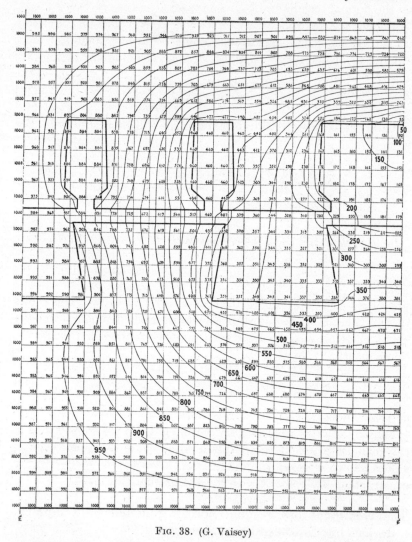

Fig. 38. (G. Vaisey)

In Fig. 24 (§ 67) B denoted a point on the boundary, A a real, and C a 'fictitious' node; the upper part of the diagram showed the string ABC as straight, and (9) was obtained on this understanding. Let E be the real (internal) node adjacent to A on this string produced, and suppose that $eabc$ (Fig. 39) is a smooth curve passing through the deflected positions of E, A, B, C. We now trace the consequences of assuming this curve to be a flat parabola (evidently a closer approximation to the membrane section than two intersecting straight lines ea, ac).

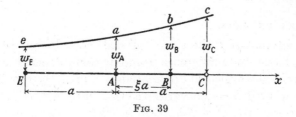

FIG. 39

We may express the parabola by

$$w = w_A + x\left(\frac{dw}{dx}\right)_A + \frac{x^2}{2!}\left(\frac{d^2w}{dx^2}\right)_A \tag{i}$$

when x is measured from left to right, as shown; and then, using the finite-difference approximations

$$2a\left(\frac{dw}{dx}\right)_A \approx w_C - w_E \tag{ii}$$

$$a^2\left(\frac{d^2w}{dx^2}\right)_A \approx w_C + w_E - 2w_A, \tag{iii}$$

we have for the deflexion at B

$$w_B = w_A + \xi a\left(\frac{dw}{dx}\right)_A + \tfrac{1}{2}\xi^2 a^2\left(\frac{d^2w}{dx^2}\right)_A$$
$$= w_A + \tfrac{1}{2}\xi(w_C - w_E) + \tfrac{1}{2}\xi^2(w_C + w_E - 2w_A). \tag{iv}$$

Rearranging this equation, we have

$$w_B - w_A(1-\xi) - \xi w_C + \tfrac{1}{2}\xi(1-\xi)(w_C + w_E - 2w_A) = 0, \tag{49}$$

which is satisfied identically when $eabc$ (Fig. 39) is straight, since then we have the relations

$$2w_A = w_E + w_C, \qquad w_B = w_A(1-\xi) + \xi w_C.$$

Regarded as an expression for the deflexion at the fictitious point C, (iv) may be written as

$$\frac{w_C}{1-\xi} = \frac{2w_B}{\xi(1-\xi^2)} - \frac{2w_A}{\xi} + \frac{w_E}{1+\xi}, \tag{50}$$

which, as the solution progresses towards finality on any particular net, may be used in place of (9), § 67, to modify the value of w_C.

Equivalent devices for improving the accuracy of the 'straight string assumption' (§ 67) have been propounded by Christopherson (Ref. 2) and Shaw (Ref. 6). All entail greater labour, and in general it would seem better to retain the simpler formulae and to rely for close approximation on the fineness of the ultimate net.

Use of 'graded' nets

92. An alternative is the use of 'graded' nets (Ref. 1, § 14). The accuracy of our finite-difference approximation depends upon the magnitudes of the neglected differentials, i.e. upon the rapidity with which the wanted function varies; consequently *a finer net may be needed in some parts of a 'field' than in others, to define the function with precision.* What then is wanted is a technique involving specially fine nets *in regions arbitrarily delimited by the computer.*

Example X: The torsion problem for a rectangular shaft with two keyways

Consider, as an example, the torsion problem for a rectangular section having two symmetrical keyways (Fig. 40). The 'stress-function' χ must satisfy the equation (8), § 64, at every point in the section, and it must vanish at every point on the boundary. We know that it has, close to the keyways, gradients which are large compared with its gradients elsewhere; so a coarse net will suffice over most of the section, compared with the net which is appropriate there. (On account of symmetry, only one-quarter of the section needs to be reproduced.)

In Fig. 40, outside of the region *abc* the mesh-side *a* is one-twelfth the length of a shorter side of the rectangle, or one-sixteenth the length of a longer side. Within *abc*, by insertion of diagonals, the meshes have been successively reduced in size (and rotated through 45°) until, within *lmn*, the mesh-side is only one-quarter of what it is outside *abc*.

93. In liquidating residuals on a net thus 'graded', care must be taken to ensure that correct 'relaxation patterns' are employed. Thus the residual force at *h* (Fig. 40) depends upon the χ-values at *h*, *g*, *b*, *d*, *e*, but the residual force at *b* depends upon the χ-values at *b*, *g*, *f*, *k*, *d*, which are nodes of a coarser net; consequently χ_b influences $\mathbf{F}_h$ but χ_h does not influence $\mathbf{F}_b$, and the notion (§ 61) of a force transmitted from *h* to *b* by the 'string' *hb*, as the result of a

'displacement' χ_h, must now be discarded. *Point h is included in the*
'relaxation pattern' appropriate to b, but b is not included in the pattern
appropriate to h.†

Moreover the sum of the residual forces will not be invariant for

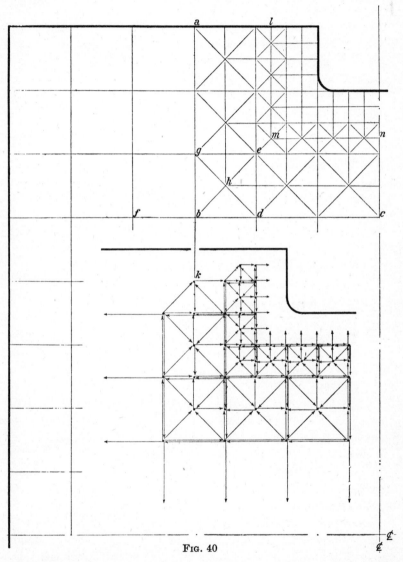

Fig. 40

† In Fig. 40 an inserted diagram shows 'patterns' drawn in accordance with
obvious conventions. These will not be needed by an experienced computer, who
will readily see the consequences of any given 'point-displacement'.

every operation, as it is when uniform nets are employed. (*e*, for example, is 'fictitious' in relation to the coarsest net of Fig. 40, and force transmitted to it as a consequence of displacement of g or d is not brought into account because $\mathbf{F}_e$ (as now defined) does not depend on χ_g or on χ_d.)

But these circumstances entail no difficulty, and the solution given in Fig. 41 was obtained (by Miss G. Vaisey) easily and more quickly than it would have been if the finest net had extended to every part of the computational field. χ-contours show the direction and (by the closeness of their spacing) the magnitude of the shear stress at every point.

RÉSUMÉ

94. This chapter, starting (§ 61) from principles developed in Chapter II, extends the range of Relaxation Methods by an elaboration of details, viz. by providing for 'irregular stars' (§§ 62–3, 67–8, 91), by introducing the concept of 'fictitious nodes' (§§ 67–8), and by evolving techniques for dealing with new forms of boundary condition and (§§ 92–3) with 'graded' nets. We can now distinguish (and solve) four classes of the plane-potential problem.

Class I, in which values of the wanted function are specified at the boundary (discussed in Chapter II and §§ 61–9);

Class II, in which values are imposed, at the boundary, on the normal gradient of the wanted function (§§ 70–7);

Class III, in which the boundary conditions are 'mixed' (§§ 78–9);

Class IV, characterized by 'refraction' at one or more 'interfaces' (§§ 80–9).

In one example, incidentally, we have (§ 90) introduced a change of variables by what amounts to an application of 'conformal transformation'. This device will receive further consideration in Chapter IV.

It is, in fact, the boundary conditions which, in any two-dimensional problem, make most demand on the intelligence of the computer. Relaxation patterns of normal type, such as were appropriate to the examples in Chapter II, can be used without understanding of their basis and significance; but when (e.g.) gradients instead of values of the wanted function are specified at the boundary, special patterns and special thinking are demanded.

One last point must be emphasized:—Usually, physical considerations prohibit multiple values of the wanted function within the

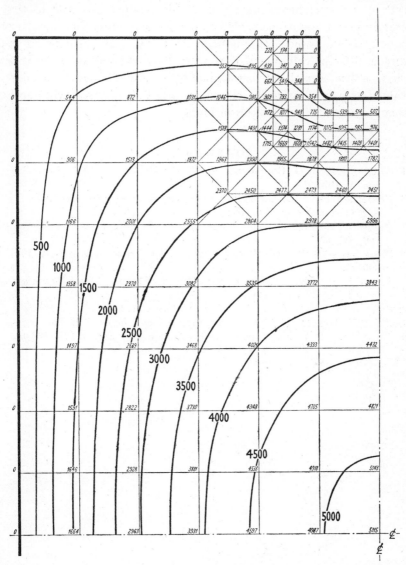

FIG. 41. The torsion problem solved for a rectangular shaft with two keyways.
(G. Vaisey)

bounded area of the problem, *but there is nothing to prohibit multiple
values at 'fictitious nodes' which lie outside that area.* (Thus

$$\psi = A \tan^{-1}(y/x)$$

is a plane-harmonic function multi-valued only at the origin of coordinates, and hence admissible if the origin is external to the area.) Near a re-entrant angle two strings may cross the boundary to end on the same fictitious node: then we must be prepared to attach different values at that point to their end deflexions, for it is obvious that we shall not thereby make the wanted function multiple-valued at points *inside* the boundary, and it is only at such points that it has real (i.e. physical) meaning.

REFERENCES

1. ALLEN, D. N. de G., SOUTHWELL, R. V., and VAISEY, G. 1945. *Proc. Roy Soc.* A, **183**, 258–83.
2. CHRISTOPHERSON, D. G. 1940. *Amer. Journ. of Applied Mechanics*, **7**, A 1–4; reprinted in *Roy. Aero. Soc. Journal*, **44**, 425–32.
3. CHRISTOPHERSON, D. G., and SOUTHWELL, R. V. 1938. *Proc. Roy. Soc.* A, **168**, 317–50.
4. HELE-SHAW, H. S., and HAY, A. 1900. *Phil. Trans. Roy. Soc.* A, **195**, 303–27.
5. JEANS, J. H. 1923. *The Mathematical Theory of Electricity and Magnetism*, 4th ed. Camb. Univ. Press.
6. SHAW, F. S. 1942. *Journ. Inst. Eng. Australia*, **14**, 273–7.
7. SHAW, F. S. 1944. *C.S.I.R. (Australia) Aero. Div. Report S.M.* **36**.
8. SOUTHWELL, R. V., and VAISEY, G. 1943. *Proc. Roy. Soc.* A, **182**, 129–51.

IV

RELAXATION METHODS APPLIED TO THE PROBLEM OF CONFORMAL TRANSFORMATION

95. In this chapter we consider a special type of problem coming (normally) within the definition of 'Class I' in § 94. One example has been given already, in §§ 89–90 of Chapter III.

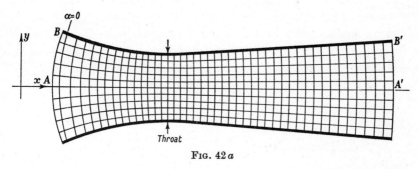

Fig. 42 a

Fig. 42 b

It often happens (as in that example) that a change of variables will leave our problem still plane-harmonic, but relating to a more convenient shape of boundary. Thus in a relaxational study of high-speed flow of air through a convergent-divergent nozzle (Ref. 5) it was found best to begin by so transforming the variables that the field of computation became a rectangle, thereby obviating the added complication of 'irregular stars'. Figs. 42 exhibit the original and the transformed field. Each is mapped with a net of which every mesh is approximately square, and to every nodal point of the curvilinear net in Fig. 42 a there corresponds a particular nodal point of the square net in Fig. 42 b.

The device by which this change of variables was effected is the relaxational equivalent of an analytical device known as conformal transformation,† which we now describe.

Basic theory

96. The existence of a plane-harmonic function ψ implies the existence of a 'conjugate' plane-harmonic function ϕ, such that

$$w = \phi + i\psi = F(x+iy) = F(z), \tag{1}$$

the form of the function F depending on the shape of the boundary and on the condition which is there imposed on ψ. In Riemann's definition of a function of a complex variable (cf., e.g., Ref. 7, § 62) not only must (1) be satisfied but dw/dz must have a value independent of the ratio dx/dy in the total increment $dz = dx+i\,dy$.

Since

$$\frac{dw}{dz} = \lim_{\delta z \to 0} \left[\frac{\delta w = \delta\phi + i\,\delta\psi}{\delta z = \delta x + i\,\delta y} \right] = \lim \frac{\left(\dfrac{\partial\phi}{\partial x} + i\dfrac{\partial\psi}{\partial x}\right)\delta x + \left(\dfrac{\partial\phi}{\partial y} + i\dfrac{\partial\psi}{\partial y}\right)\delta y}{\delta x + i\,\delta y},$$

this last requirement means that

$$i\left(\frac{\partial\phi}{\partial x} + i\frac{\partial\psi}{\partial x}\right) = i\left(\frac{dw}{dz}\right)_{\delta y = 0} = i\left(\frac{dw}{dz}\right)_{\delta x = 0} = \frac{\partial\phi}{\partial y} + i\frac{\partial\psi}{\partial y},$$

whence (by equation of real and imaginary parts) we have

$$\frac{\partial\phi}{\partial x} = \frac{\partial\psi}{\partial y}, \qquad \frac{\partial\phi}{\partial y} = -\frac{\partial\psi}{\partial x}, \tag{2}$$

and so (by elimination of ψ and ϕ)

$$\nabla^2\phi = 0, \qquad \nabla^2\psi = 0, \tag{3}$$

∇^2 standing for $\partial^2/\partial x^2 + \partial^2/\partial y^2$.

97. When the form of F, in (1), is known, then corresponding with any value of z (i.e. for any point in the x-y plane) we can deduce a value (or series of values) for w, thus fixing a corresponding point (or series of points) in the ϕ-ψ plane. Usually the possibility of multiple values can be excluded, and then we have a one-to-one correspondence of points in the x-y, or z-plane, with points in the ϕ-ψ, or w-plane; so a line-element $\delta z = \delta x + i\,\delta y$ in the z-plane corresponds with every line-element $\delta w = \delta\phi + i\,\delta\psi$ in the w-plane. The ratio of the two line-elements is given by the modulus of dw/dz, and their relative direction by its argument; therefore, since dw/dz has

† The term is explained in § 97.

(§ 96) a value independent of the ratio $\delta x/\delta y$, an elemental square in the w-plane will correspond with every elemental square in the z-plane. Usually its side will be of different length and will have a different orientation.

With any curve in the z-plane there will correspond a curve in the w-plane; and in particular, with any closed curve in the z-plane there will correspond a closed curve in the w-plane. Therefore (since any closed curve may be regarded as a boundary) a bounded region in the w-plane will correspond with every bounded region in the z-plane. We say that (1), when the form of F is given, *transforms* a region in the z-plane into a region in the w-plane; and since (as shown above) the shapes of elementary areas are conserved, we term this a **conformal transformation**.

98. As an example, let F in (1) be the logarithmic function, i.e. let

$$w = \phi + i\psi = \log z = \log r + i\theta, \tag{i}$$

where r and θ are polar coordinates in the x-y plane, so that

$$x = r\cos\theta, \qquad y = r\sin\theta, \qquad z = x + iy = re^{i\theta}. \tag{ii}$$

Then, corresponding with any point (x, y) in the z-plane, we have

$$\phi = \log r = \tfrac{1}{2}\log(x^2 + y^2), \qquad \psi = \theta = \tan^{-1}(y/x), \tag{iii}$$

i.e. we have *a series of points* in the ϕ-ψ plane, all having the same abscissa (ϕ) but with ordinates (ψ) separated by regular intervals 2π. If, however, we limit the extent of the second plane by requiring ψ to lie between 0 and 2π, then there will be a one-to-one correspondence between points in the x-y and in the ϕ-ψ plane: consequently a line-element δw in the second plane will correspond with every line-element δz in the first; and since, according to (i),

$$\frac{dw}{dz} = 1/z = (x - iy)/r^2 = \frac{1}{r}(\cos\theta - i\sin\theta), \quad \text{by (ii)}, \tag{iv}$$

the modulus of dw/dz, namely $1/r$, gives the ratio of δw to δz, and its argument, namely $2\pi - \theta$, gives their relative directions.

Fig. 43 shows the original and transformed line-elements joining points A, B which in the x-y plane are equidistant from the origin. It confirms the conclusions just stated; for the transformed line-element $A'B'$ is directed along the ψ-axis (i.e. is rotated backwards through an angle θ relatively to AB), and its length

$$\delta\psi = \delta\theta = (AB)/r.$$

(This particular conformal transformation was, in effect, employed in § 90, Chap. III.)

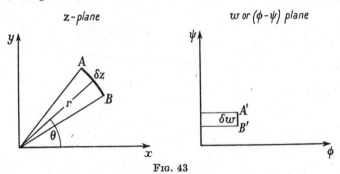

FIG. 43

99. In § 96, ϕ and ψ denoted a pair of conjugate plane-harmonic functions of x and y. Let α and β be another pair, such that

$$\gamma = \alpha + i\beta = f(x+iy) = f(z). \tag{4}$$

Then, since w and γ are both functions of z, w will also be a function of γ, and it follows, as in (2), that

$$\frac{\partial \phi}{\partial \alpha} = \frac{\partial \psi}{\partial \beta}, \qquad \frac{\partial \phi}{\partial \beta} = -\frac{\partial \psi}{\partial \alpha}. \tag{5}$$

Consequently $\qquad \nabla^2_{\alpha\beta}\phi = 0, \qquad \nabla^2_{\alpha\beta}\psi = 0, \tag{6}$

where $\qquad \nabla^2_{\alpha\beta} \equiv \dfrac{\partial^2}{\partial \alpha^2} + \dfrac{\partial^2}{\partial \beta^2}. \tag{7}$

In other words, if ϕ and ψ are plane-harmonic and conjugate when regarded as functions of x and y, they will have the same properties, regarded as functions of α and β, when these are related with x and y by an equation of the type of (4). From the geometrical standpoint of § 97, *if a region in the x-y plane can be transformed conformally into a region in the α-β plane, then any plane-harmonic function of x and y will also be a plane-harmonic function of α and β.*

Herein lies the practical value of conformal transformation. The original (specified) region in the x-y plane may be such that determination of the wanted plane-harmonic function (ψ, say) is difficult: then it may be useful to transform that region into another (in the α-β plane) for which the problem is easier. Having determined ψ as a function of α and β, we shall (in virtue of the one-to-one correspondence) also know it as a function of x and y. An example has been cited in § 95.

Standard types of transformation

100. Different transformations have value in different problems. In this chapter we shall specially consider four,—namely:

(a) transformation of the region enclosed within a given boundary into the region enclosed within a circle;

(b) transformation of the region enclosed within a given boundary into the region enclosed within a rectangle;

(c) transformation of the region external to a given boundary into the region external to a circle;

(d) transformation of a semi-infinite region into an infinite strip.

Figs. 44 (a), (b), (c), (d) show the nature of the transformations. In (b) and (d), the computed functions α and β are made Cartesian coordinates, so that the transformed boundaries are rectilinear. In (a) and (c), contours of α become lines through the origin, contours of β become concentric circles.

Thus in Fig. 44 a the region contained by an ellipse and by the two branches of a confocal hyperbola is transformed into a circle, the centres of the ellipse and circle being corresponding points. This transformation could be used (although it is not the most direct method) to solve the torsion problem of Saint-Venant, and the section illustrated has some interest from that standpoint as being an example chosen by Filon (Ref. 3) to illustrate his contention that the shear stress is not always (as had been stated by Boussinesq) greatest at those points of the boundary which are nearest the centroid.

In illustration of (b), Fig. 44 b shows a typical rail section transformed into a rectangle. This transformation could be employed as a means of solving the flexure problem for the rail section, and in this connexion would have advantages as compared with a transformation of type (a).†

In illustration of (c), Fig. 44 c shows the region external to a typical airscrew section which was studied from an aerodynamical standpoint by Bryant and Williams (Ref. 2), transformed by geometrical 'inversion' into the region external to a circle.

In illustration of (d), Fig. 44 d shows an infinite plane containing a row of circular holes, equally spaced, transformed into an infinite plane divided into parallel strips.

† Figs. 42 relate to a transformation of this type.

Later we shall consider all of these four transformations in some detail. First, however, we must give quantitative expression to the ideas of § 97.

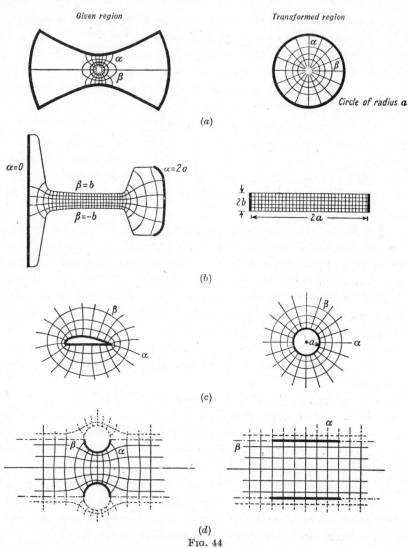

Given region   *Transformed region*

Circle of radius a

(a)

$\alpha=0$ $\alpha=2a$

$\beta=b$

$\beta=-b$

(b)

(c)

(d)
FIG. 44

The modulus of transformation

101. There it was said that elemental squares in the original and in the transformed region will correspond, but that they will have (in general) sides of different lengths. Let $\delta z = \delta x + i\,\delta y$ and $\delta\gamma = \delta\alpha + i\,\delta\beta$ be corresponding elements in a transformation from the x-y to the α-β plane. Then, clearly,

$$\frac{(\delta\alpha)^2 + (\delta\beta)^2}{(\delta x)^2 + (\delta y)^2} = \frac{|\delta\gamma|^2}{|\delta z|^2} = \left|\frac{d\gamma}{dz}\right|^2 \tag{8}$$

measures the ratio of the areas of corresponding elemental squares. This quantity will be denoted by h^2, and

$$h = \left|\frac{d\gamma}{dz}\right| \tag{9}$$

will be termed the **modulus of transformation**. In virtue of the relations

$$\frac{\partial\alpha}{\partial x} = \frac{\partial\beta}{\partial y}, \qquad \frac{\partial\alpha}{\partial y} = -\frac{\partial\beta}{\partial x} \tag{10}$$

(which can be derived like (2) of § 96), it is easy to deduce from (8), *since this holds for all ratios* $\delta x/\delta y$, that

$$\left.\begin{aligned}
h^2 &= \left(\frac{\partial\alpha}{\partial x}\right)^2 + \left(\frac{\partial\alpha}{\partial y}\right)^2 = \left(\frac{\partial\beta}{\partial x}\right)^2 + \left(\frac{\partial\beta}{\partial y}\right)^2, \\
\frac{1}{h^2} &= \left(\frac{\partial x}{\partial\alpha}\right)^2 + \left(\frac{\partial x}{\partial\beta}\right)^2 = \left(\frac{\partial y}{\partial\alpha}\right)^2 + \left(\frac{\partial y}{\partial\beta}\right)^2.
\end{aligned}\right\} \tag{11}$$

102. Again, α, β corresponding with x, y and $\alpha + \delta\alpha$, $\beta + \delta\beta$ with $x + \delta x$, y, if the line-element joining (α, β) with $(\alpha + \delta\alpha, \beta + \delta\beta)$ in the α-β plane has length δs, we may write

$$\delta\alpha = \delta s \cos\theta, \qquad \delta\beta = \delta s \sin\theta, \tag{i}$$

θ denoting the inclination of δs to the α-axis in the α-β plane. Also

$$\lim\frac{\delta s}{\delta x} = \left|\frac{d\gamma}{dz}\right| = h, \tag{ii}$$

so we have $\qquad \dfrac{\partial\alpha}{\partial x} = h\cos\theta, \qquad \dfrac{\partial\beta}{\partial x} = h\sin\theta, \tag{iii}$

and $\qquad he^{i\theta} = h(\cos\theta + i\sin\theta) = \dfrac{\partial}{\partial x}(\alpha + i\beta),$

i.e. (since in this instance y is not varied)

$$he^{i\theta} = \frac{d}{dz}(\alpha + i\beta) = f'(z) \text{ according to (4).}$$

Consequently,

$$\log h + i\theta = \log f'(z), \text{ a function of } (x + iy).$$

This means (according to the argument of § 96) that $\log h$ and θ are conjugate plane-harmonic functions of x, y and of α, β. Corresponding with (2) of § 96 we have

$$\frac{\partial}{\partial x}(\log h) = \frac{\partial\theta}{\partial y}, \qquad \frac{\partial}{\partial y}(\log h) = -\frac{\partial\theta}{\partial x},$$

and corresponding with (3)

$$\nabla^2(\log h) = 0, \qquad \nabla^2\theta = 0. \tag{12}$$

103. Finally we have

$$\frac{\partial\phi}{\partial x}\delta x = \frac{\partial\phi}{\partial\alpha}\delta\alpha + \frac{\partial\phi}{\partial\beta}\delta\beta$$

$$= \delta s\left(\cos\theta\frac{\partial\phi}{\partial\alpha} + \sin\theta\frac{\partial\phi}{\partial\beta}\right),$$

ϕ *now representing any function of* x *and* y. Hence, proceeding to the limit, we deduce that

$$\frac{\partial}{\partial x} \equiv \frac{\partial\alpha}{\partial x}\frac{\partial}{\partial\alpha} + \frac{\partial\beta}{\partial x}\frac{\partial}{\partial\beta}, \tag{13}$$

therefore

$$\frac{\partial^2}{\partial x^2} \equiv \frac{\partial^2\alpha}{\partial x^2}\frac{\partial}{\partial\alpha} + \frac{\partial\alpha}{\partial x}\frac{\partial}{\partial x}\left(\frac{\partial}{\partial\alpha}\right) + \frac{\partial^2\beta}{\partial x^2}\frac{\partial}{\partial\beta} + \frac{\partial\beta}{\partial x}\frac{\partial}{\partial x}\left(\frac{\partial}{\partial\beta}\right),$$

$$\equiv \frac{\partial^2\alpha}{\partial x^2}\frac{\partial}{\partial\alpha} + \frac{\partial^2\beta}{\partial x^2}\frac{\partial}{\partial\beta} + \left(\frac{\partial\alpha}{\partial x}\right)^2\frac{\partial^2}{\partial\alpha^2} + 2\frac{\partial\alpha}{\partial x}\frac{\partial\beta}{\partial x}\frac{\partial^2}{\partial\alpha\partial\beta} + \left(\frac{\partial\beta}{\partial x}\right)^2\frac{\partial^2}{\partial\beta^2} \tag{14}$$

if use is made again of (13). By similar treatment we have

$$\frac{\partial}{\partial y} \equiv \frac{\partial\alpha}{\partial y}\frac{\partial}{\partial\alpha} + \frac{\partial\beta}{\partial y}\frac{\partial}{\partial\beta}, \tag{15}$$

and

$$\frac{\partial^2}{\partial y^2} \equiv \frac{\partial^2\alpha}{\partial y^2}\frac{\partial}{\partial\alpha} + \frac{\partial^2\beta}{\partial y^2}\frac{\partial}{\partial\beta} + \left(\frac{\partial\alpha}{\partial y}\right)^2\frac{\partial^2}{\partial\alpha^2} + 2\frac{\partial\alpha}{\partial y}\frac{\partial\beta}{\partial y}\frac{\partial^2}{\partial\alpha\partial\beta} + \left(\frac{\partial\beta}{\partial y}\right)^2\frac{\partial^2}{\partial\beta^2}, \tag{16}$$

and on adding (14) and (16), with a use of (11), we see that

$$\nabla^2 \equiv \frac{\partial^2}{\partial x^2} + \frac{\partial^2}{\partial y^2}$$

$$\equiv \nabla^2\alpha\frac{\partial}{\partial\alpha} + \nabla^2\beta\frac{\partial}{\partial\beta} + h^2\left[\frac{\partial^2}{\partial\alpha^2} + \frac{\partial^2}{\partial\beta^2}\right] + 2\left(\frac{\partial\alpha}{\partial x}\frac{\partial\beta}{\partial x} + \frac{\partial\alpha}{\partial y}\frac{\partial\beta}{\partial y}\right)\frac{\partial^2}{\partial\alpha\partial\beta}$$

$$\equiv h^2\left[\frac{\partial^2}{\partial\alpha^2} + \frac{\partial^2}{\partial\beta^2}\right] \equiv h^2\nabla^2_{\alpha\beta}, \tag{17}$$

in virtue of the relations (10), whereby $\nabla^2\alpha = \nabla^2\beta = 0$. This confirms the conclusion reached in § 99, that a function plane-harmonic in x and y is also plane-harmonic in α and β.

Approximate calculation of h

104. Suppose that we have determined (approximately) one of the conjugate *plane-harmonic* functions α, β, so as to have for a net in the x-y plane values of that function at every nodal point. Then we can deduce (again, approximately) values of the modulus of transformation h; for it is easy to verify that

$$\tfrac{1}{2}\nabla^2(\alpha^2) \equiv \alpha\nabla^2\alpha + \left(\frac{\partial\alpha}{\partial x}\right)^2 + \left(\frac{\partial\alpha}{\partial y}\right)^2,$$

and hence, according to (11), it follows that

$$h^2 = \tfrac{1}{2}\nabla^2(\alpha^2) - \alpha\nabla^2\alpha, \left.\begin{array}{c}\\[1ex]\end{array}\right\} \qquad (18)$$
$$= \tfrac{1}{2}\nabla^2(\beta^2) - \beta\nabla^2\beta \text{ (similarly).}$$

Now we saw in § 17 that (whether $N = 3$ or 4 or 6)

$$\frac{1}{N}\sum_{a,N}(w) - w_0$$

$$= \frac{a^2}{4}(\nabla^2 w)_0 + \text{(terms in } a^4 \text{ and higher powers of } a^2\text{)}, \quad (19)$$

a denoting a mesh-size of the chosen net. Consequently with neglect of a^4 and higher powers of a we may replace the first of (18) by

$$N\frac{a^2}{2}(h^2)_0 = \sum_{a,N}(\alpha^2) - N\alpha_0^2 - 2\alpha_0\left\{\sum_{a,N}(\alpha) - N\alpha_0\right\}$$

$$= \sum_N [(\alpha_k - \alpha_0)^2] = \sum_N (\Delta\alpha)^2, \quad \text{say,}$$

in which $\Delta\alpha = (\alpha_k - \alpha_0)$ typifies the change in α as we pass from 0 to one of the N points grouped symmetrically round it at the standard distance a. Thus with an error of fractional order a^2 (at most) we may deduce h^2 from the expression

$$h^2 = \frac{2}{Na^2}\sum_N (\Delta\alpha)^2, \left.\begin{array}{c}\\[3ex]\end{array}\right.$$

or from the similar expression

$$h^2 = \frac{2}{Na^2}\sum_N (\Delta\beta)^2. \left.\begin{array}{c}\\[1ex]\end{array}\right\} \qquad (20)$$

Elimination of singularities in plane-potential problems

105. In proceeding to relaxational aspects of conformal transformation we shall meet a feature not presented in earlier examples—

namely, 'singularities' which imply that concentrated forces act in the membrane analogue. In Chapter II, Z as well as w was treated as a 'smooth' function of x and y, representable by a polynomial in the vicinity of any nodal point. Such treatment excludes 'point loadings', which of course would entail infinite displacement of the membrane, and as such are unlikely to occur in physical applications. But here we are concerned with purely mathematical problems, and while no allowance has to be made for distributed loadings (since the governing equation has the form of (3), § 96,—i.e. since $Z = 0$), point loading is required for transformation (a) of § 100.

It entails no special difficulty, (i) because (since equation (3) is linear) *solutions can be superposed*, and (ii) because an exact solution of (3) is known for the case of a single concentrated load, namely,

$$\phi_1 = \frac{1}{2\pi} \log r, \ \Big\}$$

where

$$r^2 = x^2 + y^2, \ \Big\} \tag{21}$$

and the origin is at the point of loading. It is easy to verify that $\nabla^2\phi_1 = 0$ when $r \neq 0$, also (by applying Green's theorem to a circle of radius a and centred at the origin) to show that the total force at that point is Z where

$$-Z = \iint \nabla^2\phi_1 \, dx dy = \oint \frac{\partial\phi_1}{\partial\nu} \, ds = \oint \frac{\partial\phi_1}{\partial r} r \, d\theta$$

$$= 1, \text{ according to (21).}$$

Using (21) with an appropriate multiplier and origin ($r = 0$), we can dispose of each and every 'point loading' *in advance*, thereby leaving for subsequent attack by Relaxation Methods a plane-potential problem of normal kind. For if ϕ, the wanted function, is expressed in the form

$$\phi = (\phi_1 + \ldots + \phi_n) + \phi', \tag{22}$$

where $\phi_1, \ldots, \phi_n$ relate to the specified point loadings *and are therefore known*, then we have to make $\nabla^2\phi' = 0$ everywhere and to satisfy a boundary condition which can be derived from the boundary condition for ϕ.

Conformal transformation by the Relaxation Method. Type (a), § 100

106. The transformation denoted by (a) in § 100 is a particular case of the more general transformation whereby a region contained between two closed boundaries A and B is transformed into the annular region between two concentric circles. The analytical problem is to determine the form of the function f in (4) of § 99: our (equivalent) problem is to determine α and β, in (4), at nodal points of the chosen net, so that β has a constant value on each of A, B, and α (its conjugate) is cyclic.

Without loss of generality β may be required to vanish on the outer boundary A and to have the value 1 at every point of the inner boundary B: then β is definite, also the cyclic constant $\boldsymbol{\alpha}$ of its conjugate α. In the transformed plane, the functional relation between $\gamma = \alpha + i\beta$ and $z = r'e^{i\theta'}$ is

$$\frac{z}{a} = \left(\frac{a}{b}\right)^{i\gamma}, \tag{23}$$

as is easily verified. For according to (23)

$$\left.\begin{array}{l} \dfrac{z}{a} = \left(\dfrac{b}{a}\right)^{\beta}(\cos\theta' + i\sin\theta'), \\[2mm] \theta' = \alpha\log\dfrac{a}{b}; \end{array}\right\} \tag{24}$$

where

consequently the contours $\beta = 0$, $\beta = 1$ are concentric circles of radius a and b respectively.

In order that the region between A and B may transform into a complete circular annulus, θ' must be cyclic with constant 2π. Therefore, according to (24), the relation

$$\log\frac{a}{b} = 2\pi/\boldsymbol{\alpha}$$

must be satisfied, so that *while either a or b may be chosen at will, the ratio a/b must have a particular value.* This result has a physical interpretation (Ref. 1, § 3): the original and the transformed region, regarded as conducting sheets of equal resistivity, must offer the same total resistance to the passage of electric current between their inner and outer boundaries.

107. But on that understanding, if (as in this example) B is contracted indefinitely, then a/b must tend to infinity. Therefore *any* closed boundary A, and *any* interior point B, can be transformed into a complete circle and its centre. This is the transformation (a) of § 100, and *it entails a singularity at B.*

Proceeding in the manner of § 105, we express the wanted solution in two parts by writing

$$\alpha = \theta - \phi, \qquad \beta = \log \frac{r_0}{r} - \psi, \tag{25}$$

r, θ being polar coordinates in the x, y plane (with origin at B), and r_0 being an arbitrary constant. Then ϕ and ψ, like α and β, must be conjugate plane-harmonic functions, and having no singularity inside A they will be defined completely (except as regards a nugatory constant in α) by the requirement that $\beta = 0$ at every point on that boundary.

Retaining the significance of γ and z in (23), but now replacing that relation by

$$\frac{z}{a} = e^{i\gamma} = e^{-\beta}(\cos\alpha + i\sin\alpha)$$

$$= \frac{r}{r_0} e^{\psi}\{\cos(\theta - \phi) + i\sin(\theta - \phi)\}, \tag{26}$$

we see that A (i.e. the contour $\beta = 0$) is transformed into a circle of chosen radius a, and B (where $r = 0$ and ψ is finite) into the origin $z = 0$. Since ϕ is single-valued, α like θ will be cyclic with cyclic constant 2π.

Example XI: Conformal transformation of an area into a circle

108. As an example we now proceed to compute ψ (and therefore β) for a doubly symmetrical region bounded by an ellipse and the two branches of a confocal hyperbola (Filon's torsion section: cf. § 100). As the point B we take the common centre of the ellipse and hyperbola.

Fig. 45 exhibits the solution of this initial problem (by R. W. G. Gandy: Ref. 4, § 6). Nothing in the treatment calls for special notice: triangular nets were employed, with meshes successively reduced in the manner of §§ 52–3 (Chap. II). In Fig. 45, which shows the finest net of the series, figures to the left of nodal points give ψ as computed from the finite-difference relation, figures to the right give 'residual forces'.† As usual, all figures have been multiplied with the object of avoiding decimals in computation. If r_0 (§ 107) is identified with

† On the convention adopted by Gandy (Ref. 4), residual forces were less in the ratio 1:6 than they would be as calculated from the formulae of this and of preceding chapters.

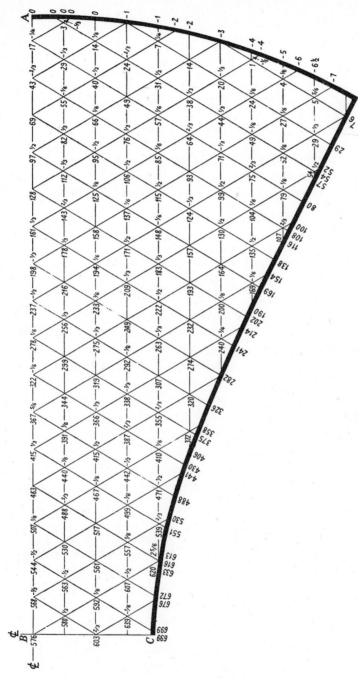

Fig. 45. (R. W. G. Gandy)

the distance BA in Fig. 45, the boundary values there given are such as satisfy the equation

$$\psi + 1000 \log_{10}(r/r_0) = 0, \qquad (27)$$

and a comparison of (27) with (25) shows that in consequence the computed values (at internal points) contain a multiplying factor

$$1000 \log_{10} e = 434 \cdot 2945.$$

109. Having evaluated ψ with an accuracy deemed to be sufficient, to complete the solution we must associate with it a similar approximation to its conjugate ϕ. The exact solutions for ϕ and ψ satisfy the relations

$$\frac{\partial \phi}{\partial x} = \frac{\partial \psi}{\partial y}, \qquad -\frac{\partial \phi}{\partial u} = \frac{\partial \psi}{\partial x}, \qquad (2)\,bis$$

and are, moreover, without singularities and single-valued in the sense that both $\oint \dfrac{\partial \phi}{\partial s} \, ds$ and $\oint \dfrac{\partial \psi}{\partial s} \, ds$ vanish when the integrals relate to any closed curve which lies within the outer boundary. But our solution for ψ, being only an approximation, though single-valued is not strictly plane-harmonic: therefore *it will not be possible to satisfy both of* (2) *by any single-valued* ϕ, and a problem is presented which we have not encountered previously.

Later (§ 125) we shall develop an argument to show that ϕ, for optimum results, should be computed without reference to any existing (approximate) solution for ψ. This, however, would entail an expenditure of labour comparable with what was needed for the determination of ψ, and results sufficiently accurate, though in some degree arbitrary, can usually be obtained by the quicker process now to be described.

110. The two conditions (2), § 109, imply that both will also hold when Ox, Oy are rotated through any angle. Accordingly, in Fig. 46 a, $\partial \phi / \partial x'$ should be equal to $\partial \psi / \partial y'$; and the finite-difference approximation to this relation is

$$\phi_Q - \phi_P = \frac{a}{b} (\psi_R - \psi_S), \qquad (28)$$

terms of the third and higher orders in a and b being neglected in comparison with a or b. Such approximations being the essence of a relaxational treatment, in what follows we may with consistency replace (2) by (28).

Suppose that ψ has been determined *approximately* at nodal points of the triangular net shown by fine lines in Fig. 46 b. In that diagram

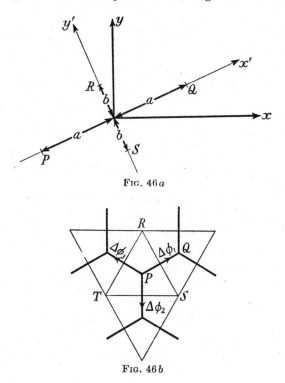

Fig. 46 a

Fig. 46 b

the points lettered P, Q, R, S have the same spatial relations as in Fig. 46 a if

$$\frac{a}{b} = \frac{PQ}{RS} = \frac{1}{\sqrt{3}},$$

therefore according to (28) we have

$$\phi_Q - \phi_P = \frac{\psi_R - \psi_S}{\sqrt{3}}, \tag{29}$$

and so, knowing ψ_R, ψ_S, we can attach a numerical value to $\Delta\phi_1$ in Fig. 46 b. (An arrow is used to indicate the direction in which this increment is measured.) In exactly the same way we can attach a unique value to $\Delta\phi$ for every link of the bold-line hexagonal net in Fig. 46 b.

Because ψ is single-valued, the circuital relation $\oint \dfrac{\partial \psi}{\partial s}\, ds = 0$ is satisfied for the triangle RST, and therefore

$$\Delta\phi_1 + \Delta\phi_2 + \Delta\phi_3 = \sum_N (\phi) - 3\phi_P = 0. \tag{30}$$

This means that on the hexagonal net ϕ as calculated from the $\Delta\phi$'s will satisfy exactly (for $N = 3$) the finite-difference approximation to Laplace's equation (3). But because ψ does not exactly satisfy the similar relation (with $N = 6$) which is appropriate to its triangular net, the integral $\oint \dfrac{\partial \phi}{\partial s}\, ds$ taken round one of the bold-line hexagons will not in general vanish,—i.e. the $\Delta\phi$'s will *not* in general determine a single-valued function ϕ. *This is the finite-difference equivalent of the difficulty noticed in § 109.*

111. Starting with ψ as presented (e.g.) in Fig. 45, we can deduce $\Delta\phi$'s in accordance with (29) and from these, having given an arbitrary value to ϕ at any one point, we can deduce its value at any other by summing along any selected path. Values so calculated will be unique provided that the path is not self-cutting; but they will *not* (usually) constitute a unique solution, because different values would have been obtained if another path had been chosen. To that extent they are indeterminate, and we have now to eliminate this undesirable feature. In other words, only some of the calculated $\Delta\phi$'s have been used to obtain a solution, and the same weight should be given to all.

When ϕ is interpreted as transverse displacement of an actual net, a procedure for adjusting calculated $\Delta\phi$'s is at once apparent. If the values of ϕ at two adjacent nodes are not compatible with the value which has been attached to $\Delta\phi$ for the 'string' connecting them, then before this can be fitted into place its ends must be given a relative displacement $\Delta\phi'$ additional to $\Delta\phi$: therefore according to § 61 (Chap. III) transverse forces $\pm\Delta\phi'$ must be applied at its two ends, entailing 'residual forces' on the corresponding 'constraints'. Eliminating in this manner every discrepancy of the type denoted by $\Delta\phi'$, we obtain a solution for ϕ which is single-valued *but entails residual forces*: these must be liquidated in order that it may satisfy our approximation (30) to Laplace's equation.

Alternatively, the total residual force entailed at any point by the ϕ's can be calculated from the formula

$$\mathbf{F_0} = \sum_{a,N}(\phi) - N\phi_0. \tag{31}$$

The result will be the same, since the right-hand side of (31)

$$= \sum_N (\Delta\phi + \Delta\phi'), \text{ in the notation used above,}$$

$$= \sum_N (\Delta\phi'),$$

because the $\Delta\phi$'s sum to zero as exemplified in (30).

112. There are now two possibilities: either the residual forces are of an order neglected in the ψ-solution, and so with consistency can be disregarded, or they will call for liquidation by normal methods. In the latter event (since we have seen that every discrepancy entails equal and opposite forces at adjacent nodes) liquidation may be expected to be rapid.

Greater accuracy can be attained by dealing with ϕ on the basis of a triangular instead of a hexagonal net, and the change can be made without difficulty either before or after the final liquidation. For every hexagon centre we can derive a value of ϕ from the finite-difference equation

$$N\phi_0 = \sum_{a,N}(\phi), \tag{32}$$

with $N = 6$: then the residual force will vanish at the hexagon centres, and for a corner it can be calculated in terms of the six surrounding values of ϕ, from the formula

$$\mathbf{F_0} = \sum_{a,N}(\phi) - N\phi_0, \tag{31}\,bis$$

N again having the value 6.

113. Fig. 47 serves to illustrate the suggested procedure. In its left-hand portion values of ψ (from Fig. 45) are shown for the hexagon centres, and numbers are attached to $\Delta\phi$ for every hexagon side.†
In its central portion are given values of ϕ deduced from the $\Delta\phi$'s by summation along paths (arbitrarily chosen) which are indicated

† The factor $1/\sqrt{3}$ which occurs in equation (29) has been disregarded, but the given values of ϕ were divided by $\sqrt{3}$ before the α-contours (Fig. 48) were constructed.

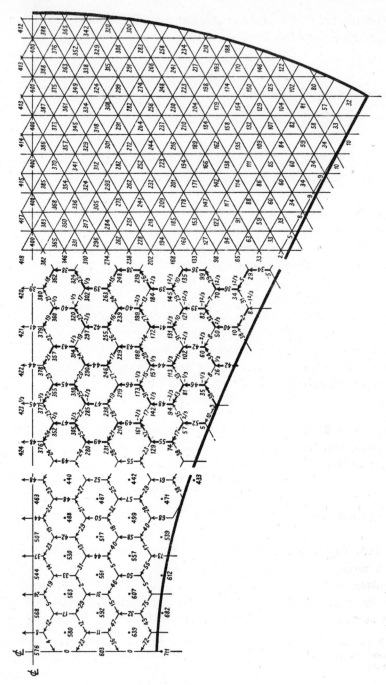

Fig. 47. (R. W. G. Gandy)

in bold lines.† These values, shown by figures to the left of the hexagon corners,‡ are in some instances incompatible with the $\Delta\phi$'s attached to the sides of hexagons which did *not* form paths of summation (and on that account are shown in fine lines): therefore residual forces are entailed in accordance with (31), and these are shown by figures to the right of the hexagon corners. Only a few have magnitudes in excess of 2/3—a figure which was neglected in the computation of ψ (Fig. 45); and all can be brought below that magnitude by a final liquidation (in relation to a finer triangular net) in the manner of § 112. The right-hand part of Fig. 47 shows the accepted ϕ-solution.

It remains to allow for the arbitrary addition of 400 to the values of ϕ (cf. footnote) and for the multiplier (434·2945) which was introduced in § 108; then, to deduce values of α and β in accordance with the expressions (25), and using these to construct the α–β net. Fig. 48 exhibits the accepted solution of this problem in conformal transformation.

Conformal transformation by the Relaxation Method. Type (b), § 100

114. This transformation (exemplified in Figs. 42 and 44 *b*) can be effected similarly. In illustration we transform a flanged 'bullhead' rail section (Fig. 49) into a rectangle such that one pair of opposite sides corresponds with the top and bottom of the rail, the other pair with its curved sides.§

Here the shape of the boundary to be transformed makes a square mesh ($N = 4$) more convenient, and the relative simplicity of its boundary condition suggests the desirability of calculating first that function (here denoted by β) which has to take a constant value along each curved side. On account of symmetry only one-half of the section need be considered if β is made zero on the centre-line:

---

† The paths should be roughly orthogonal to the boundary, since $\partial\phi/\partial\nu$ is specified.

‡ It is known (from the symmetry of ψ) that ϕ has a constant value along both the lines BA, BC in Fig. 45, also variations skew-symmetrical with respect to both. Accordingly the natural procedure would be to make the constant value zero; but in these calculations an arbitrary value 400 was given to the constant, with the object of keeping ϕ positive.

§ The points which have to become corners of the rectangle were chosen arbitrarily.

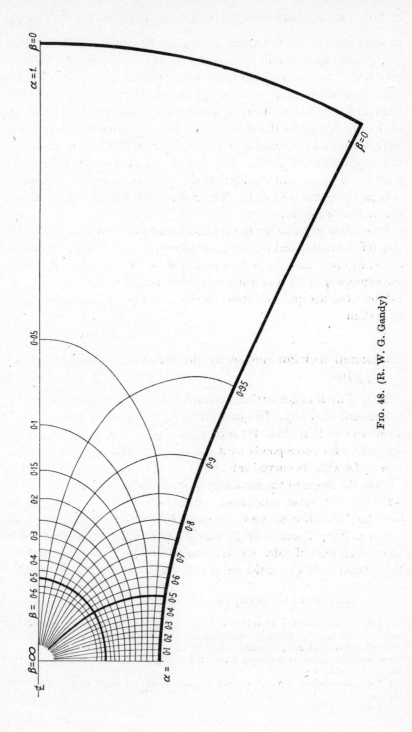

FIG. 48. (R. W. G. Gandy)

at internal nodes it must satisfy the finite-difference relation (akin to (32), but with $N = 4$)

$$4\beta_0 = \sum_{a,4} (\beta).\tag{33}$$

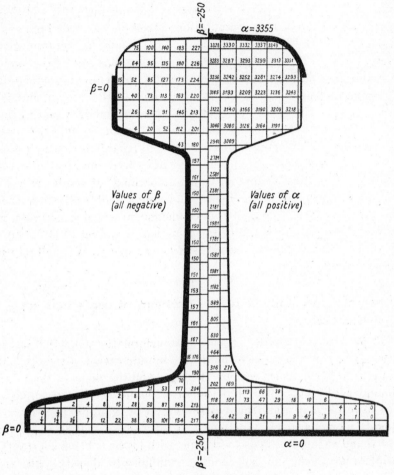

FIG. 49. (R. W. G. Gandy)

Example XII: Conformal transformation of a rail section into a rectangle

115. The computation of β, as of ψ in § 108, is effected by the standard methods of Chapters II and III; and when β is known its conjugate α can be determined by methods exactly similar to those §§ 109–12, except that for the square-mesh net the factor $\sqrt{3}$ in

(29) is replaced by unity and N in (31) $= 4$. Accordingly this problem may be left to the reader as an example. The accepted values of α and β are recorded in Fig. 49, and the resulting 'map' in Fig. 50.†

The bold-line curves in Fig. 50 call, on the other hand, for explanation. They are contours of the quantity h defined in § 101, and they have been derived from computations based on the second of equations (20), § 104. The numbers attached to the bold-line contours give values of h on the assumption that $h = 1$ in the region of the 'web' of the rail section, where the contours of α and β are approximately straight. Actually, of course, h must vary in this region; but its variation is too slight to be calculated accurately, and for that reason the contour $h = 1$, as being somewhat uncertain, is indicated by a broken line. Similar uncertainties exist in regard to contours near the corners of the rail section, and these have been similarly indicated.

When h is thus computed, some 'smoothing' of results may be necessary, since we are in effect performing a double differentiation of the computed β; and in this connexion, when high accuracy is wanted, use may be made of the fact that according to (12), § 102, $\log h$, *like β, is a plane-harmonic function of x and y.* We shall return to this point in § 122.

'Inversion' as applied to the problem of conformal transformation

116. A relaxational treatment of transformation (c), § 100, introduces new considerations owing to the infinite extent of the original and of the transformed regions. In Fig. 44 (c) the shape of the inner boundary B is specified, and the outer boundary A is at infinity: we have to 'map' the region *external to B* by contours of two conjugate plane-harmonic functions α, β, of which $\beta = 0$ at all points on B and at infinity tends to identity with $\log r/c$ (c being constant), while α is a cyclic function tending at infinity to identity with $-\theta$. Thus the 'field' in which β must be determined cannot be shown on a drawing of finite size: to circumvent this practical difficulty, we have recourse to the analytical process known as **inversion**.

If
$$x' = \frac{c^2 x}{x^2 + y^2}, \qquad y' = \frac{c^2 y}{x^2 + y^2}, \tag{34}$$

† The actual computations (by R. W. G. Gandy: Ref. 4) were carried to a net twice as fine as that shown in Fig. 49.

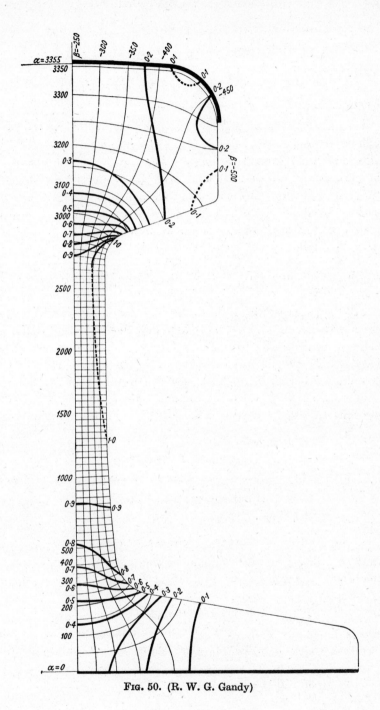

FIG. 50. (R. W. G. Gandy)

c being constant, then

$$r' = \sqrt{(x'^2+y'^2)} = c^2/r, \qquad \theta' = \tan^{-1}(y'/x') = \theta, \qquad (35)$$

and

$$\left.\begin{array}{l} z' = x'-iy' = c^2(x-iy)/(x^2+y^2) = c^2/z, \end{array}\right\} \qquad (36)$$

when, as in § 96, $\qquad\qquad z = x+iy.$

Consequently, z' is a function of z, like γ as defined in (4); and it follows, as in § 99, that *any function plane-harmonic in x and y will also be plane-harmonic in x' and y'*. The transformation represented by (34), and known as 'inversion', is a type of conformal transformation. It transforms any boundary B which encloses the origin into some new closed curve C (say), the region external to B into the region *internal to C*, and all points at infinity (i.e. the boundary A) into the origin of the coordinates x', y'.

Conformal transformation by the Relaxation Method. Type (c), § 100

117. Thus transformed, the problem of computing α and β becomes exactly similar to the problem treated in §§ 106–13, except that $\alpha+i\beta$, being a function of $x+iy$ or of $re^{i\theta}$ (§ 98), is now required to be a function of $r'e^{-i\theta'}$,—i.e. of $x'-iy'$ according to (34) or (36),—so $\alpha-i\beta$ is required to be a function of $x'+iy'$.† (In order that $\alpha+i\beta$ may be a function of $x'+iy'$, the operation of inversion must be accompanied by 'reflection' with respect to the axis of x.) The condition

$$\beta \to \log(r/c) \quad \text{as } r \to \infty$$

becomes $\qquad\qquad \beta \to \log(c/r') \quad \text{as } r' \to 0,$

by (35); and since β must vanish on B, in the transformed problem

$$\beta = 0 \text{ at all points on } C. \qquad (37)$$

Proceeding on the lines of § 107, we write

$$-\alpha = \theta'+\phi, \qquad \beta = \log(c/r')+\psi, \qquad (38)$$

thus requiring ϕ and ψ to be plane-harmonic without singularity at the origin, and $\phi+i\psi$ to be a function of $x'+iy'$. Then (37) imposes the relation

$$\psi = \log(r'/c) \text{ at points on } C, \qquad (39)$$

and it remains to evaluate ψ and ϕ (approximately) at nodal points inside C, and to draw contours of α and β in accordance with (38).

† A different significance was attached to r', θ' in § 106, where they stood for polar coordinates in the *transformed* plane.

Finally, the required contours (external to B) can be obtained from these by a further application of inversion as defined in (34) and (35).

Example XIII: Conformal transformation of the region external to an airscrew section

118. As an example we now consider a typical airscrew section which was used by Bryant and Williams (Ref. 2) for a study of two-dimensional flow round an aerofoil in a wind-tunnel. Fig. 51 shows the aerofoil section B, the chosen **circle of inversion** (viz. the circle of radius c), and the resulting boundary C. In Ref. 4, §16, values of ψ on this 'inverted boundary' were calculated from the formula

$$\psi = 1000 \log_{10}(r'/c), \tag{40}$$

and in consequence the calculated values of ψ contained a multiplying factor

$$1000 \log_{10} e = 434 \cdot 2945$$

(cf. §108). So when ψ has the calculated values, and if values of ϕ (such that $\phi + i\psi$ is a function of $x + iy$) are deduced in the manner of §§ 109–13, the formulae (38) are replaced by

$$\left.\begin{aligned}
-434 \cdot 2945\alpha &= 434 \cdot 2945\theta + \phi, \\
434 \cdot 2945\beta &= 434 \cdot 2945 \log(c/r') + \psi, \\
&= 1000 \log_{10}(c/r') + \psi.
\end{aligned}\right\} \tag{41}$$

ϕ being non-cyclic, $-\alpha$ like θ is cyclic with constant 2π, and contours of α, for equal spacing, must be drawn for sub-multiples of this quantity. In Ref. 4 it was decided to plot 40 α-contours for values of α separated by $\pi/20$: this means, according to (41),

$$\text{contours of } \frac{200}{\pi}\left(\theta + \frac{\phi}{434 \cdot 2945}\right) \text{ for values differing by 10,}$$

i.e.   contours of $\dfrac{10}{9}\theta° + \dfrac{200\phi}{\pi \times 434 \cdot 2945}$ for values differing by 10,

where $\theta°$ stands for θ expressed in angular degrees. The contour values of β must be separated by the same interval as those of α: therefore according to (41) contours must be drawn for values of $\{\psi - 1000 \log_{10}(r'/c)\}$ which differ by $434 \cdot 2945 \times \pi/20$ ($= 68 \cdot 22$) and start with C as the contour ($\beta = 0$).

119. Fig. 51 shows the accepted values of ψ,[†] contours of β as deduced from these, and the contours which result by inversion. Fig. 52 shows, similarly, accepted values of ϕ, contours of α as

† To avoid confusion no values have been inserted within the circle of inversion.

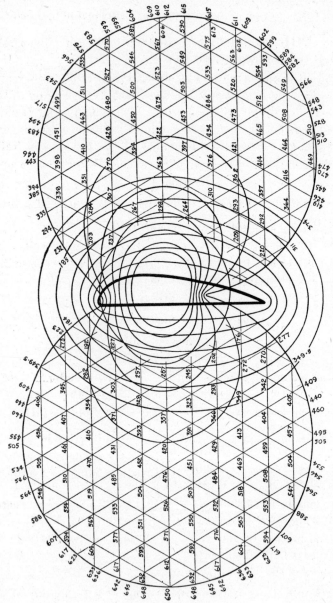

Fig. 51. (R. W. G. Gandy)

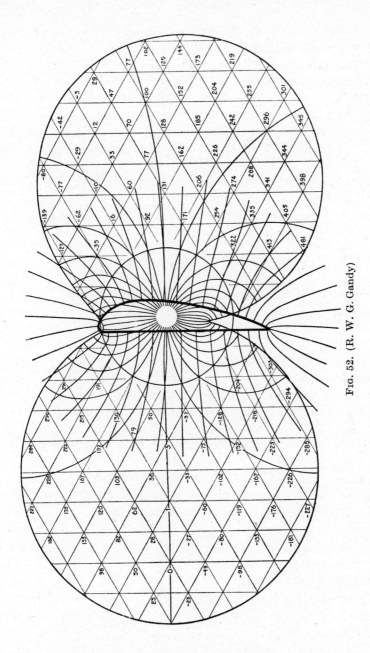

Fig. 52. (R. W. G. Gandy)

deduced from these, and the contours which result from inversion. Near the 'waist' of the inverted boundary C (corresponding with the leading and trailing edges of the aerofoil section) ϕ and ψ vary rapidly and contours were not easy to determine with accuracy. Accordingly in that region values were calculated for nodal points of a considerably finer net, extended into regions where the variation of ϕ or ψ was sufficiently slow to permit a reliable estimation of boundary values. Interpolation was then a straightforward problem.

Conformal transformation by the Relaxation Method. Type (d), § 100

120. Given a transformation of type (c), § 100, we have only to apply the further transformation

$$\phi+i\psi = k\left(z+\frac{a^2}{z}\right) \quad (z = x+iy) \tag{42}$$

in order that the circle $x^2+y^2 = a^2$ together with the line $y = 0$ may correspond with the axis $\psi = 0$, and the semi-infinite region (external to the circle) in which $y > 0$ with the half-plane in which $\psi > 0$. It is thus unnecessary to consider further the problem of transformation into a half-plane, except in relation to *multiply-connected* regions which have symmetry such that in effect a region finite in one direction has to be transformed into a strip of infinite length and uniform breadth. This is transformation (d) of § 100.

Example XIV: Conformal transformation of a notched strip into a rectangle

121. Fig. 53 presents a problem of this kind which has been discussed by Poritsky and others (Ref. 8),—namely, to transform the notched strip shown into a strip with parallel sides, and thereby to transform a plane containing one straight row of circular holes into a plane containing one straight row of parallel slits (Fig. 44 d). The computations embodied in Fig. 53 were made (Ref. 4, § 17) by L. Fox and Miss A. Pellew.

The required solution was expressed in two parts by writing

$$\alpha = \frac{x}{d}-\phi, \qquad \beta = \frac{y}{d}-\psi, \tag{43}$$

where x and y relate to an origin at the centre of the strip and d is the half-width of the unnotched part; and the methods described above were employed to find forms for ϕ and ψ which give β the value ± 1 on the two edges of the strip, and a zero value on the centre line. On account of symmetry, only one-quarter of the field needs to be reproduced. Contours of α, β, and h are plotted in Fig. 53.

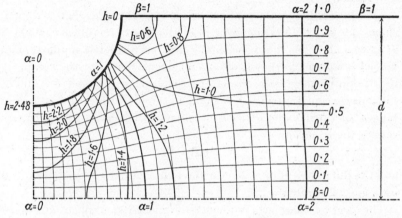

Fig. 53. (L. Fox and A. Pellew)

122. As in § 115 the formulae (20), § 104, were employed to compute values of h, but in this instance the results were 'smoothed', not (as in Fig. 50) by judgement applied to cross-plottings, but (as suggested in § 115) by making use of the circumstance that $\log h$ is plane-harmonic. For each computed value of h the corresponding value of $\log h$ was recorded as a 'displacement' of the appropriate nodal point; then the corresponding 'residual forces' were liquidated by the normal procedure. Liquidation was carried far enough to make the fractional uncertainty the same for h as for α and β, viz. 0·1 per cent.

In problems calling for an accurate determination of h, this systematic procedure (also employed in Ref. 5 to effect the transformation shown in Fig. 42, § 95) would appear to have advantages over the customary 'smoothing' treatment.

Computation of the electrical capacity of cables and condensers

123. In § 106 the transformation (a) of Fig. 44 (§ 100) was described as a particular case of the more general transformation whereby a region contained between two closed boundaries A and B is transformed into the annular region contained between two concentric circles. The function β has to take a constant value on each of A and B, and α (its conjugate) must be cyclic. By requiring β to vanish on the outer boundary A and to have the value 1 at every point of the inner boundary B, we make β definite, also the cyclic constant **α** of its conjugate α.

§ 107 proceeded on the understanding that B had negligible dimensions—i.e. was an interior *point*. But the more general case in which B as well as A has finite size could have been treated similarly, and indeed is simpler in that it entails no singularity. For the computer it is a problem exactly similar to the torsion problem for hollow sections, except that in it β is plane-harmonic ($\nabla^2\beta = 0$) and has to take a specified value at each boundary, whereas in § 64 χ had to satisfy the equation

$$\nabla^2\chi + 2 = 0,$$

and the difference of its values at the two boundaries was determined by a special condition.

The general case has, moreover, an electrical application, being presented when we require to calculate the 'capacity' of a cable or (cylindrical) condenser. For β, defined as in § 106 by the requirement that it vanishes on the outer boundary A and has the value 1 at every point of the inner boundary B, can be interpreted as the electrical potential in the space between an inner conductor B and an outer conductor A which is 'earthed': then (Ref. 1, § 11) α is the electric current-function and **α**, its cyclic constant, has the value ρ/R, ρ denoting the (uniform) resistivity and R the total resistance of the medium between A and B. It can, moreover, be shown (Ref. 6, § 386) that $4\pi R/\rho = 1/C$, where C is the capacity (per unit length) of A and B regarded as electrodes of an air condenser. Accordingly we have

$$4\pi C = \frac{\rho}{R} = \oint \frac{\partial\alpha}{\partial s}\,ds = -\oint \frac{\partial\beta}{\partial\nu}\,ds \qquad (44)$$

(ν denoting the outward normal), when the integral relates to any contour surrounding B and lying within the outer boundary A. As shown in § 27 (Chap. I), when β is accurately plane-harmonic all such contours yield the same value.

Using (44) we can estimate C without difficulty, given values of β computed for some regular net. For such estimation the current function α is not required.

Example XV: Capacity of a square-section cable in a square sheath

124. A problem of this kind was solved by R. W. G. Gandy in Ref. 4, §§ 18–20; it presents no difficulty, so may be left to the reader as an example. Both A and B were taken as square (Fig. 54), their

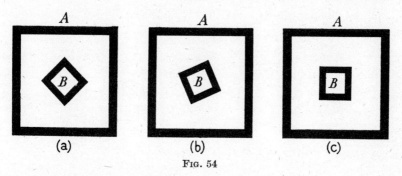

A   A   A

(a)   (b)   (c)

FIG. 54

sides being in the ratio $2\sqrt{2}$. The capacity C was computed for three different arrangements (a), (b), (c).

The results were:

$$4\pi C = \rho/R = 6\cdot71_5 \text{ in arrangement } (a), \\ = 6\cdot57_5 \quad ,, \quad\quad ,, \quad (b), \\ = 6\cdot71_5 \quad ,, \quad\quad ,, \quad (c), \Big\} \quad (45)$$

—showing that the capacity fluctuates within narrow limits as B is rotated relatively to A. The contour integral in (44) was computed from the formula (52) of § 27, and because in each determination of β some residuals were left unliquidated, the integration was effected for several contours and the resulting figures were meaned. The first of the figures (45) is the mean of 5, the second of 5, and the third of 7 estimates.

Optimal approximation to the conjugate of an approximately determined plane-harmonic function

125. It was remarked in § 109 that the conjugate (ϕ) to an approximately determined function (ψ) ought strictly to be computed independently (i.e. without reference to the existing solution) We now give the grounds for that assertion.†

When (owing to unavoidable errors of computation) ψ is not strictly plane-harmonic, no single-valued function ϕ will satisfy *both*

† § 125 is reproduced from Ref. 9, § 5.

of (2), § 109, and we have the problem of choosing ϕ to minimize the residual error. We may take as the measure of this error the integral

$$Q = \iint \left\{ \left(\frac{\partial \phi}{\partial x} - \frac{\partial \psi}{\partial y}\right)^2 + \left(\frac{\partial \phi}{\partial y} + \frac{\partial \psi}{\partial x}\right)^2 \right\} dx\, dy \tag{46}$$

evaluated for the whole 'field' contained within the specified boundary: i.e., given ψ we may say that the optimal approximation to its conjugate function ϕ is that which makes Q a minimum.

Let
$$\phi = \phi_0 + \phi', \tag{47}$$

where ϕ_0 satisfies the conditions

$$\left.\begin{array}{ll} \nabla^2 \phi_0 = 0, & \text{everywhere in the 'field',} \\[2mm] \dfrac{\partial \phi_0}{\partial v} = \dfrac{\partial \psi}{\partial s}, & \quad\text{,,} \qquad \text{on the boundary.} \end{array}\right\} \tag{48}$$

Then on substituting in (46) from (47) we have

$$Q = \iint \left\{ \left(\frac{\partial \phi_0}{\partial x} - \frac{\partial \psi}{\partial y}\right)^2 + \left(\frac{\partial \phi_0}{\partial y} + \frac{\partial \psi}{\partial x}\right)^2 \right\} dx\, dy +$$

$$+ \iint \left\{ \left(\frac{\partial \phi'}{\partial x}\right)^2 + \left(\frac{\partial \phi'}{\partial y}\right)^2 \right\} dx\, dy +$$

$$+ 2 \iint \left\{ \frac{\partial \phi'}{\partial x}\left(\frac{\partial \phi_0}{\partial x} - \frac{\partial \psi}{\partial y}\right) + \frac{\partial \phi'}{\partial y}\left(\frac{\partial \phi_0}{\partial y} + \frac{\partial \psi}{\partial x}\right) \right\} dx\, dy, \tag{49}$$

and the last of the integrals in this expression

$$= 2 \oint \phi'\left(\frac{\partial \phi_0}{\partial v} - \frac{\partial \psi}{\partial s}\right) ds - 2 \iint \phi' \nabla^2 \phi_0 \, dx\, dy,$$

by Green's transformation,

$$= 0, \text{ in virtue of the relations (48).}$$

Again, since ϕ_0 and ψ are invariant so also is the first integral in (49). Consequently Q has its minimum value when

$$\iint \left\{ \left(\frac{\partial \phi'}{\partial x}\right)^2 + \left(\frac{\partial \phi'}{\partial y}\right)^2 \right\} dx\, dy = 0.$$

i.e. when $\phi' = \text{const.}$ so that ϕ (like ϕ_0) satisfies (48).

According to this conclusion, *the optimal approximation to ϕ is governed by (48) and accordingly is independent of any errors in the computation of ψ*: its determination is a plane-harmonic problem of the type termed Class II in Chapter III (§ 94). A relaxational treatment of such problems was described in §§ 71–4 of that chapter. It can be used when special accuracy is wanted, but it entails more

labour than the somewhat arbitrary treatment which has been
described in §§ 110–13.

Mixed boundary conditions in plane-potential problems. Method 2

126. One method of dealing with 'mixed' boundary conditions
was described in § 78, and exemplified in § 79 of Chapter III. A
second method (due in principle to J. R. Green: Ref. 9, § 20) utilizes
the conjugate property of plane-harmonic functions, so is appropriate to this chapter.

The principle of superposition, employed in § 105 to dispose of
singularities in advance, permits us to confine attention to a governing equation of the form of (3), because a particular integral of the
more general equation

$$\nabla^2 \psi + Z(x, y) = 0$$

can always be formulated. (Denoting this solution by ψ_1, and writing
the complete solution in the form

$$\psi = \psi_1 + \psi',$$

we shall (cf. § 105) have $\nabla^2 \psi' = 0$, also a boundary condition for ψ'
which (ψ_1 being known) can be deduced from the boundary condition
for ψ.) Here, then, we consider the problem of satisfying mixed
boundary conditions imposed on a function which at every point
within the boundary satisfies

$$\nabla^2 \psi = 0. \tag{3 bis}$$

127. Suppose in the first place that the boundary consists (Fig. 55)
of two portions only—a part ABC on which the wanted function ψ
is specified, and a part CDA along which values are imposed upon
its normal gradient. We can assume that ψ being plane-harmonic
has a conjugate function ϕ related with it by the equations (2); and we
arrange the *square mesh* net so that AC coincides with one line of
nodal points.

Then along CDA, where $\partial \psi / \partial \nu$ is specified, we have values of $\partial \phi / \partial s$
in virtue of the relations (2), so can integrate to obtain ϕ. The
constant of integration is immaterial, so ϕ_C can be given any arbitrary value and a definite value will then be imposed upon ϕ_A. We
also know ψ_A and ψ_C, but we do not (initially) know the values of
ϕ or of ψ at nodal points *between* A and C. If these were given, we
should be confronted with two plane-harmonic problems of Class I,

§ 94—namely, evaluation of ψ within the region $ABCA$, and evaluation of ϕ within the region $CDAC$, Fig. 55. Our problem is to attach
such values to ϕ and ψ, at nodal points between A and C, that the
resultant solutions are compatible; i.e. that ψ as deduced for the
region $ABCA$, and ψ' the conjugate of ϕ as deduced for the region
$CDAC$, merge without discontinuity along the junction line AC.

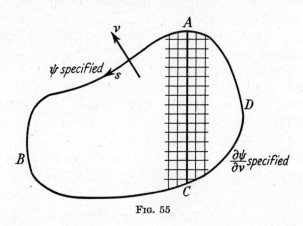

FIG. 55

Identifying the directions of Oy and of CA, we may state the
conditions of such mergence as follows:

$$\text{along } AC, \qquad \left. \begin{aligned} \frac{\partial \psi}{\partial x} &= \frac{\partial \psi'}{\partial x} = -\frac{\partial \phi}{\partial y}, \\ \frac{\partial \psi}{\partial y} &= \frac{\partial \psi'}{\partial y} = \frac{\partial \phi}{\partial x}, \end{aligned} \right\} \text{ by (2).} \tag{50}$$

128. Let 0, Fig. 56, be any nodal point in the line AC, and let
1, 2, 3, 4 denote the four surrounding points. Then the usual finite-
difference approximations replace

$$\left. \begin{aligned} 2a\frac{\partial \psi}{\partial x} &\text{ by } \psi_1 - \psi_3, \\ 2a\frac{\partial \psi}{\partial y} &\text{ by } \psi_2 - \psi_4, \end{aligned} \right\} \tag{i}$$

and similar expressions hold for $\partial \phi/\partial x$, $\partial \phi/\partial y$. But 1 in relation to ψ
is a 'fictitious point', and ψ_1 (since ψ is plane-harmonic) must satisfy
the approximate relation

$$\psi_1 + \psi_2 + \psi_3 + \psi_4 = 4\psi_0; \tag{51}$$

consequently the first of (i) can be replaced by

$$2a\frac{\partial \psi}{\partial x} = 4\psi_0-(\psi_2+2\psi_3+\psi_4),\qquad\text{(ii)}$$

which involves only values of ψ at 'actual' points in $ABCA$, Fig. 55. The corresponding approximation to $\partial\phi/\partial x$ is

$$2a\frac{\partial \phi}{\partial x} = 4\phi_0-(\phi_4+2\phi_1+\phi_2),\qquad\text{(iii)}$$

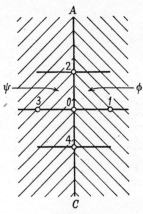

Fig. 56

involving only values of ϕ at 'actual' points in $CDAC$, Fig. 55.

The expressions for $\partial\psi/\partial y$, $\partial\phi/\partial y$ call for no modification. Substituting from (ii) and (iii), we deduce that the following may be employed as finite-difference approximations to (50):

$$\left.\begin{aligned}\text{along } AC, \quad 4\psi_0-(\psi_2+2\psi_3+\psi_4) &= \phi_4-\phi_2, \\ 4\phi_0-(\phi_4+2\phi_1+\phi_2) &= \psi_2-\psi_4.\end{aligned}\right\}\qquad\text{(52)}$$

The mesh-side (a) does not appear in these expressions, which accordingly hold for every size of net, and whether x, y, ϕ, ψ have 'dimensional' or purely numerical significance.

129. We have now transformed our problem into one suited to attack by standard methods. The function ψ is to be evaluated at nodal points in the region $ABCA$, ϕ at nodal points in the region $CDAC$, both ψ and ϕ at nodal points in the line AC. The wanted functions are specified on the curved boundary, so the methods of Chapter III can be employed to deal with 'irregular stars'. Separating the regions $ABCA$ and $CDAC$ as shown in Fig. 57, we need not (in computation) distinguish between ψ and ϕ. Each is plane-harmonic within its own domain, so special relaxation patterns are entailed only near the curved boundaries (due to irregular stars) and at points near the lines AC, $A'C'$.

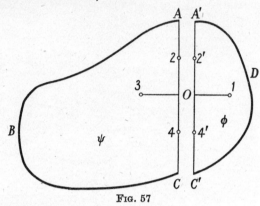

FIG. 57

For the latter, they may be derived from (52) in the way by which the standard pattern was derived from (51). Thus for the first of (52), introducing the concept of residual forces, we may substitute

$$F_0 = -4\psi_0 + (\psi_2 + 2\psi_3 + \psi_4) + \phi_{2'} - \phi_{4'} = 0 \qquad (53)$$

(dashes now denoting points on the line $A'C'$ of Fig. 57). This gives the changes induced in the residual force at 0 by unit 'displacements' (ψ or ϕ) imposed severally at the nodal points numbered 0, 2, 3, 4, 2', 4', therefore decides one numeral in the 'pattern' for each such point. The second of (52) may be treated similarly. Excepting (possibly) at A and C, all of the 'strings' have standard lengths, so the patterns are simple to construct and apply.

In special cases that part of the boundary on which normal gradients are specified may be straight: i.e. CDA, Fig. 55, may degenerate into the line CA. Then ϕ will be known initially for points on AC, so that $\phi_{2'}$, $\phi_{4'}$ are invariant and the first of (52) is recognizable as an expression for $\partial\psi/\partial x$, at 0, in terms of ψ_0, ψ_2, ψ_3, ψ_4. No further condition is imposed by the second of (52), since 1, in this instance, is a fictitious point in relation to ϕ as well as ψ, and accordingly ϕ_1 may have any value.

130. Occasionally it may not be convenient to arrange the chosen net (as in § 127) so that AC coincides with a line of nodal points. In that event the barrier between the ψ and ϕ regions may be chosen to coincide with *two* such lines, as in Fig. 58 *a*. No new question of principle is entailed.

But our discussion as it stands does not cover problems in which normal gradients are specified on more than one portion of the boundary. The reason is indicated in Fig. 58 *b*: knowing $\partial\phi/\partial s$ at all

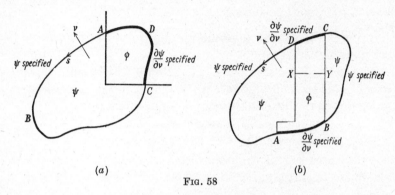

$$(a) \qquad\qquad\qquad (b)$$

$$\text{Fig. 58}$$

points in AB, CD, we can attach an arbitrary value to ϕ_A and thence deduce ϕ_B; but we cannot go on to deduce ϕ_C and ϕ_D severally (though we can calculate $\phi_D - \phi_C$), and we are not entitled arbitrarily to introduce another constant in order to make them definite.

We can, on the other hand (taking advantage of the principle of superposition), obtain the required solution by a synthesis of two solutions (a) and (b), of which

    (a) is obtained on the assumption $\phi_A = \phi_C = 0$,

    (b) ,,   ,,   ,,   ,, $\phi_A = 0, \phi_C = 1,$

and both can be obtained in the manner of §§ 127–8. Denoting these two solutions by ψ_a, ϕ_a and ψ_b, ϕ_b, we can derive a third solution ψ, ϕ by attaching any value to k in the expressions

$$\psi = \psi_a - k\psi_b, \qquad \phi = \phi_a - k\phi_b. \tag{54}$$

To make the derived solution acceptable, k must be so chosen that on any line XY parallel to Ox

$$\psi_Y - \psi_X = \int_X^Y \frac{\partial\psi}{\partial x}\,dx \quad \text{as determined from } \phi \text{ according to (2),}$$

$$= -\int_X^Y \frac{\partial\phi}{\partial y}\,dx;$$

so we have from (54)

$$k\{(\psi_b)_Y - (\psi_b)_X\} + k \int_X^Y \frac{\partial \phi_b}{\partial y}\, dx = (\psi_a)_Y - (\psi_a)_X + \int_X^Y \frac{\partial \phi_a}{\partial y}\, dx. \quad (55)$$

Every line of nodal points like XY will yield a separate estimate of k, and the estimates will differ only on account of unavoidable errors of computation.

Example XVI: Mixed boundary conditions in relation to a rectangular area

131. To test these methods L. Fox (Ref. 9, § 24) applied them to the two problems indicated in Fig. 59. For both the boundary conditions were framed so that the wanted function was†

$$\psi = \tan^{-1} y/x \atop \text{(corresponding with } \phi = \log r + \text{const.)} \Big\} \quad (56)$$

when the axes are as shown in the diagrams. But in Example XVI A (illustrative of §§ 127–9) boundary values of ψ were assumed to be

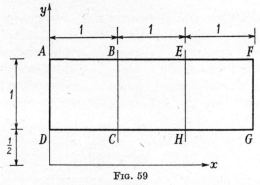

Fig. 59

specified over the length $EBADCH$, normal gradients of ψ over the length $EFGH$, so that a single barrier EH separated a ψ-region from a ϕ-region; in Example XVI B (illustrative of § 130) boundary values of ψ were assumed to be specified both over $BADC$ and over $EFGH$, normal gradients of ψ over the lengths BE and HC, so that a single ϕ-region separated two ψ-regions. The choice of a rectangular boundary obviated the inessential complication of 'irregular stars'.

Example XVI A presented no difficulty. Three successive nets were employed, the finest having 8 mesh sides in a shorter side of the rectangle. The final (accepted) values of ψ (shown in Fig. 60) are nowhere in error by $\frac{1}{3}$ per cent.

† The advantages of this function have been stated in § 75.

1571	1488	1406	1326	1249	1176	1107	1043	983	927	876	829	785	745	709	675	643	2302	2340	2382	2420	2456	2492	2528	2563	2596
1571	1480	1391	1304	1221	1143	1071	1004	942	885	833	785	742	702	666	633	601	2272	2313	2355	2395	2434	2472	2509	2545	2581
1571	1471	1373	1278	1189	1106	1029	959	895	837	785	738	695	656	621	588	559	2243	2286	2330	2372	2413	2453	2491	2529	2565
1571	1460	1351	1248	1151	1062	981	908	843	784	732	686	644	606	572	541	513	2215	2260	2305	2351	2393	2435	2475	2514	2552
1571	1446	1326	1210	1105	1010	925	850	784	726	674	629	588	552	520	491	464	2188	2238	2285	2331	2375	2418	2459	2499	2537
1571	1428	1291	1164	1050	949	860	784	718	661	610	567	528	494	464	438	414	2164	2217	2266	2313	2359	2403	2445	2486	2526
1571	1405	1248	1106	982	875	784	708	643	587	540	499	464	432	405	381	360	2144	2198	2249	2298	2345	2390	2433	2475	2515
1571	1373	1189	1029	895	785	694	620	558	507	464	427	395	367	343	322	304	2125	2181	2234	2285	2333	2379	2423	2466	2506
1571	1326	1107	927	785	675	588	519	464	418	381	349	322	298	278	261	245	2109	2168	2221	2274	2322	2369	2415	2458	2499

Fig. 60. (L. Fox)

132. The test imposed in Example XVI B was somewhat different, being concerned with the accuracy attainable by the procedure suggested in § 130. By that method we derive a series of estimates for the constant k in (54), in number depending on the fineness of the chosen net. In this example it was arranged that the correct value of k should be 805, and on a net having 8 mesh-sides in the length of a smaller side of the rectangle the following were obtained as estimated values:

795,   797,   807,   813,   807,   799,   799   (mean 802).

Acceptance of the mean value 802 entails an error of less than 0·4 per cent.

RÉSUMÉ

133. In this chapter the standard methods of preceding chapters have been applied to effect four common types of conformal transformation, likely to be useful in physical problems. Seen from this standpoint, conformal transformation requires a computation of two conjugate plane-harmonic functions α and β. It is shown in § 125 that strictly α and β should be determined independently; but it has also been established by examples (§§ 110–21) that less labour is involved, and sufficient accuracy (for most purposes) is attainable, by treatment in which, when one of α and β has been determined, the other can be deduced.

In §§ 127–30 the theory of conjugate plane-harmonic functions has been utilized to develop a new approach to problems characterized by 'mixed' boundary conditions, alternative to what was given in § 78 of Chapter III. This part of the chapter, and the theory in § 125, have been taken from Ref. 9. The remainder of the chapter closely reproduces Ref. 4.

Electrical analogies of conformal transformation

134. Its examples, for the most part, have no directly practical application, conformal transformation being regarded (§ 99) merely as a device by which computation can sometimes be rendered simpler. But in § 123 it has been shown that transformation (a), § 100, has a physical application,—namely, to the estimation of electrical capacity. Example XV (§ 124) dealt with a cable of dimensions comparable with those of the surrounding sheath; but transformation (a), in Figs. 44 a and 48, can be given a like interpretation,—the only difference being, that here the cable is replaced by a wire of negligible cross-section.

In fact, all four of the standard transformations of § 100 can be regarded as solutions to problems in electricity, β standing for the electric potential and α for the electric current-function, *or vice versa*. Thus when β has been determined for transformation (c) we can deduce the capacity of a specified (straight) conductor infinitely remote from 'earth'.

REFERENCES

1. BRADFIELD, K. N. E., HOOKER, S. G., and SOUTHWELL, R. V. 1937. *Proc. Roy. Soc.* A, **159**, 315–46.
2. BRYANT, L. W., and WILLIAMS, D. H. 1925. *Phil. Trans.* A, **225**, 199–245.
3. FILON, L. N. G. 1899. *Phil. Trans.* A, **193**, 309–52.
4. GANDY, R. W. G., and SOUTHWELL, R. V. 1940. *Phil. Trans. Roy. Soc.* A, **238**, 453–75.
5. GREEN, J. R., and SOUTHWELL, R. V. 1944. *Phil. Trans. Roy. Soc.* A, **239**, 367–86.
6. JEANS, J. H. 1923. *The Mathematical Theory of Electricity and Magnetism*, 4th ed. Camb. Univ. Press.
7. LAMB, H. 1932. *Hydrodynamics*, 6th ed. Camb. Univ. Press.
8. PORITSKY, H., SNIVELY, H. D., and WYLIE, C. R. 1939. *J. Appl. Mech.*, **6**, A–63–6.
9. SOUTHWELL, R. V., and VAISEY, G. 1943. *Proc. Roy. Soc.* A, **182**, 129–51.

V

'QUASI-PLANE-POTENTIAL' PROBLEMS

The 'quasi-plane-harmonic' equation, and its physical significance

135. IN all of Chapters II–IV our concern has been with governing equations of the 'plane-harmonic' form, viz.

$$\left[\frac{\partial^2}{\partial x^2}+\frac{\partial^2}{\partial y^2}\right]\psi+Z(x,y)=0,\tag{1}$$

$Z(x,y)$ being a specified function. We now consider the more general equation

$$\frac{\partial}{\partial x}\left(\chi\frac{\partial\psi}{\partial x}\right)+\frac{\partial}{\partial y}\left(\chi\frac{\partial\psi}{\partial y}\right)+Z=0,\tag{2}$$

in which χ, as well as Z, is a function of x and y. When χ is constant (2) degenerates into the form of (1), and on that account we term it a **quasi-plane-harmonic equation**.

We have met this type of equation already, in § 85, Chap. III. If Ω denotes the 'magnetic potential', μ the 'permeability' of the material at any point (x,y,z) in a magnetic field, when everything is independent of z (so that $\partial\Omega/\partial z = \partial\mu/\partial z = 0$), then Ω satisfies the equation

$$\frac{\partial}{\partial x}\left(\mu\frac{\partial\Omega}{\partial x}\right)+\frac{\partial}{\partial y}\left(\mu\frac{\partial\Omega}{\partial y}\right)=0,\tag{3}$$

in which μ is not necessarily uniform (as it was assumed to be in the examples of §§ 87–90), but may be a specified function of x and y. The 'magnetic flux function' ψ (§ 86) was shown to satisfy a similar equation, viz.

$$\frac{\partial}{\partial x}\left(\frac{1}{\mu}\frac{\partial\psi}{\partial x}\right)+\frac{\partial}{\partial y}\left(\frac{1}{\mu}\frac{\partial\psi}{\partial y}\right)=0.\tag{4}$$

136. Associated equations of the type of (3) and (4) govern the flow of electric current, and the electric potential, in a plane conducting sheet. Let i_x, i_y stand for the line-intensities of current in the directions Ox, Oy, and suppose that both surfaces of the sheet are insulated: then (since no current, *on the whole*, can enter or leave an element)

$$\frac{\partial}{\partial x}i_x+\frac{\partial}{\partial y}i_y=0,$$

so we can write $\qquad i_x=\dfrac{\partial\psi}{\partial y},\qquad i_y=-\dfrac{\partial\psi}{\partial x},$

thereby expressing i_x, i_y in terms of a single **current function** ψ.

Let ρ denote the 'resistivity' of the conducting sheet, V the electric potential at the point (x, y). Then, by Ohm's law,

$$-\frac{\partial V}{\partial x} = \rho i_x = \rho \frac{\partial \psi}{\partial y}, \qquad -\frac{\partial V}{\partial y} = \rho i_y = -\rho \frac{\partial \psi}{\partial x},$$

and successive elimination of V and ψ from these equations leads to

$$\left. \begin{array}{c} \dfrac{\partial}{\partial x}\left(\rho \dfrac{\partial \psi}{\partial x}\right) + \dfrac{\partial}{\partial y}\left(\rho \dfrac{\partial \psi}{\partial y}\right) = 0, \\[2mm] \dfrac{\partial}{\partial x}\left(\rho^{-1} \dfrac{\partial V}{\partial x}\right) + \dfrac{\partial}{\partial y}\left(\rho^{-1} \dfrac{\partial V}{\partial y}\right) = 0. \end{array} \right\} \tag{5}$$

and to

This, and the magnetic example of § 135, suggest a physical interpretation of the quasi-plane-harmonic equation:—The function χ, in (2), is a measure of something in the nature either of 'resistance' (ρ) or of 'admittance' (ρ^{-1}), which varies from point to point. When it measures a resistance, the wanted function measures something having the nature of a flux; when an admittance, something having the nature of potential.†

137. In both examples the function $Z(x, y)$ is zero, and from (3)–(5) we see that on that understanding (2) will be associated with a second equation similar but not identical in form. Mathematically, when $Z(x, y) = 0$ in (2) the existence of a solution ψ implies that we may write

$$\chi \frac{\partial \psi}{\partial y} = \frac{\partial \phi}{\partial x}, \qquad -\chi \frac{\partial \psi}{\partial x} = \frac{\partial \phi}{\partial y}, \tag{6}$$

and by elimination of ψ from these relations the equation

$$\frac{\partial}{\partial x}\left(\chi^{-1} \frac{\partial \phi}{\partial x}\right) + \frac{\partial}{\partial y}\left(\chi^{-1} \frac{\partial \phi}{\partial y}\right) = 0 \tag{7}$$

is obtained. When χ is constant, (6) reduce to the 'conjugate relations' (2) of § 96. There, the related functions ϕ and ψ both satisfied the 'two-dimensional Laplace equation' (§ 34): here they satisfy two similar but not identical equations, which we describe as **adjoint**.

Since

$$\left. \begin{array}{c} \dfrac{\partial}{\partial v} \equiv \cos(x, v)\dfrac{\partial}{\partial x} + \sin(x, v)\dfrac{\partial}{\partial y}, \\[2mm] \dfrac{\partial}{\partial s} \equiv \cos(x, v)\dfrac{\partial}{\partial y} - \sin(x, v)\dfrac{\partial}{\partial x}, \end{array} \right\} \tag{8}$$

† It will be observed that μ, in § 135, has the nature of an admittance.

when the senses of ν and s are as shown in Fig. 5, we have

$$\frac{\partial\phi}{\partial\nu} = \chi\frac{\partial\psi}{\partial s}, \qquad \frac{\partial\phi}{\partial s} = -\chi\frac{\partial\psi}{\partial\nu} \tag{9}$$

according to (6), which thus imply that $\partial\psi/\partial\nu = 0$ at every point of a ϕ-contour ($\phi =$ const.), $\partial\phi/\partial\nu = 0$ at every point of a ψ-contour ($\psi =$ const.). These again are generalizations of properties already established (in Chap. IV) for plane-harmonic functions.

138. When $Z(x,y) \neq 0$ in (2), an adjoint equation can still be formulated. Let Ω be a function such that

$$\nabla^2\Omega = Z(x,y). \tag{10}$$

Then (2), written in the form

$$\frac{\partial}{\partial x}\left(\chi\frac{\partial\psi}{\partial x} + \frac{\partial\Omega}{\partial x}\right) + \frac{\partial}{\partial y}\left(\chi\frac{\partial\psi}{\partial y} + \frac{\partial\Omega}{\partial y}\right) = 0,$$

shows that we may write

$$\chi\frac{\partial\psi}{\partial y} + \frac{\partial\Omega}{\partial y} = \frac{\partial\phi}{\partial x}, \qquad -\left(\chi\frac{\partial\psi}{\partial x} + \frac{\partial\Omega}{\partial x}\right) = \frac{\partial\phi}{\partial y}, \tag{11}$$

and from these relations the equation

$$\frac{\partial}{\partial x}\left(\chi^{-1}\frac{\partial\phi}{\partial x}\right) + \frac{\partial}{\partial y}\left(\chi^{-1}\frac{\partial\phi}{\partial y}\right) + \chi^{-2}\left(\frac{\partial\chi}{\partial x}\frac{\partial\Omega}{\partial y} - \frac{\partial\chi}{\partial y}\frac{\partial\Omega}{\partial x}\right) = 0 \tag{12}$$

is obtained by elimination of ψ. Since χ is specified and Ω is deducible from (10), the last term on the left of (12) may be regarded as a *specified* function of x and y.

139. A further example of the quasi-plane-harmonic equation is presented in the theory of torsional stresses in a bar of circular section but non-uniform diameter (Ref. 11, §§ 8 and 11). On certain assumptions (akin to those made by Saint-Venant in his theory of torsion for prismatic bars of non-circular section), these consist solely of shearing stress on axial (z, r) planes, having components

$$\widehat{\theta z} = -\frac{1}{r^2}\frac{\partial\phi}{\partial r}, \qquad \widehat{\theta r} = \frac{1}{r^2}\frac{\partial\phi}{\partial z}, \tag{13}$$

where ϕ is a function of r and z which satisfies the condition

$$\phi = \text{const.} \tag{14}$$

along a generator of the (stress-free) boundary, together with the equation

$$\frac{\partial}{\partial r}\left(\frac{1}{r^3}\frac{\partial\phi}{\partial r}\right) + \frac{\partial}{\partial z}\left(\frac{1}{r^3}\frac{\partial\phi}{\partial z}\right) = 0 \tag{15}$$

at every point in the material. Equation (15) is (2) with

$$Z(x,y) = 0, \qquad \chi = r^{-3}, \qquad \psi = \phi.$$

Membrane analogue of the quasi-plane-harmonic equation

140. A 'membrane analogue' of (2) can be stated. Suppose that the membrane tension T, which in § 36 was taken as uniform, now has an intensity, $T\chi$, which varies from point to point; and let ψ denote the small transverse displacement. Proceeding exactly as in § 36, it is easy to obtain (2) as the condition of transverse equilibrium for an element at (x, y), TZ denoting the surface-intensity of the external (transverse) loading. There is no objection to the postulation of a variable tension, since this can be maintained by external forces acting always in directions parallel to the plane of the undeflected membrane, and accordingly having no influence on *transverse* equilibrium. The surface-intensity of the external forces will have components

$$X = -T\frac{\partial \chi}{\partial x}, \qquad Y = -T\frac{\partial \chi}{\partial y}, \tag{16}$$

—i.e. *it is derivable from a potential* $T\chi$.

Relaxational treatment of the quasi-plane-harmonic equation

141. As with plane-potential problems (§ 94), three cases are presented according as values of the wanted function, or of its normal gradient, are specified on the given boundary. Thus ψ, as governed by (2), may be specified at every point (Class I), or $\partial\psi/\partial\nu$ may be specified at every point (Class II), or ψ may be specified at some points and $\partial\psi/\partial\nu$ at others (Class III). In this chapter we shall be concerned solely with examples of Class I.[†]

A second classification of quasi-plane-potential problems is possible, since χ, in (2) or (7), may either (A) be a specified function of x and y or (B) be related by a known equation with ψ and/or with its differentials. Class (A) is simpler, and we shall treat it first (§§ 142–56).

142. χ being known, a relaxational treatment of (2) presents no difficulty. We assume that the equation is in 'non-dimensional' form (so that x, y, χ, and ψ are purely numerical), and we proceed to develop its finite-difference approximation.

† Quasi-plane-potential problems of Class II received attention in Ref. 2.

Referring to Fig. 61, we have the usual approximations (cf. (18), § 12)

$$a\left(\frac{\partial\psi}{\partial x}\right)_{\mathrm{I}} \approx \psi_1 - \psi_0, \left.\begin{array}{r}\\\\\end{array}\right\}$$

$$a\left(\frac{\partial\psi}{\partial x}\right)_{\mathrm{III}} \approx \psi_0 - \psi_3, \qquad\qquad \text{(i)}$$

therefore (similarly)

$$a^2\left[\frac{\partial}{\partial x}\left(\chi\frac{\partial\psi}{\partial x}\right)\right]_0 \approx a\left(\chi\frac{\partial\psi}{\partial x}\right)_{\mathrm{I}} - a\left(\chi\frac{\partial\psi}{\partial x}\right)_{\mathrm{III}}$$

$$\approx \chi_{\mathrm{I}}(\psi_1 - \psi_0) - \chi_{\mathrm{III}}(\psi_0 - \psi_3). \qquad \text{(ii)}$$

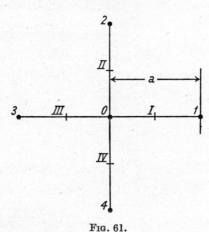

Fig. 61.

By a like argument we have

$$a^2\left[\frac{\partial}{\partial y}\left(\chi\frac{\partial\psi}{\partial y}\right)\right]_0 \approx \chi_{\mathrm{II}}(\psi_2 - \psi_0) - \chi_{\mathrm{IV}}(\psi_0 - \psi_4), \qquad \text{(iii)}$$

and hence, as the required approximation to (2),

$$\mathbf{F}_0 = \mathsf{F}_0 + F_0 = 0, \left.\begin{array}{r}\\\\\end{array}\right\}$$

where $\qquad \mathsf{F}_0 = a^2 Z_0, \qquad F_0 = \sum_4 (\chi_{\mathrm{I}}\,\psi_1) - \psi_0 \sum_4 (\chi_{\mathrm{I}}). \qquad$ (17)

In these equations I, II, III, IV (for which χ-values must be given) are points half-way between 0 and 1, 2, 3, 4 respectively,—i.e. they are (cf. Fig. 61) the middle points of the sides of the relaxation net.

143. It is an easy matter to deduce from (17) the 'relaxation pattern' corresponding with an isolated displacement $\Delta\psi_0 = 1$. This is shown in Fig. 62 a: it is very simple, and reduces (as it should) to the standard plane-harmonic pattern (Fig. 10 b) when $\chi = 1$ everywhere.

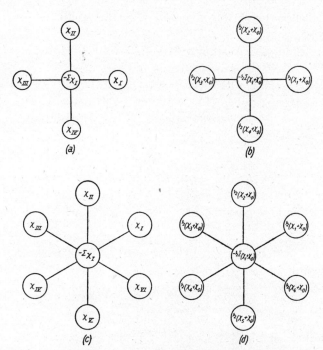

FIG. 62. Quasi-plane-harmonic 'relaxation patterns'.

Alternatively we may proceed as follows. The quantity

$$2\left\{\frac{\partial}{\partial x}\left(\chi\frac{\partial\psi}{\partial x}\right)+\frac{\partial}{\partial y}\left(\chi\frac{\partial\psi}{\partial y}\right)\right\}=2\left\{\chi\nabla^2\psi+\frac{\partial\chi}{\partial x}\frac{\partial\psi}{\partial x}+\frac{\partial\chi}{\partial y}\frac{\partial\psi}{\partial y}\right\}$$
$$=\nabla^2(\chi\psi)+\chi\nabla^2\psi-\psi\nabla^2\chi: \qquad \text{(i)}$$

therefore, using the standard (square-net) approximation

$$a^2(\nabla^2 w)_0 \approx \sum_{a,4}(w)-4w_0 \qquad \text{(ii)}$$

in relation to the terms of the right of (i), we obtain in replacement of the last of (17)

$$2F_0 = \sum_{a,4}(\chi\psi)-4\chi_0\psi_0+\chi_0\left\{\sum_{a,4}(\psi)-4\psi_0\right\}-\psi_0\left\{\sum_{a,4}(\chi)-4\chi_0\right\}$$
$$=\sum_4[\psi_1(\chi_1+\chi_0)]-\psi_0\sum_4(\chi_1+\chi_0). \qquad \text{(18)}$$

The corresponding pattern is as shown in Fig. 62 b, reducing to identity with Fig. 62 a when we identify

$$2(\chi_\mathrm{I}, \chi_\mathrm{II}, \chi_\mathrm{III}, \chi_\mathrm{IV}) \text{ with } \chi_0 + (\chi_1, \chi_2, \chi_3, \chi_4),$$

and to identity with the standard plane-harmonic pattern when $\chi = 1$ everywhere.

Within the approximation of our finite-difference expressions for $\partial\psi/\partial\chi$, etc., *Figs.* 62, *a and b, are equivalent*; that is to say, their differences are of an order (a^4) which is here neglected. An advantage of the treatment leading to (18) is that it can be applied as well to triangular nets ($N = 6$), if we replace (ii) by its generalization

$$N\frac{a^2}{4}(\nabla^2 w)_0 \approx \sum_{a,N}(w) - Nw_0, \tag{iii}$$

in which (cf. (36) of §17) terms of order a^4 are suppressed. Substituting from (i) and (iii) in (2), we obtain the first of (17) with expressions as under for F_0, F_0:

$$\mathsf{F}_0 = N\frac{a^2}{4}Z_0, \qquad 2F_0 = \sum_N[\psi_1(\chi_1+\chi_0)] - \psi_0\sum_N(\chi_1+\chi_0). \tag{19}$$

The second of these reduces to (18) when $N = 4$, and with an error of order a^4 which is here neglected we may replace it by

$$F_0 = \sum_N(\chi_\mathrm{I}\psi_1) - \psi_0\sum_N(\chi_\mathrm{I}), \tag{20}$$

which reduces similarly to the last of (17) when $N = 4$. Figs. 62, c and d, give for $N = 6$ the relaxation patterns corresponding with (20) and (19) respectively.

Net analogue of the finite-difference approximation

144. The results of §§ 142–3 can be interpreted mechanically, as relating to a tensioned net. The treatment follows exactly on the lines of §§ 38–41 (Chap. II), except that now *the string tension* T *varies from mesh to mesh*. Exactly as in § 140, equilibrium in the plane of the undeflected net can be ensured by an application of suitable forces which have no influence on the *transverse* equilibrium of nodal points.

Here the membrane tension is given (§ 140) by

$$T = \mathsf{T}\chi,$$

T being constant but χ a function of x and y. Referring to Fig. 9 (§ 40), when $N = 6$ we concentrate the loading $\mathsf{T}Z$ at nodal points (as in § 39) according to the rules of Statics; but when $N = 3$ or 4 the best that we can do (cf. § 40) is to concentrate at O the whole of the pressure acting on the surrounding polygon $abc...a$. Then, for $N = 6$, the external force at O is given by

$$\mathbf{F}_0 = \tfrac{1}{4}N\mathbf{T}\tan\frac{\pi}{N}\left[a^2Z_0+\frac{a^4}{16}(\nabla^2Z)_0\right], \tag{i}$$

as in (v) of § 39; when $N = 3$ or 4 it is given by

$$\mathbf{F}_0 = \tfrac{1}{4}N\mathbf{T}\tan\frac{\pi}{N}a^2Z_0, \tag{ii}$$

as in (i) of § 40.

As in § 39 we concentrate in a string OB of the substituted net (Fig. 8) the whole force which is the membrane tension T acting on the length $kl = a\tan\pi/N$. Then, with neglect of quantities of order a^3,

$$\mathbf{T} = \mathbf{T}a\tan\frac{\pi}{N}\chi_\mathrm{I}, \tag{iii}$$

I denoting (as before) the middle point of the string: so we have the expression

$$\mathbf{T}\Delta\psi/a = \mathbf{T}\tan\frac{\pi}{N}\chi_\mathrm{I}\Delta\psi \tag{iv}$$

for the force exerted by a string in consequence of a relative transverse displacement $\Delta\psi$ of its two ends; and hence the expression

$$F_0 = \mathbf{T}\tan\frac{\pi}{N}\sum_N\left[\chi_\mathrm{I}(\psi_1-\psi_0)\right] \tag{v}$$

for the total transverse force imposed at O by reason of displacements $\psi_0,\ \psi_1,...,\ \psi_N$.

145. Accordingly the condition of transverse equilibrium is

$$\mathbf{F}_0 = \mathbf{F}_0+F_0 = 0, \tag{17}\textit{bis}$$

where $\mathbf{F}_0$ and F_0 are given by (i) or (ii) and (v). But this condition is not altered if $\mathbf{F}_0$, F_0 are multiplied in the same proportion, and, moreover, since terms of order a^3 have been neglected in obtaining (iv), we are no longer justified in retaining the second term of (i). Therefore, cancelling (or equating to unity) the factor $\mathbf{T}\tan\pi/N$,† we now associate with (17) the expressions

$$\begin{aligned} \mathbf{F}_0 &= \tfrac{1}{4}Na^2Z_0,\\ F_0 &= \sum_N\left[\chi_\mathrm{I}(\psi_1-\psi_0)\right] = \sum_N(\chi_\mathrm{I}\psi_1)-\psi_0\sum_N(\chi_\mathrm{I}), \end{aligned}\left.\right\} \tag{21}$$

† A corresponding cancellation was effected in § 41, Chap. II. Cf. also (11) of § 71, Chap. III.

which, for $N = 4$, are identical with the second and third of (17). The 'force per string' must be modified accordingly: i.e. in place of (iv) we now have

$$T\Delta\psi/a = \chi_I \Delta\psi,$$

and in place of (iii) $$T = a\chi_I,$$ (22)

—reducing to the first of (16), § 41, when $\chi = 1$ everywhere.

Because, with neglect of terms of order a^2,

$$2\chi_I = \chi_1 + \chi_0, \dots, \quad \text{etc.},$$

the last of (21) is equivalent to (18) as shown in § 143, and (22) is equivalent to

$$2T = a(\chi_0 + \chi_1).$$ (23)

Knowing the tension in every string, we can deal as in §§ 71–9 (Chap. III) with problems in Class II or Class III, § 141.

146. Occasionally, when χ, in (2) or (7), is a function only of x or y, it may be advantageous to change the variables.

Fixing attention on (7), suppose that χ is a function of x but not of y, and let

$$\frac{d\xi}{dx} = \chi = \frac{1}{f(\xi)}, \quad \text{say,}$$

so that $$\chi^{-1}\frac{\partial}{\partial x} = \frac{\partial}{\partial\xi}.$$ (24)

Then (7) is equivalent to

$$\frac{\partial^2\phi}{\partial\xi^2} + f^2\frac{\partial^2\phi}{\partial y^2},$$ (25)

f being written for $f(\xi)$. The finite-difference approximation to (25) leads to a pattern even simpler than what is shown in Fig. 62 a.

Applying these notions to the problem of § 139 (where, in equation (7), $\chi = r^3$), we should write

$$R = r^4, \quad \text{so that} \quad \frac{dR}{dr} = 4r^3 = 4R^{\frac{3}{4}},$$ (i)

and thus transform (15) to obtain

$$16\frac{\partial^2\phi}{\partial R^2} + R^{-\frac{3}{2}}\frac{\partial^2\phi}{\partial z^2} = 0.$$ (ii)

Example XVII: Torsion of a shaft of circular section but non-uniform diameter

147. When ϕ is independent of z in (13)–(15), § 139, its variation with r will be given by

$$\phi = Ar^4 + B,$$ (26)

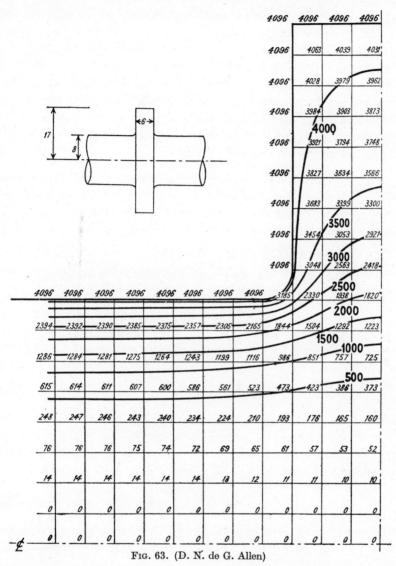

FIG. 63. (D. N. de G. Allen)

A and B being constants; and without affecting the stresses we may make B zero. Then according to (13) we have

$$\widehat{r\theta} = 0, \qquad \widehat{\theta z} = -4Ar, \qquad (27)$$

and (14) requires that $r = \text{const.}$ on a stress-free generator,—i.e. (26) is the familiar solution for a *cylindrical* shaft.

Now consider the problem shown in the sketch attached to Fig. 63, viz. a long shaft of radius 8 units carrying a collar, of length 6 and radius 17 units, which is joined by a fillet of radius 1 unit. Saint-Venant's principle implies that at points remote from the collar (27) and therefore (26) will apply; moreover (B being zero) the magnitude of A is immaterial, because within the elastic limit (by Hooke's law) stresses may be multiplied in any proportion. If we say that $\phi = 1$ when $r = 1$ (non-dimensional) unit, then A in (26) is determined, also the value which ϕ must assume, by (14), at all points on the stress-free generator, including the fillet.

148. But now a new consideration is presented: in thus adopting the known solution (26) at points remote from the fillet *we must take account of intrinsic errors in our finite-difference approximations* (21). In this example (§ 139) $\chi = r^{-3}$ in (2), so that

$$\chi_I = \chi_{III} = r_0^{-3}, \qquad \chi_{II} = (r_0 + \tfrac{1}{2}a)^{-3}, \qquad \chi_{IV} = (r_0 - \tfrac{1}{2}a)^{-3}$$

when I, II, III, IV are the points so denoted in § 142, and with neglect of terms of order a^2 we may write

$$\chi_{II} = r_0^{-3}\left(1 - \frac{3}{2}\frac{a}{r_0}\right), \qquad \chi_{IV} = r_0^{-3}\left(1 + \frac{3}{2}\frac{a}{r_0}\right);$$

consequently with neglect of terms of order a^4 (17) may be replaced (F_0 being zero) by

$$r_0^3 F_0 = \phi_1 + \phi_2 + \phi_3 + \phi_4 - 4\phi_0 - \frac{3}{2}\frac{a}{r_0}(\phi_2 - \phi_4) = 0, \qquad (28)$$

and the relaxation pattern is as shown in Fig. 64.†

Now in adopting this pattern we must (for consistency) assume that at points remote from the fillet, where $\partial\phi/\partial z \approx 0$, the ϕ-values satisfy (28) as simplified by the relations $\phi_0 = \phi_1 = \phi_3$, —i.e.

$$r_0^3 F_0 = \phi_2 + \phi_4 - 2\phi_0 - \frac{3}{2}\frac{a}{r_0}(\phi_2 - \phi_4) = 0. \qquad (29)$$

Hence, assuming ϕ to be zero when $r = 0$ and to have the value 4096 ($= 8^4$)‡ when $r = 8$ units, we deduce (for $a = \frac{1}{2}$ unit)§ that

---

† §§ 147–51 reproduce the treatment given in the original paper (not yet released for open publication). The alternative treatment leading to Figs. 62, a and b, was devised later (Ref. 2): it would have avoided the anomalies to which attention is drawn in §§ 148 and 150.

‡ This value was adopted in order to facilitate comparison with the work of Thom and Orr.

§ A different series of numbers will be obtained from (29) for every value of a. In Fig. 63 ($a = 1$), the solution obtained on a larger working diagram ($a = \frac{1}{2}$) has been transferred for the purpose of reproduction.

when $r = 1,\quad 2,\quad 3,\quad 4,\quad 5,\quad 6,\quad 7,\quad 8,$

then $\phi = 0,\quad 14,\quad 76,\quad 248,\quad 615,\quad 1286,\quad 2394,\quad 4096,$

as shown on the left of Fig. 63.

When ϕ has this distribution at great distances from the fillet, it must also have the value 4096 all along the stress-free boundary, and it must vanish at all points on the centre-line ($r = 0$). Liquidation is affected on the basis of special 'patterns' (e.g. Fig. 64). In

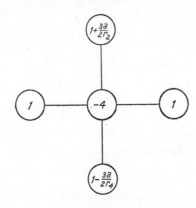

FIG. 64

the treatment of this problem by Mr. D. N. de G. Allen, a finer net was used in way of the fillet to obtain a more reliable estimate of the local stress-intensification, and a diagram compared the relaxational solution with that of Thom and Orr (Ref. 12), who had dealt with Example XVII by a different technique.

Torsional stresses in an incomplete tore

149. A closely similar problem is presented by an incomplete tore subjected to torsion by actions, on its terminal sections, of which the resultants are equal and opposite forces directed along its axis of revolution. The stresses thereby induced approximate to those which obtain in a helical spring *of small pitch* subjected to axial tension or compression.

The tore is generated by rotation about its axis Oz of a closed boundary of specified form. It can be shown† that the stresses (when

† Cf., e.g., Ref. 11, §§ 8–10.

the actions are suitably applied) are determinable from a stress-function ϕ which satisfies the equation

$$\frac{\partial}{\partial r}\left(r^{-3}\frac{\partial\phi}{\partial r}\right)+\frac{\partial}{\partial z}\left(r^{-3}\frac{\partial\phi}{\partial z}\right)=r^{-3}, \tag{30}$$

together with the condition

$$\phi=0 \tag{31}$$

at every point on the closed boundary. They are shearing stresses given by

$$\widehat{\theta z}=-\frac{A}{r^2}\frac{\partial\phi}{\partial r}, \qquad \widehat{\theta r}=\frac{A}{r^2}\frac{\partial\phi}{\partial z}, \tag{32}$$

A being constant; and their resultant is a force along Oz of magnitude

$$\mathbf{Z}=\iint\widehat{\theta z}\,drdz=-A\iint\frac{1}{r^2}\frac{\partial\phi}{\partial r}\,drdz,$$

$$=\tfrac{1}{2}A\oint\left\{\cos(r,\nu)\log r-\frac{1}{r}\frac{\partial\phi}{\partial\nu}\right\}ds, \tag{33}$$

so that ($\mathbf{Z}$ being given) A can be determined when ϕ is known.

Equation (30) is 'dimensional'; but by writing

$$r' \text{ for } r/L, \quad z' \text{ for } z/L, \quad A' \text{ for } A/L, \quad \phi' \text{ for } \phi/L^2,$$

where L denotes some representative dimension of the cross-section, we leave its form unchanged; and the same is true of (32), by which the stress-components are expressed in terms of ϕ, also of (33)—when ν and s are similarly interpreted—except that $\mathbf{Z}$, on the left-hand side, is now replaced by $\mathbf{Z}/L^2$. This means that every quantity in (30)–(33) may be regarded as purely numerical, provided that (33) is now replaced by

$$2\mathbf{Z}/L^2=A\oint\left\{\cos(r,\nu)\log r-\frac{1}{r}\frac{\partial\phi}{\partial\nu}\right\}ds, \tag{33a}$$

so that A, in (32) and (33a), becomes a multiple of $\mathbf{Z}/L^2$ (a stress). The expressions (32) then define $\widehat{r\theta}$, $\widehat{\theta z}$ as multiples of $\mathbf{Z}/L^2$.

We adopt this non-dimensional interpretation of r, z, ν, s, A, ϕ, but without actually inserting dashes in the equations.

150. Proceeding as in § 148, we replace (30) by (17) with

$$\mathbf{F}_0=-a^2, \qquad F_0=\sum_{a,4}(\phi)-4\phi_0-\frac{3}{2}\frac{a}{r_0}(\phi_2-\phi_4). \tag{34}$$

Hence, starting with ϕ zero, we have initially

$$\mathbf{F}=-a^2, \quad \text{everywhere,} \tag{35}$$

but the 'relaxation pattern' employed to liquidate the **F**'s will be different for every row of nodes parallel to Oz. Thus when $r_0 = 3a$ so that $r_1 = r_3 = 3a$, $r_2 = 4a$, $r_4 = 2a$, the effects of unit displacement at 0 (i.e. $\Delta\phi_0 = 1$) are

$$\Delta\mathbf{F}_0 = -4, \qquad \Delta\mathbf{F}_1 = \Delta\mathbf{F}_3 = 1, \qquad \Delta\mathbf{F}_2 = \tfrac{11}{8}, \qquad \Delta\mathbf{F}_4 = \tfrac{1}{4}, \tag{36}$$

—summing nearly *but not exactly*† to zero.

Example XVIII: Torsion of a tore of square section

151. This problem has been treated by Mr. D. N. de G. Allen, and may with advantage be worked by the reader. The side of the square section was taken as the governing dimension L, and a was given the values 1/8 and 1/16 in successive nets. Fig. 65 records the accepted values of ϕ as computed on the final net, with contours of constant ϕ.‡

From the second of (8), replacing x and y by z and r respectively, we have

$$\cos(z, v)\frac{\partial\phi}{\partial r} - \sin(z, v)\frac{\partial\phi}{\partial z} = \frac{\partial\phi}{\partial s},$$

$$= 0 \tag{i}$$

when s and v (as in § 137) are measured along and perpendicular to a contour of constant ϕ. Hence and from (32) it follows that the component shear stress in the direction v, viz.

$$\widehat{\theta z}\cos(z, v) + \widehat{r\theta}\sin(z, v) = -\frac{A}{r^2}\frac{\partial\phi}{\partial s} = 0, \tag{ii}$$

and for the component shear stress in the direction of s we have, similarly,

$$S \text{ (say)} = -\widehat{\theta z}\sin(z, v) + \widehat{r\theta}\cos(z, v) = \frac{A}{r^2}\frac{\partial\phi}{\partial v}. \tag{iii}$$

Thus the ϕ-contours in Fig. 65 have at every point the direction of the resultant shear-stress S; but their spacing (viz. $\partial\phi/\partial v$) is not a measure of S but of Sr^2. Accordingly Fig. 66 is appended to show the variation of the shear intensity S over the cross-section. Figs. 65 and 66 in combination present the whole solution.

† This is a new feature, due to the occurrence of r in (34). Cf. footnote to § 148.
‡ In Fig. 65, ϕ has been multiplied by -256000 in order to eliminate negative signs and decimals from the recorded values.

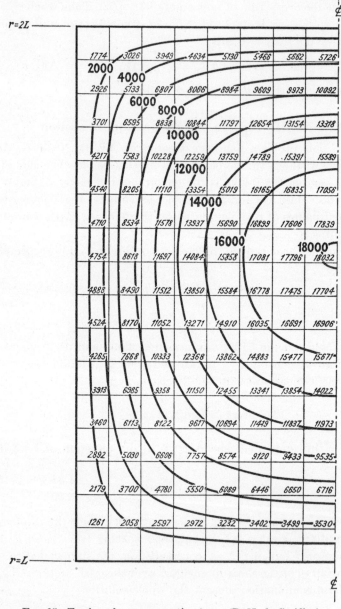

FIG. 65. Torsion of a square-section tore. (D. N. de G. Allen)

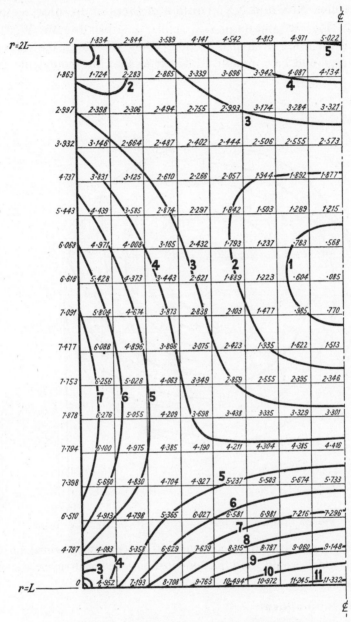

FIG. 66. Shear-stress contours in a square-section tore.
(D. N. de G. Allen)

Examples XIX and XX: Torsion of tores of circular section

152. Figs. 67 and 68 present similar solutions (by Mr. W. E. A. Acum) for tores of circular section. They are left to the reader as examples, and have practical interest as showing the extent of the

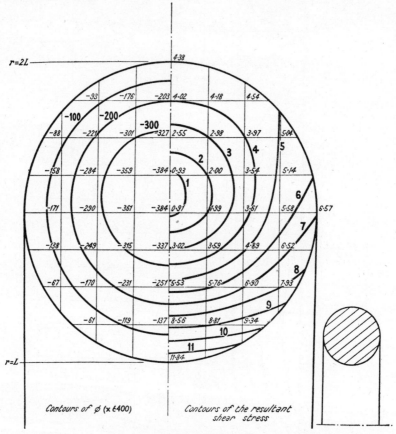

Fig. 67. Torsion of a tore of circular section. (W. E. A. Acum)

inaccuracy involved by a conventional treatment of helical springs (§ 149), which would yield, in these instances, concentric circles both for the ϕ- and for the shear intensity-contours.

Conduction of heat

153. The distribution of temperature in a solid body (e.g. the piston of an internal-combustion engine) depends upon the thermal capacity and conductivity of its material. When these are uniform

(as is usual in problems having engineering importance), the governing
equation is (Ref. 3, § 5)

$$\frac{\partial v}{\partial t} = \kappa \left[\frac{\partial^2}{\partial x^2} + \frac{\partial^2}{\partial y^2} + \frac{\partial^2}{\partial z^2} \right] v, \tag{37}$$

v denoting the temperature and κ the 'thermometric conductivity'
of the material. It often happens that we can attach values to v at

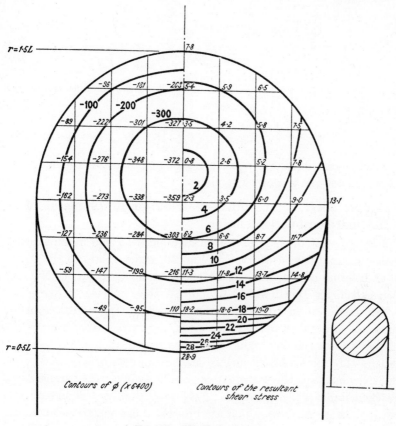

Contours of ϕ ($\times 6400$)   Contours of the resultant
shear stress

FIG. 68. (W. E. A. Acum)

points on the boundary, and require (e.g. for the estimation of
'thermal stresses') to know its distribution in the interior of the solid.
When the boundary values are steady (i.e. invariant with time), the
internal distribution will also be steady, so (37) simplifies to

$$\left[\frac{\partial^2}{\partial x^2} + \frac{\partial^2}{\partial y^2} + \frac{\partial^2}{\partial z^2} \right] v = 0 \tag{38}$$

and no longer involves κ. When in addition everything is invariant with respect to z, (38) simplifies further to

$$\nabla^2 v = 0 \tag{39}$$

and we have a plane-potential problem.†

154. When, on the other hand, everything has axial symmetry with respect to Oz, then in cylindrical coordinates r, θ, z,

$$\frac{\partial^2}{\partial x^2} + \frac{\partial^2}{\partial y^2} + \frac{\partial^2}{\partial z^2} \equiv \frac{\partial^2}{\partial r^2} + \frac{1}{r}\frac{\partial}{\partial r} + \frac{1}{r^2}\frac{\partial^2}{\partial \theta^2} + \frac{\partial^2}{\partial z^2},$$

$$\equiv \frac{\partial^2}{\partial r^2} + \frac{1}{r}\frac{\partial}{\partial r} + \frac{\partial^2}{\partial z^2} \tag{40}$$

since there is no variation with respect to θ. In that event the governing equation (38) reduces to

$$\left[\frac{\partial}{\partial r}\left(r\frac{\partial}{\partial r}\right) + \frac{\partial}{\partial z}\left(r\frac{\partial}{\partial z}\right)\right]v = 0, \tag{41}$$

and the determination of v is a quasi-plane-potential problem of the kind discussed in preceding sections.

Example XXI: Temperature-distribution in the piston of an internal-combustion engine

155. In view of that discussion little need be said in explanation of the computations recorded in Fig. 70, which relate to the piston of an internal-combustion engine, and were made by Mr. D. N. de G. Allen (Ref. 2). It will suffice to indicate their bearing on design.

The piston of an internal-combustion engine takes heat from the products of combustion through its upper surface and transmits it mainly to the cylinder walls, which are cooled. Some heat is transmitted through its lower surface to the contents of the crank-case, but in comparison this is negligible. Similarly of the heat transmitted to the cylinder walls, because oil has low conductivity almost all goes through those surfaces which are brought most nearly into contact, viz. (1) those surfaces of each piston ring and groove which are pressed together by reason of the (frictional and inertial) resistance to the piston's motion, (2) the outer surface of each ring, and that part of the cylinder wall against which it presses. Neglecting the local flow of heat to the gudgeon-pin and connecting-rod, we may

† H. W. Emmons (*Trans. Amer. Soc. Mech. Eng.*, 1943) has suggested a thermal analogue of the relaxation method as an alternative to the mechanical (net) analogue which was developed in Chapter II.

assume the boundary temperature to be invariant with respect to θ and to have the (arbitrary) values 100 and 0, respectively, on the crown of the piston and on the surfaces (2); and at other boundaries,

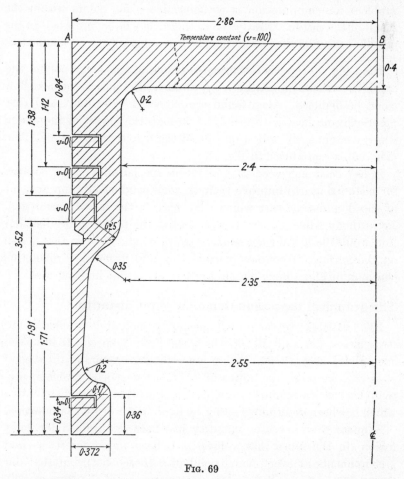

FIG. 69

assuming the heat transmission to be negligible, we may impose the condition

$$\frac{\partial v}{\partial \nu} = 0. \tag{42}$$

Simplifying the true conditions in this way, Allen attacked the computational problem shown in Fig. 69. *No* heat was assumed to pass through any of the surfaces (other than the heated top surface) which are shown in thick line, and *no* insulating effect was attributed to the thin oil films which separate the piston rings from their grooves and from the cylinder walls (so that in effect continuous metal was assumed to occupy the space shown by continuous shading). The problem for computation is to determine v for points within the metal of the piston. Clearly the isothermals will be 'crowded' in the neighbourhood of the piston rings, so a use of graded nets is indicated.

156. Fig. 70 records the accepted values of v at nodal points, and exhibits contours of constant v from which (if required) the heat-flow could be deduced. Allen found the expected 'crowding', and that practically no heat is transmitted through the lowest of the piston rings: consequently only a portion of the whole computational field (Fig. 69) is reproduced in Fig. 70.

It has been suggested that in future special alloys may be used for piston rings, to improve their thermal conductivity, on account of the dominating part which they play in the heat-transmission. Accordingly Allen also investigated what the temperature distribution would be if the rings were *infinitely* conducting (so that $v = 0$ on the surface of contact of each ring and groove). Broken-line contours in Fig. 70 exhibit the isothermals in this limiting case.

The graphical representation of a vector quantity

157. In §141 we separated quasi-plane-potential problems into two classes, (A) and (B), of which the first (χ specified) has been exemplified in §§147–56. Before proceeding to exemplify the second class (B), we now take notice of a somewhat special problem, presented when we require to exhibit graphically a stress-distribution which has been determined either by experiment or by computation.

Suppose that a vector quantity has been determined for some region (in the sense that values have been found for its x- and y-components at every nodal point of a chosen net), but that our theory has not provided functional expressions of the type of (32), so that the construction of curves like those in Fig. 65 is not a straightforward matter. For example, suppose that we know the two components

$$X_z = S\cos\theta, \qquad Y_z = S\sin\theta \tag{43}$$

of a shear stress S, on the (x, y) plane, which has a direction inclined at θ to the axis Ox. Since

$$S^2 = X_z^2 + Y_z^2, \tag{44}$$

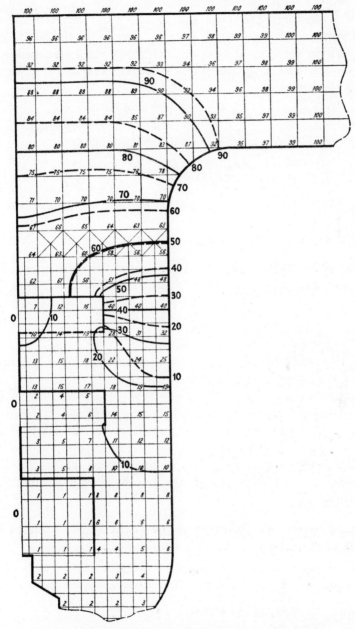

Fig. 70. Temperature-distribution in an I.C. engine piston.
(D. N. de G. Allen)

it is easy to construct contours, like the curves of Fig. 66, along which S has constant values. But we also want **trajectories** of the shear stress—i.e. curves which have at every point the direction θ. These will be contours of some function β, not yet determined, such that $\partial\beta/\partial s = 0$ when the direction s is inclined at θ to Ox; so β must satisfy the equation

$$\cos\theta\frac{\partial\beta}{\partial x}+\sin\theta\frac{\partial\beta}{\partial y} = 0, \tag{45}$$

which (provided S is nowhere infinite) is the same as

$$X_z\frac{\partial\beta}{\partial x}+Y_z\frac{\partial\beta}{\partial y} = 0. \tag{46}$$

Our problem is to deduce β from this equation, which implies that

$$X_z = -\alpha\frac{\partial\beta}{\partial y}, \qquad Y_z = \alpha\frac{\partial\beta}{\partial x}, \tag{47}$$

α being some other function of x and y, not yet determined. The function α will be easy to deduce when β has been found, since

$$\alpha^2\left\{\left(\frac{\partial\beta}{\partial x}\right)^2+\left(\frac{\partial\beta}{\partial y}\right)^2\right\} = X_z^2+Y_z^2 = S^2, \tag{48}$$

by (47) and (44).

Solutions will be in some degree arbitrary, since (46) is still satisfied when β is replaced by any function of β. For the same reason, any values may be given to β along contours which are known initially, either as being parts of a stress-free boundary, or from considerations of symmetry. But there is nothing arbitrary in the *shapes* of the resulting contours, which alone have practical importance; and the problem yields without difficulty to a relaxational treatment, $\partial\beta/\partial x$ and $\partial\beta/\partial y$ in (46) being replaced, as usual, by their finite-difference approximations.

Example XXII: Trajectories of the shear stress induced by uniform shearing action in a beam of oval section

158. Details will be explained most easily in relation to a particular example. It can be shown that when Poisson's ratio $\sigma = \frac{1}{4}$, then

$$X_z = x^2-a^2, \qquad Y_z = \tfrac{1}{2}xy \tag{49}$$

represent (with omission of a constant which for our purpose is immaterial) the shear stress called into play when a uniform shearing action is imposed upon an elastic cylinder of which the cross-sections are bounded by the curve

$$x^2/a^2 + 16y^4/a^4 = 1. \tag{50}$$

This curve is symmetrical with respect both to Ox and to Oy, and clearly Ox is one of the wanted contours, since at every point on it $Y_z = 0$. Accordingly β may be given the values 0 along Ox, 100 along the curved boundary (50). Since β must also have symmetry about Oy, computation may be confined to a single quadrant.

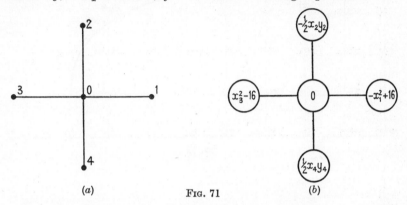

(a)   Fig. 71   (b)

159. The finite-difference approximation to (46) is

$$\mathbf{F}_0 = (X_z)_0(\beta_1 - \beta_3) + (Y_z)_0(\beta_2 - \beta_4) = 0, \tag{51}$$

i.e. (in this instance)

$$\mathbf{F}_0 = (x_0^2 - a^2)(\beta_1 - \beta_3) + \tfrac{1}{2}x_0 y_0(\beta_2 - \beta_4) = 0, \tag{52}$$

the suffixes 0, 1, 2, 3, 4 relating to points so denoted in Fig. 71 a. When 0 lies on Ox (52) is satisfied identically, and when 0 lies on Oy it is satisfied in virtue of symmetry (in both instances because $\beta_1 = \beta_3$). From (52) we deduce the 'relaxation pattern' shown in Fig. 71 b, which represents the effect on the $\mathbf{F}$'s of a unit increment $\Delta\beta_0$ made to β at an isolated point 0. Different patterns hold for different points.

In Fig. 72—where the semi-axes are 4 and 2, so that $a = 4$ in (49) and (50)—values of $(x^2 - 16)$ and of $\tfrac{1}{2}xy$ are recorded at nodal points, and the lengths of all 'irregular' strings are shown (in square brackets). Proceeding on normal lines, D. N. de G. Allen obtained (Ref. 1) the solution which is exhibited in Fig. 73. Trial values for β gave calculable residuals at the internal nodes, and these were liquidated by driving them towards the axis Oy, where β, being unrestricted, could be altered to remove residuals at neighbouring (internal) nodes.

In Fig. 73 the fine lines are correct trajectories, bold lines are

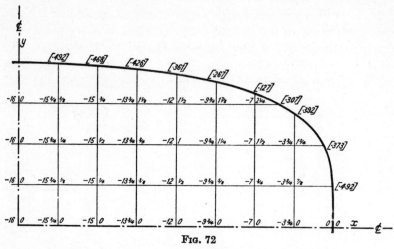

Fig. 72

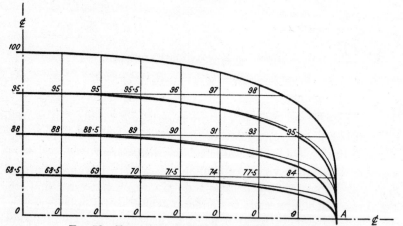

Fig. 73. Shear-stress trajectories. (D. N. de G. Allen)

trajectories derived by Relaxation Methods on the fairly coarse net shown. The computed values (shown to the left of nodal points) are not sufficiently numerous to determine the contour forms near A; but here their exact shapes do not matter, since the shear stress tends to zero at A.†

† Because 'shear stress cannot cross an unloaded boundary'. Cf. (e.g.) *Elasticity*, § 129.

Graphical representation of a tensor quantity

160. In general stress is not a vector but a tensor quantity, having three components even in two dimensions. In a state of 'plane stress', for example,

$$Z_x = Z_y = Z_z = 0 \tag{53}$$

and the other stress components have the expressions

$$X_x = \frac{\partial^2 \chi}{\partial y^2}, \qquad Y_y = \frac{\partial^2 \chi}{\partial x^2}, \qquad X_y = -\frac{\partial^2 \chi}{\partial x \partial y} \tag{54}$$

in terms of a stress-function χ which satisfies the 'biharmonic equation'

$$\nabla^4 \chi = 0. \tag{55}$$

More generally, i.e. when (53) are not satisfied, six quantities (in all) are needed for its specification. But Z_z can be exhibited by contours, and the shear stress of which Z_x, Z_y are components can be represented by contours and by stress-trajectories in the manner of §§ 157–9; so the only problem remaining is to represent, for all points in a specified plane (x, y), a state of stress specified by its components X_x, Y_y, X_y, when these are *not* given by functional expressions of the type of (54).

A stress defined by X_x, Y_y, X_y will be completely represented by (*a*) a set of orthogonally intersecting trajectories directed along the planes of principal shear stress, together with (*b*) contours exhibiting the local intensity of the principal shear stress, and (*c*) contours exhibiting the distribution of $(X_x + Y_y)$—a quantity which is invariant for change of axes. The intensity of the principal shear stress is given by

$$|S| = \tfrac{1}{2}\sqrt{\{(X_x - Y_y)^2 + 4X_y^2\}}, \tag{56}$$

and the planes of principal shear stress are inclined to Ox at angles θ_1, θ_2 which are roots of the equation

$$\cot 2\theta = -2X_y/(X_x - Y_y). \tag{57}$$

Thus all of $|S|$, θ_1, θ_2, $(X_x + Y_y)$ are calculable, and (*b*) and (*c*) present no difficulty. To plot the trajectories (*a*) it is required to know the distribution of some function β such that

$$\cos\theta \frac{\partial\beta}{\partial x} + \sin\theta \frac{\partial\beta}{\partial y} = 0, \tag{45 bis}$$

when θ is identified either with θ_1 or θ_2. *This problem has been considered already*, since the forms of (45) and (46) are identical.

Example XXIII: Trajectories of principal shear stress for a system of plane strain

161. Although we have not yet discussed the application of Relaxation Methods to the 'biharmonic' equation (55), we may exemplify the graphical representation of stresses so obtained. Fig. 74 records computed values of $(X_x - Y_y)$ and of X_y for a case

908	903	888	862	827	781	727	664	592	510	412	278	0
0	10	21	34	51	72	99	134	179	238	315	424	600
993	386	966	932	885	823	748	657	550	423	285	51	-237
0	16	32	51	72	97	128	165	210	264	329	389	456
1049	1041	1017	976	919	844	750	637	501	339	146	-80	-311
0	20	41	63	88	115	146	182	223	269	317	353	374
1075	1066	1039	994	930	846	741	613	459	280	76	-138	-336
0	23	46	71	96	123	152	183	216	251	283	304	316
1074	1064	1036	990	923	836	726	593	434	251	49	-156	-339
0	25	50	75	101	126	151	176	200	222	241	256	267
1046	1037	1010	965	900	815	710	581	429	253	58	-143	-323
0	27	54	80	105	128	149	168	182	193	201	210	221
991	983	959	918	859	784	689	575	441	285	105	-93	-286
0	30	59	87	113	135	154	167	174	174	169	167	172
906	900	879	845	797	735	659	569	463	342	199	18	-208
0	34	67	99	127	151	170	182	184	176	158	137	$\frac{X_x - Y_y}{X_y}$ 108
794	789	774	748	712	668	614	552	483	407	321	211	0
0	40	78	115	147	175	196	209	211	199	169	111	0

Fig. 74

of 'plane strain' in which specified boundary displacements are imposed on a rectangle having sides in the proportion 3 : 1. (It was postulated that $u = 0$ on all four edges, $v = 0$ on all except the top edge, where it has a parabolic distribution tending to induce compression. For our purpose absolute magnitudes are not material.) Hence, using (57), we can deduce values of θ_1 and θ_2: Fig. 75 records nodal values of θ_1, and the second root $\theta_2 = \theta_1 + 90$. There is no question of the value appropriate to each family of trajectories, and for each family computation proceeds on the lines of § 159, but from (45) as governing equation instead of (46).

This problem too was solved by D. N. de G. Allen in Ref. 1. The two orthogonally intersecting families are exhibited in Fig. 76,

45°0'	45°39'	46°22'	47°17'	48°31'	50°14'	52°38'	56°1'	60°36'	66°30'	73°23'	80°55'	90°0'
45°0'	45°55'	46°55'	48°7'	49°38'	51°39'	54°26'	58°18'	63°40'	70°41'	79°0'	88°7'	97°16'
45°0'	46°7'	47°18'	48°41'	50°24'	52°37'	55°38'	59°52'	65°51'	73°55'	83°31'	93°14'	101°17'
45°0'	46°14'	47°33'	49°3'	50°50'	53°6'	56°9'	60°26'	66°39'	75°25'	86°9'	96°24'	104°1'
45°0'	46°21'	47°46'	49°20'	51°9'	53°23'	56°17'	60°19'	66°17'	75°15'	87°7'	98°28'	106°12'
45°0'	46°30'	48°3'	49°43'	51°34'	53°44'	56°25'	59°59'	65°11'	73°23'	85°55'	99°24'	108°5'
45°0'	46°44'	48°31'	50°22'	52°20'	54°31'	57°1'	60°4'	64°8'	70°21'	81°19'	97°47'	109°53'
45°0'	47°10'	49°21'	51°34'	53°50'	56°11'	58°38'	61°17'	64°14'	67°57'	73°55'	88°4'	111°55'
45°0'	47°52'	50°43'	53°31'	56°14'	58°50'	61°18'	63°34'	65°34'	67°11'	68°13'	68°10'	

FIG. 75

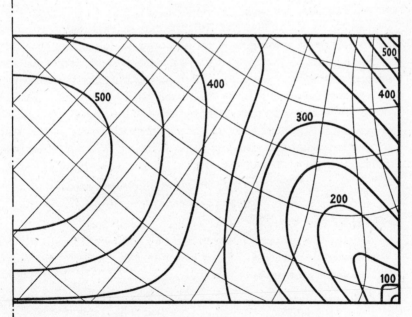

FIG. 76. Shear-stress trajectories. (D. N. de G. Allen)

together with bold-line contours, deduced from (56), which give the intensity of the principal shear. No feature calls for special notice.

'Film lubrication.' Basic theory

162. We now revert to the class of problem which in § 141 was termed Class (B)—namely, problems in which χ, in (2), is additionally related with ψ and/or its differentials. An important example is presented in Osborne Reynolds's theory of 'oil-film lubrication', where χ involves the oil viscosity μ. If μ were constant, χ could be specified

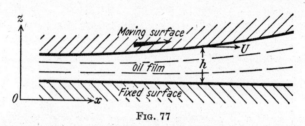

Fig. 77

initially; but in fact (cf. Fig. 80) μ depends both on pressure and on temperature, so χ must be altered as the solution proceeds. Relaxation Methods have been applied to this problem by D. G. Christopherson (Ref. 4).

As shown by Reynolds (Ref. 10), the film of oil which separates a journal from its bearing acquires its power to do so from the fact that, being thin, it is subjected to high rates of shear and in consequence develops high pressures. Because it is thin, its motion even in a cylindrical bearing may be treated as occurring in a plane. Taking this as the (x, y) plane, we postulate that w is zero and $\partial u/\partial x$, $\partial u/\partial y$, $\partial v/\partial x$, $\partial v/\partial y$ negligible in comparison with $\partial u/\partial z$, $\partial v/\partial z$. We also postulate that the viscosity (μ) is invariant with z. Then our problem reduces to the solving of[†]

$$\frac{\partial}{\partial x}\left(\frac{h^3}{\mu}\frac{\partial p}{\partial x}\right)+\frac{\partial}{\partial y}\left(\frac{h^3}{\mu}\frac{\partial p}{\partial y}\right) = 6\left\{\frac{\partial}{\partial x}(hU)+\frac{\partial}{\partial y}(hV)\right\}, \qquad (58)$$

in which (cf. Fig. 77)

h denotes the distance between the two sliding surfaces—which distance is a function of x and y such that $\partial h/\partial x$, $\partial h/\partial y$ are small,

p denotes the pressure of the fluid,

[†] Cf. H. Lamb, *Hydrodynamics* (6th ed. 1932), § 330 a. Lamb follows Reynolds (Ref. 10, p. 259) in neglecting variation of μ, which accordingly appears as a factor on the right of his equation (24).

μ denotes the viscosity of the fluid,

U and V are the components of velocity of the moving surface.

163. In the cases treated by Christopherson, $V = 0$ and U is constant. 'Dimensional' factors may be eliminated by writing

$$x = Lx', \qquad y = Ly', \qquad h = Hh_0, \qquad \mu = M\mu_E,$$

where L is the length of the bearing in the direction of U,

  h_0 is the minimum thickness of the oil film, and

  μ_E is the viscosity of the oil at entry;

$$\left.\begin{array}{c}\end{array}\right\} \quad (59)$$

and if

$$p = \left(\frac{6\mu_E UL}{h_0^2}\right) P,$$

then P is 'non-dimensional' like x', y', H, and M. By this change of variables (58) is transformed into the standard form

$$\frac{\partial}{\partial x'}\left(\chi\frac{\partial P}{\partial x'}\right) + \frac{\partial}{\partial y'}\left(\chi\frac{\partial P}{\partial y'}\right) = \frac{\partial H}{\partial x'}, \qquad (60)$$

where $\chi = H^3/M$ and $\partial H/\partial x'$ is specified. This *with omission of the dashes* we adopt as our governing equation. Given the shapes and relative positions of the fixed and of the moving surface, we can deduce $\partial H/\partial x'$; and P is specified at the oil-film boundary (where p is atmospheric).

164. All of this rests on the assumption (made in the deduction of (58), and justifiable *a posteriori*) that second differentials of μ with respect to x and y are negligible. Subject to that restriction, μ may have any specified variation with x and y, but (§ 162) we assume it to be independent of z. The line-intensities of flow are

$$Q_x = \tfrac{1}{2}Uh_0\left(H - \chi\frac{\partial P}{\partial x}\right)$$

in the x-direction, and (when $V = 0$)

$$\left.\begin{array}{c}\end{array}\right\} \quad (61)$$

$$Q_y = -\tfrac{1}{2}Uh_0\chi\frac{\partial P}{\partial y}$$

in the y-direction (*in our notation, and x and y having non-dimensional significance*). From these expressions (60) can be deduced as the 'condition of continuity'

$$\frac{\partial}{\partial x}Q_x + \frac{\partial}{\partial y}Q_y = 0 \qquad (62)$$

and (by integration) we can also deduce (if required) the quantity of oil which enters or leaves any part of the oil-film boundary. The net entry for the whole boundary must of course be zero, so a check can be imposed upon the accuracy of a computation.

The surface-intensity of the resistance (in the x-direction) to motion of the bearing is given by

$$S = \frac{\mu_E U}{h_0}\left(\frac{M}{H} + 3H\frac{\partial P}{\partial x}\right),\tag{63}$$

in our notation, x again having non-dimensional significance. From this, when the variation of P has been determined, the frictional moment can be deduced by an appropiate integration, also the magnitude and line of action of the force on the shaft.

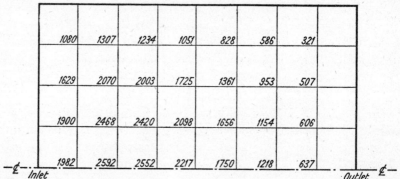

1080	1307	1234	1051	828	586	321	
1629	2070	2003	1725	1361	953	507	
1900	2468	2420	2098	1656	1154	606	
1982	2592	2552	2217	1750	1218	637	

Inlet   Outlet

Fig. 78. Square slider bearing: computed values of $P \times 10^5$. (D. G. Christopherson)

Example XXIV: Pressure-distribution in a plane slider bearing

165. Everything thus turns on the solution of (60), and since that equation has the standard form of (2), §135, the problem needs no further discussion when μ is specified at every point. Christopherson, in Ref. 4, took first a problem previously treated by A. G. M. Michell (Ref. 9)—a flat slider bearing of length and breadth L, tilted so that $\partial H/\partial x' = -1$, $\partial H/\partial y' = 0$ everywhere. (This means an inlet clearance twice the exit clearance.†) Fig. 78 records his accepted values of $P \times 10^5$, which he regarded as accurate within 0·1 per cent. Integrated, they gave the resultant load as

$$W = 0 \cdot 01153\left(\frac{6\mu_E U L^3}{h_0^2}\right)\tag{64}$$

and the distance of its line of action from the exit edge as

$$\mathbf{x} = 0 \cdot 4196L:$$

Michell's coefficients in these expressions were $0 \cdot 0114_9$ and $0 \cdot 419_0$.

† A slip in Christopherson's paper has been corrected.

Example XXV: Pressure-distribution in a partial-journal bearing (1) for oil of specified and constant viscosity

166. Since μ was treated as constant, the above example falls within Class (A) of § 141, and the same is true of the second example

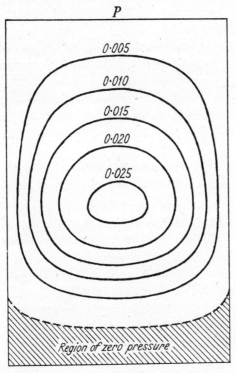

FIG. 79. Partial-journal bearing: computed values of P.
(D. G. Christopherson)

treated by Christopherson—a 120° partial-journal bearing of arc-length L, breadth $\frac{2}{3}L$, clearance $3h_0$ (h_0 denoting, as in § 163, the minimum film thickness), in which the line of centres is supposed to fall 30° from the exit edge, so that the oil film is divergent in the last quarter of its length. For this his computed contours of P are reproduced in Fig. 79 (Fig. 4 of Ref. 4).

The main interest of his treatment lies in its rejection of the negative pressures which appeared on the exit side of the bearing: thereby a region of zero pressure was obtained (shaded in Fig. 79) of which the boundary (shown in broken line) was characterized by *zero pressure-gradients as well as by zero pressure.*

Approximate allowance for the rise of temperature

167. From this solution Christopherson went on to compute the temperature rise of the oil in passing through the bearing,—making two assumptions:

(1) that the heat developed by friction all goes to raise the temperature of the oil;

(2) that the temperature rise of the oil leaving the sides of the bearing averages one-half of the total temperature rise.

Then, still using results obtained on the basis of a constant viscosity. but now taking as its value the mean of the viscosities at inlet and at outlet, from an empirical temperature-viscosity relation of the type of Fig. 80 he was able to deduce the temperature-rise in the oil.

Example XXVI: Pressure-distribution in a partial-journal bearing (2) with full allowance for rise of temperature

168. Finally Christopherson proceeded to a more elaborate treatment of the problem (falling within Class (B) of §141) in which at every point the viscosity was given a value appropriate to the computed temperature. Making the assumptions

(1) that the temperature is a function of x and y only,—i.e. uniform throughout the thickness of the oil-film,

(2) that the temperature-distribution is negligibly affected by conduction of heat through the oil-film, and

(3) that the heat developed by friction all goes to raise the oil temperature,

he formulated in accordance with them the work-equation

$$\frac{\partial}{\partial x}(\theta Q_x) + \frac{\partial}{\partial y}(\theta Q_y) = \frac{USL}{\sigma\rho J},$$

in which x and y have non-dimensional significance,

θ denotes the rise of temperature,

ρ „ „ density and

σ „ „ specific heat of the oil,

J „ „ mechanical equivalent of heat,

$$(65)$$

and Q_x, Q_y, S have the same significance as in (61) and (63). Substituting from those equations in (65), he obtained (in our notation)

$$\frac{\partial\theta}{\partial x}\left(1 - \frac{\chi}{H}\frac{\partial P}{\partial x}\right) - \frac{\partial\theta}{\partial y}\frac{\chi}{H}\frac{\partial P}{\partial y} = \frac{2L\mu_E U}{\sigma\rho J h_0^2}\left(\frac{M}{H^2} + 3\frac{\partial P}{\partial x}\right), \qquad (66)$$

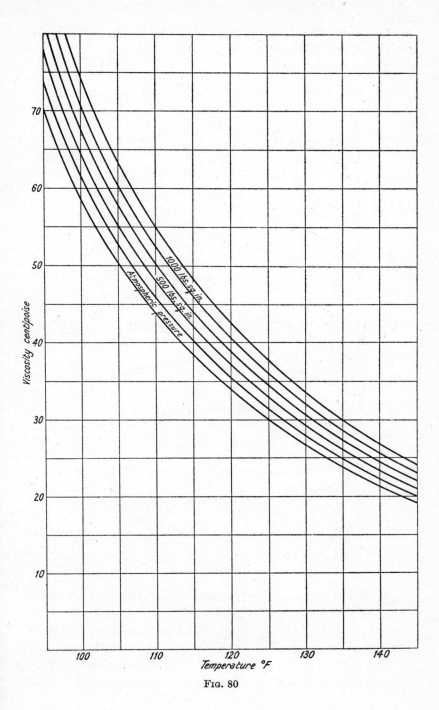

Fɪɢ. 80

whence, after substitution of their finite-difference approximations for the differential coefficients, θ could be deduced from known distributions of χ and P.

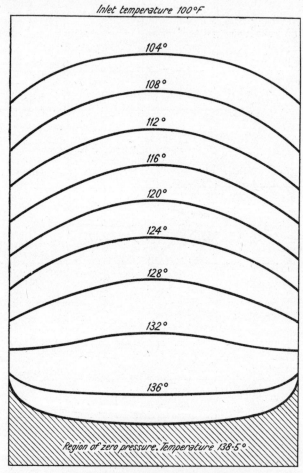

Inlet temperature 100°F

104°

108°

112°

116°

120°

124°

128°

132°

136°

Region of zero pressure. Temperature 138·5°

FIG. 81. Temperature-distribution in a partial-journal bearing.
(D. G. Christopherson)

169. Solutions were derived by an iterative process, starting from an assumed distribution of P. Christopherson started with P zero everywhere, then deduced θ from (66) and hence, using a temperature-viscosity chart of the type of Fig. 80, the distribution of μ and so of χ. Equation (60) could then be solved to obtain a second approximation to P, and the whole cycle of operations was repeated.

Three such cycles were judged to be sufficient, and Christopherson takes note of a circumstance making for convergence: 'Suppose that the temperature estimate at some stage is too high: then the esti-

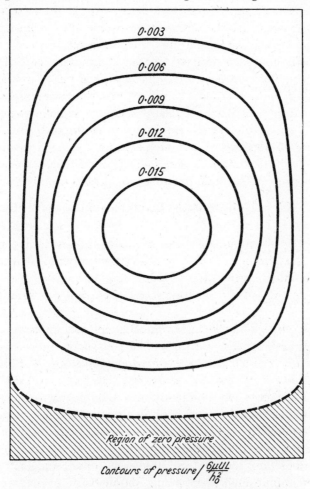

FIG. 82. Pressure-distribution in a partial-journal bearing.
(D. G. Christopherson)

mated viscosity is too low, the heat developed by friction too low, and the consequent temperature increment too low, so the error in this increment tends to reduce the original error in the temperature estimate.'

His accepted solutions for the temperature and pressure are recorded in Figs. 81 and 82 (Figs. 7 and 8 of Ref. 4). A feature of interest in Fig. 81 is that although at most sections the temperature varies somewhat widely across the width of the bearing, it is more or less uniform across this width at exit. Taken by itself, this last result might lead to a belief (on which many previous treatments have been based) that the temperature varies only in the direction of motion: Fig. 81 shows the belief to be erroneous.

Both diagrams were derived on the assumption that frictional losses are negligible after the oil film has given place to a layer of air between the bearing and the shaft; but the assumption is not essential, and it could be dropped if contrary evidence were forthcoming. A check on over-all accuracy can be imposed, because the total work done against friction should be the work-equivalent of the heat communicated to the oil which issues from the sides and exit edge: Christopherson found these quantities to agree within 0·3 per cent.

Example XXVII: Flow of gas through a convergent-divergent nozzle

170. Our last example in Class (B), § 141, relates to flow of compressible fluid through a convergent-divergent nozzle. This problem was first studied on the basis of Relaxation Methods by J. R. Green (Ref. 7). Its details are intricate, and space will not permit a full account.

But one remark may be made which has general application:—*An inexact 'pattern' can be used to liquidate residuals, provided that we compute with precision the effects of the displacements which it indicates, so that residuals are recorded accurately throughout.* (Cf. *Rel. Meth. E. S.*, § 165, where a like standpoint was adopted.) Here, in equation (2), χ is related with ψ by an additional equation—the 'equation of state'; consequently as ψ alters in the progress of the solution, χ also alters, and hence the patterns appropriate to particular points. Strictly, therefore, each pattern applies but once, and then only in respect of infinitesimal increments; but in fact we may use it to estimate the effects of fairly large increments, and for this a roughly estimated pattern will suffice, provided that at fairly frequent intervals we recalculate the residuals exactly.

171. Green's computations related to the shape of (two-dimensional) nozzle which is shown in Fig. 83.† Air was assumed to start

† This shape had been employed at the Engineering Laboratory, Oxford, in some experiments on the flow of steam (Binnie, A. M., and Woods, M. W., *Proc. Inst. Mech. Engrs.*, **138** (1938), 229).

from rest in a reservoir where its temperature is 15° C. and its pressure 100 lb./sq. in. (absolute), and to expand through the nozzle at a series of different rates (depending on the pressure at exit). To limit the field of computation it was further assumed that the pressure, density, and velocity of the fluid have uniform values on two

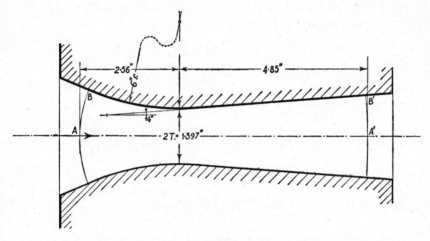

FIG. 83

circular arcs AB, $A'B'$ which cut the nozzle wall orthogonally at points B, B' well upstream and well downstream of the 'throat'; and to simplify computation the Cartesian coordinates (x, y) of the problem as presented were replaced by curvilinear coordinates α, β, related with x and y by a conformal transformation so chosen as to make β vanish on the centre line of the (symmetrical) nozzle, have a constant value β_1 (say) on the nozzle wall, and increase from 0 to that value at uniform rates along AB, $A'B'$. By this procedure α and β are made conjugate plane-harmonic functions of x and y: they may be interpreted as the velocity-potential and stream-function, respectively, of an incompressible fluid entering the nozzle radially across AB and leaving it radially across $A'B'$.

The conformal transformation was effected by relaxation methods, and has been noticed in § 95 of Chapter IV. It simplifies the subsequent computations, since these can be made on rectangular (α-β) nets having no 'irregular stars'. Figs. 84 a, b, c (at end of book) exhibit Green's solution of this problem: Fig. 84 a records his accepted values of α, β, and log h, all of which are plane-harmonic functions of x and y; Fig. 84b shows contours of α, β, and h in the x-y plane; Fig. 84c records h-values at nodal points of the α-β net.

Basic theory

172. The theory of two-dimensional motion of a compressible fluid is as follows:—Postulating an absence of rotation, we can express the component velocities u and v as derivatives of a velocity-potential ϕ; also the 'equation of continuity'

$$\frac{\partial}{\partial x}(\rho u)+\frac{\partial}{\partial y}(\rho v)=0 \tag{67}$$

permits the introduction of a 'mass-flow function' ψ. So we may write

$$\frac{1}{\rho}\frac{\partial \psi}{\partial y}=u=-\frac{\partial \phi}{\partial x}, \qquad -\frac{1}{\rho}\frac{\partial \psi}{\partial x}=v=-\frac{\partial \phi}{\partial y}, \tag{68}$$

and then, eliminating ψ and ϕ in turn from (68), we have

$$\frac{\partial}{\partial x}\left(\rho\frac{\partial \phi}{\partial x}\right)+\frac{\partial}{\partial y}\left(\rho\frac{\partial \phi}{\partial y}\right)=0 \tag{69}$$

and

$$\frac{\partial}{\partial x}\left(\frac{1}{\rho}\frac{\partial \psi}{\partial x}\right)+\frac{\partial}{\partial y}\left(\frac{1}{\rho}\frac{\partial \psi}{\partial y}\right)=0 \tag{70}$$

as alternative forms of the governing equation. (Cf. § 136.)

But here ρ is additionally related with u and v in virtue of its dependence on the local pressure. If we postulate that there is no transfer of energy between contiguous elements of the fluid,† and if the fluid is assumed to start from rest in a reservoir where its state is known, then its total energy will have the same known value at every point: if p, ρ, and q denote its pressure, density, and velocity, and if no body forces are operative, then

$$\int_0^{}\frac{dp}{\rho}+\tfrac{1}{2}q^2=0 \tag{i}$$

when the lower limit 0 of integration relates to the starting conditions, so that $q_0=0$. Moreover p and ρ will conform with some known law of adiabatic expansion,—e.g.

$$p/\rho^\gamma=\text{const.}=p_0/\rho_0^\gamma \tag{ii}$$

for a perfect gas, γ denoting (as usual) the ratio of the specific heats at constant pressure and at constant volume. Consequently by

† Already, in postulating irrotational motion, we have excluded the possibility of transfer due to friction; and heat conduction will be negligible when the speed of flow is high. But cf. § 180.

eliminating p we can relate the density and velocity at any point in the fluid field.

As obtained from (i) and (ii) the relation is

$$q^2 = \frac{2}{\gamma-1}(a_0^2-a^2), \tag{71}$$

a standing for the velocity of sound at the point in question, so that

$$a^2 = \gamma p/\rho = \gamma p_0 \rho^{\gamma-1}/\rho_0^\gamma \text{ according to (ii).} \tag{72}$$

On our assumptions (71) and (72) will hold exactly in respect of a perfect gas, and with sufficient accuracy (γ having the value 1·4) in respect of air. For steam, (ii) and therefore (71) will hold approximately when γ is replaced by an appropriate constant of the order of 1·3 (Ewing, Ref. 5, § 134). Alternatively, (71) and (72) may be replaced by an empirical relation between ρ and q^2.

173. Thus for any fluid we can relate ρ and q^2, therefore ρ and $\rho^2 q^2$. That is, the form of F is known in the expression

$$\chi^2 \text{ (say)} = \frac{1}{\rho} = F(\rho^2 q^2)$$
$$= F\left\{\left(\frac{\partial \psi}{\partial x}\right)^2 + \left(\frac{\partial \psi}{\partial y}\right)^2\right\}, \tag{73}$$

by (68), since $q^2 = u^2 + v^2$. Equation (70) can now be written as

$$\frac{\partial}{\partial x}\left(\chi^2 \frac{\partial \psi}{\partial x}\right) + \frac{\partial}{\partial y}\left(\chi^2 \frac{\partial \psi}{\partial y}\right) = 0, \tag{74}$$

and this in turn (multiplied throughout by $1/\chi$) as

$$\nabla^2(\chi\psi) - \psi\nabla^2\chi = 0, \tag{75}$$

∇^2 denoting the operator $\partial^2/\partial x^2 + \partial^2/\partial y^2$. Equation (74) has the form of (2), § 135, except that χ in that equation is now replaced by χ^2, with a view to the step which yields (75).[†]

The boundary conditions (for a symmetrical nozzle) are

$$\left.\begin{array}{l} \psi = 0 \text{ on the centre line} \\ \psi = \text{const.} = M \text{ (say), on the nozzle wall.} \end{array}\right\} \tag{76}$$

Then, according to (68),

$$2M \text{ measures the total mass-flow through the nozzle.} \tag{77}$$

Preliminaries to computation by the Relaxation Method

174. In order to eliminate 'dimensional' factors we now express the relation (73) as a relation between ρ/ρ_0 and q/a_0, a_0 being the

[†] Cf. the alternative treatments of equation (2) in §§ 142 and 143.

velocity of sound in the fluid in its initial state of rest in the reservoir. Writing

$$x = Tx', \qquad y = Ty', \qquad \rho = \rho_0 \rho', \qquad \psi = M\psi', \quad \Bigg\}$$
and $\qquad \chi'^2$ for $1/\rho' = \rho_0 \chi^2, \qquad q'$ for $q/a_0,$ $\qquad$ (78)

where (cf. Fig. 83) $2T$ denotes the throat-width and M has the significance stated in (77), we have from (71) and (72)

$$q'^2 = \frac{2}{\gamma-1}\left(1 - \frac{a^2}{a_0^2}\right) = \frac{2}{\gamma-1}(1 - \rho'^{\gamma-1}), \qquad \text{(i)}$$

and (73) can be replaced by

$$\chi'^2 = 1/\rho' = F(\rho'^2 q'^2), \qquad \text{(ii)}$$

—F having now, of course, a slightly altered significance. Also

$$\rho^2 q^2 = \left(\frac{\partial\psi}{\partial x}\right)^2 + \left(\frac{\partial\psi}{\partial y}\right)^2 = \frac{M^2}{T^2}\left\{\left(\frac{\partial\psi'}{\partial x'}\right)^2 + \left(\frac{\partial\psi'}{\partial y'}\right)^2\right\},$$

according to (68) and (78); consequently (ii) may be written as

$$\chi'^2 = \frac{1}{\rho'} = F(\rho'^2 q'^2) = F\left[\mu^2\left\{\left(\frac{\partial\psi'}{\partial x'}\right)^2 + \left(\frac{\partial\psi'}{\partial y'}\right)^2\right\}\right], \quad \Bigg\}$$
where $\qquad \mu = M/\rho_0 a_0 T,$ $\qquad$ (79)

so that μ denotes the average mass-flow per unit throat-area, expressed as a fraction of $\rho_0 a_0$.

The forms of (75) and (76) are conserved; i.e. we obtain

$$\nabla'^2(\chi'\psi') - \psi'\nabla'^2\chi' = 0, \quad \Bigg\}$$
∇'^2 denoting the operator $\partial^2/\partial x'^2 + \partial^2/\partial y'^2,$ $\qquad$ (80)

and

$$\psi' = 0 \text{ on the centre line}, \quad \Bigg\}$$
$$\psi' = 1 \text{ on the nozzle wall}, \quad \Bigg\} \qquad \text{(81)}$$

on substituting in them from (78).

175. Finally we change the variables from x', y' to α, β, derived by conformal transformation as described in § 171.

Any convenient value β_1 may be attached to β at the nozzle wall, and any convenient number of contours may be mapped: in Fig. 84 *b* the contour values of β increase from 0 to 10^5 by increments of 2×10^4, and the same increments separate contour values of α. A one-to-one correspondence obtains between points on the curvilinear net, Fig. 84 *b*, and on the rectangular net, Fig. 84 *c*; so any physical quantity determined as a function of α and β in Fig. 84 c can be plotted as a function of x' and y' in Fig. 84 b.

As in § 101, let h stand for the modulus of transformation. Then

$$h^2 = \left| \frac{d(\alpha+i\beta)}{d(x'+iy')} \right|^2 = \left(\frac{\partial\alpha}{\partial x'}\right)^2 + \left(\frac{\partial\alpha}{\partial y'}\right)^2 = \left(\frac{\partial\beta}{\partial x'}\right)^2 + \left(\frac{\partial\beta}{\partial y'}\right)^2, \qquad (82)$$

and in (79) and (80) we may substitute

$$\left.\begin{array}{c} h^2\left\{\left(\frac{\partial\psi'}{\partial\alpha}\right)^2 + \left(\frac{\partial\psi'}{\partial\beta}\right)^2\right\} \quad \text{for} \quad \left(\frac{\partial\psi'}{\partial x'}\right)^2 + \left(\frac{\partial\psi'}{\partial y'}\right)^2 \\[2mm] \text{and} \qquad\qquad h^2\nabla^2_{\alpha,\beta} \text{ for } \nabla'^2, \\[2mm] (\nabla^2_{\alpha,\beta} \text{ denoting the operator } \partial^2/\partial\alpha^2 + \partial^2/\partial\beta^2). \end{array}\right\} \qquad (83)$$

Thereby we obtain

$$\left.\begin{array}{c} \chi'^2 = F\left[\mu^2 h^2\left\{\left(\frac{\partial\psi'}{\partial\alpha}\right)^2 + \left(\frac{\partial\psi'}{\partial\beta}\right)^2\right\}\right] \\[2mm] \text{and} \qquad \nabla^2_{\alpha,\beta}(\psi'\chi') - \psi'\nabla^2_{\alpha,\beta}\chi = 0 \\[2mm] \text{as governing equations, and as boundary conditions} \\[2mm] \psi' = 0 \text{ when } \beta = 0, \\[2mm] \psi' = 1 \text{ when } \beta = \beta_1. \end{array}\right\} \qquad (84)$$

The problem will be specified when we have settled (a) the shape of the nozzle, (b) the value of the mass-flow constant μ as defined in (79), (c) the form of the function F in (84).

The computational problem

176. *Hereafter we shall suppress the dashes which have been attached to χ and ψ, so that in what follows*

$$\left.\begin{array}{l} \chi^2 \text{ stands for } \rho_0/\rho; \ M\psi \text{ is the mass-flow function (§172)}. \\[2mm] \text{We shall, moreover, write } \nabla^2, \text{ simply, for } \nabla^2_{\alpha,\beta} \equiv \dfrac{\partial^2}{\partial\alpha^2} + \dfrac{\partial^2}{\partial\beta^2}. \end{array}\right\} \qquad (85)$$

On this understanding, in 'non-dimensional' coordinates α, β, and on a rectangular net, our problem is to satisfy

$$\nabla^2(\psi\chi) - \psi\nabla^2\chi = 0, \qquad (86)$$

together with

$$\chi^2 = F(\rho'^2 q'^2) = F\left[\mu^2 h^2\left\{\left(\frac{\partial\psi}{\partial\alpha}\right)^2 + \left(\frac{\partial\psi}{\partial\beta}\right)^2\right\}\right], \qquad (87)$$

at every point. In (87),

$$\left.\begin{array}{l} h^2 \text{ has a distribution known from the conformal trans-} \\ \quad \text{formation,} \\ \mu = M/\rho_0\, a_0\, T \text{ is a specified ('mass-flow') parameter,} \\ \rho' \text{ stands for } \rho/\rho_0,\ q' \text{ stands for } q/a_0, \text{ where} \\ \rho \text{ is the local density, } q \text{ is the local velocity,} \\ \rho_0 \text{ is the starting density of the fluid, and (cf. § 172)} \\ a_0 \text{ is the speed of sound in the fluid when at rest.} \end{array}\right\} \quad (88)$$

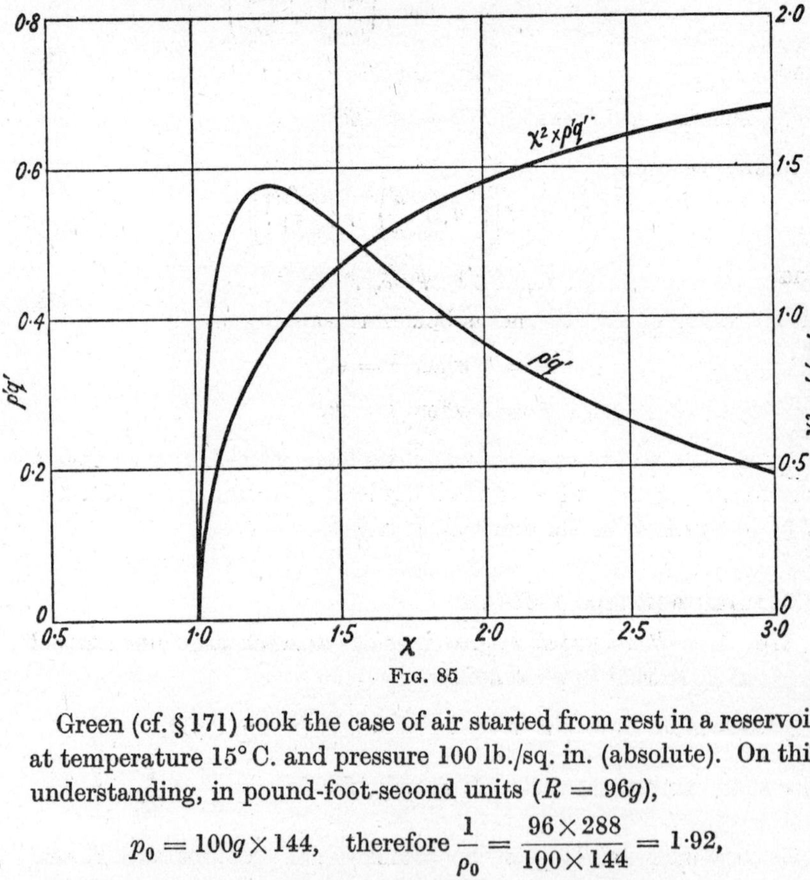

Fig. 85

Green (cf. § 171) took the case of air started from rest in a reservoir at temperature 15° C. and pressure 100 lb./sq. in. (absolute). On this understanding, in pound-foot-second units ($R = 96g$),

$$p_0 = 100g \times 144, \quad \text{therefore } \frac{1}{\rho_0} = \frac{96 \times 288}{100 \times 144} = 1.92,$$

and giving to γ for air the value 1·4 we have from (72)

$$a_0^2 = \gamma p_0/\rho_0 = 140g \times 144 \times 1.92 = 1,246,372 \text{ ft.-sec. units.}$$

Equation (i), § 174, becomes

$$q'^2 = \left(\frac{q}{a_0}\right)^2 = \frac{2}{\gamma-1}\left\{1 - \left(\frac{\rho}{\rho_0}\right)^{\gamma-1}\right\} = 5(1 - \rho'^{0.4});$$

consequently

$$\rho'^2 q'^2 = 5\rho'^2(1-\rho'^{0.4}) = 5\chi^{-4}(1-\chi^{-0.8}), \tag{89}$$

when χ has non-dimensional significance. From (89) we can derive, for Green's assumed conditions, the form of F in (87).

Fig. 85 shows $\rho'q'$ and q' $(= \chi^2\rho'q')$ plotted against χ. We deduce from (89) that $\rho'q'$, therefore μ in (87), cannot exceed

$$(5/6)^3 = 0.578{,}704 \quad (\mu^2 \not> 0.335).$$

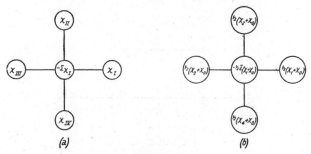

FIG. 86

Introduction of the relaxation technique

177. The finite-difference approximation to (86) can be derived in the manner of § 143. For a net of square mesh it is

$$\mathbf{F}_0 = \sum_{a,4} (\chi\psi) - \psi_0 \sum_{a,4} (\chi) = 0, \tag{90}$$

and two equivalent forms of the corresponding 'pattern' are shown in Fig. 86. The χ^2-values are to be related with the ψ-values by (87), in which, since

$$2\left\{\left(\frac{\partial\psi}{\partial\alpha}\right)^2 + \left(\frac{\partial\psi}{\partial\beta}\right)^2\right\} \equiv \nabla^2(\psi^2) - 2\psi\nabla^2\psi,$$

we use the finite-difference approximation

$$\left(\frac{\partial\psi}{\partial\alpha}\right)^2 + \left(\frac{\partial\psi}{\partial\beta}\right)^2 \approx \frac{2}{a^2}\left[\psi_0^2 + \tfrac{1}{4}\left\{\sum_{a,4}(\psi^2) - 2\psi_0\sum_{a,4}(\psi)\right\}\right]. \tag{91}$$

(A like approximation was used to compute h^2 according to (82).)

For any chosen value of the mass-flow parameter μ, having calculated ψ approximately we can deduce χ^2 at nodal points from (87) combined with (91). Then the pattern appropriate to each point is definite, and we can proceed to a more complete liquidation of the residuals as defined in (90). *It is here that importance attaches to the remark in § 170.*

178. Ref. 7 (§ 14) outlined a slightly different procedure, formally more exact but (for the reason just indicated) not obligatory. We reproduce it here, in order to repair certain omissions in the original presentation.

Writing x^2 for the quantity on the left of (91), we replace (87) by

$$\chi = f(\mu^2 h^2 x^2),\qquad\text{(i)}$$

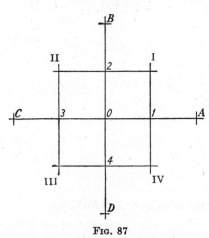

Fig. 87

in which the form of f is known from that of F; and then for infinitesimal increments

$$\delta\chi = f'(\mu^2 h^2 x^2)\mu^2 h^2(\delta x^2).\qquad\text{(ii)}$$

Now from (90) we may deduce that an infinitesimal increment $\delta\psi_0$ given to ψ_0 (ψ being left unaltered at every other point) will entail increments to the residual forces as under:

$$\left.\begin{aligned}
\delta\mathbf{F}_0 &= \sum_{a,4}(\psi\,\delta\chi) - \psi_0\sum_{a,4}(\delta\chi) - \delta\psi_0\sum_{a,4}(\chi),\\
\delta(\mathbf{F}_1,\mathbf{F}_2,\mathbf{F}_3,\mathbf{F}_4) &= \delta\psi_0\chi_0 + \psi_0\delta\chi_0 - (\psi_1,\psi_2,\psi_3,\psi_4)\delta\chi_0,\\
\delta(\mathbf{F}_A,\mathbf{F}_B,\mathbf{F}_C,\mathbf{F}_D) &= (\psi_1-\psi_A)\delta\chi_1,(\psi_2-\psi_B)\delta\chi_2,(\psi_3-\psi_C)\delta\chi_3,(\psi_4-\psi_D)\delta\chi_4,\\
\delta(\mathbf{F}_I,\mathbf{F}_{II},\mathbf{F}_{III},\mathbf{F}_{IV}) &= (\psi_1-\psi_I)\delta\chi_1 + (\psi_2-\psi_I)\delta\chi_2,\text{ etc.,}
\end{aligned}\right\}\text{(iii)}$$

$\delta\chi$ denoting the increment to χ which is entailed by $\delta\psi_0$, and the suffixes $1, 2, 3, 4, A, B, C, D, I, II, III, IV$ relating to points so designated in Fig. 87; and according to (91) an increment $\delta\psi_0$ in ψ_0 *only* leaves x^2 unaltered at A, B, C, D, I, II, III, IV, and makes

$$\left.\begin{aligned}
(\delta x^2)_0 &= \frac{\delta\psi_0}{a^2}\Big[4\psi_0 - \sum_{a,4}(\psi)\Big],\\
(\delta x^2)_{1,2,3,4} &= \frac{\delta\psi_0}{a^2}(\psi_0 - \psi_{1,2,3,4}).
\end{aligned}\right\}\text{(iv)}$$

Consequently in the expressions (iii) we may write

$$\left. \begin{aligned}
\delta\chi_0 &= \frac{\mu^2 h^2}{a^2} f'(\mu^2 h^2 x^2)\left[4\psi_0 - \sum_{a,4}(\psi)\right]\delta\psi_0, \\
\delta\chi_{1,2,3,4} &= \frac{\mu^2 h^2}{a^2} f'(\mu^2 h^2 x^2)(\psi_0 - \psi_{1,2,3,4})\delta\psi_0,
\end{aligned} \right\} \tag{v}$$

and then, if G is defined by

$$G = \frac{\mu^2 h^2}{a^2} f'(\mu^2 h^2 x^2) = \frac{\mu^2 h^2}{a^2}\frac{d\chi}{d(\rho'^2 q'^2)}, \text{ by (ii) and (87),} \tag{92}$$

it follows that when quantities of the second and higher orders in $\delta\psi_0$ are neglected

$$\left. \begin{aligned}
\delta F_0 &= -\delta\psi_0\left\{\sum_{a,4}(\chi) + G\sum_{a,4}[(\psi-\psi_0)^2]\right\}, \\
\delta F_1 &= \delta\psi_0\left[\chi_0 + G(\psi_1-\psi_0)\left\{\sum_{a,4}(\psi) - 4\psi_0\right\}\right], \\
&\;\;\cdot \qquad\;\; \cdot \qquad\;\; \cdot \qquad\;\; \cdot \\
\delta F_A &= -\delta\psi_0\, G(\psi_1-\psi_0)(\psi_1-\psi_A), \\
&\;\;\cdot \qquad\;\; \cdot \qquad\;\; \cdot \qquad\;\; \cdot \\
\delta F_I &= G\,\delta\psi_0\{(\psi_0+\psi_I)(\psi_1+\psi_2) - (2\psi_0\psi_I+\psi_1^2+\psi_2^2)\}, \\
&\;\;\cdot \qquad\;\; \cdot \qquad\;\; \cdot \qquad\;\; \cdot
\end{aligned} \right\} \tag{93}$$

Fig. 88 (deduced from Fig. 85) shows χ and $d\chi/d(\rho'^2 q'^2)$ plotted against $\rho'^2 q'^2$ as related with ψ by (87). Using (93), for any point 0 we can (given ψ-values for 0, 1, 2, 3, 4, A, B, C, D, I, II, III, IV and χ-values for 0, 1, 2, 3, 4) compute a 'pattern' giving the effects of a *small* increment $\delta\psi_0$ upon the residual forces at all points in Fig. 87 Here again nothing is gained by computing very exact *patterns*, but residual forces must be known with certainty, and to that end χ-values must be accurately computed in the later stages of the work—i.e. with all the accuracy which is permitted by (91) and by the similar approximation to h^2.

179. Having thus explained the basis of Green's computations, we now proceed to summarize his results. It has been shown (§ 176) that μ must be less than 0.5787 ($\mu^2 < 0.335$), this being the value at which the velocity of sound is attained at the throat. Green, approaching this value from below, explored the flow in four subsonic cases, as under:†

Case	μ	$(M/T)^2$ (lb. ft. sec. units)
1	$0.486,4_5$	800,000
2	$0.515,9_5$	900,000
3	$0.543,8_5$	1,000,000
4	$0.575,5_5$	1,120,000

† Errors in the original table have been corrected.

Case 4 was expected (and was found) to give velocities just attaining to the speed of sound at a point in the throat section and on the nozzle wall. The computations, though laborious, entailed no diffi-

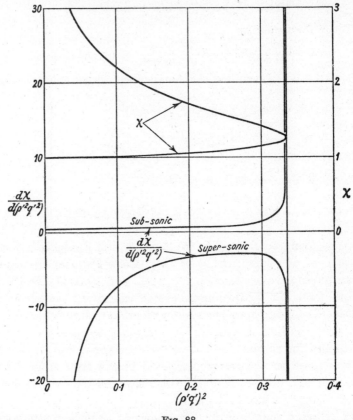

FIG. 88

culty, and 3-figure accuracy (at least) was claimed for the results presented in Figs. 89–92 (folding diagrams at end of book).

180. Under supersonic conditions, on the other hand, the technique failed to yield definite results. The failure was ascribed to some kind of instability appearing downstream of the throat, whereby any disturbance (implicit in an assumed solution) would be magnified without limit. (As Fig. 88 shows, G, in (92), tends to an infinite value corresponding with the speed of sound; so near the throat, and for supersonic flow, the 'relaxation patterns' which come from (93) must involve very large numbers.)

To meet the difficulty an alternative method was devised, *not involving the relaxational technique.* (Since that technique in its initial stages presupposes that disturbing forces are operative, it could hardly be expected to determine régimes intrinsically unstable.) The new method was successful, and in Cases 1 and 4 (Figs. 89 and 92) yielded the contours shown in broken line, with identical results elsewhere. In a subsequent paper (Ref. 6) L. Fox, with assistance from Miss G. Vaisey, used it to compute both the limiting subsonic régime (Fig. 93) and the supersonic régime (Fig. 94), i.e. that (unique) régime in which the pressure and density of the gas decrease continuously in its passage from end to end.† Their nozzle shape was practically identical with Green's (Fig. 83).

The two régimes imply two different values of the pressure at exit, and for intermediate pressures (on the assumption that the flow is everywhere irrotational) there is no solution of the problem. As shown by von Karman (Ref. 8) on the basis of Osborne Reynolds's simplified treatment, the explanation is that 'shock waves' make an appearance and *the flow is no longer isentropic.* Recently H. W. Emmons, in a paper not yet released, has shown shock waves to be amenable to relaxational treatment; so the two-dimensional theory of the flow of gas through nozzles may now be regarded as complete.

RÉSUMÉ

181. This chapter deals with governing equations of the form

$$\frac{\partial}{\partial x}\left(\chi\frac{\partial\psi}{\partial x}\right)+\frac{\partial}{\partial y}\left(\chi\frac{\partial\psi}{\partial y}\right)+Z = 0 \qquad\qquad (2)\,bis$$

in which χ, like Z, is a function of x and y. They are presented in a wide variety of physical problems, some of which receive notice in §§ 135–9. To orthodox analysis they oppose greater difficulty than the plane-harmonic equations treated hitherto, but for Relaxation Methods, when χ is specified, they entail only minor modifications of the normal technique, and even when χ is additionally related by some other equation with ψ and/or with its differentials (i.e. in problems of 'Class (B)', § 141) solutions can still be found without great difficulty—though at greater cost in labour—by processes in

† Figs. 93 and 94 are folding diagrams at the end of this book. In Fig. 93, shading indicates regions at the 'throat' in which the velocity attains the local speed of sound.

which the 'relaxation patterns' are modified as 'liquidation' becomes more and more complete. Consequently for some of the problems in this chapter Relaxation Methods are a necessary rather than an alternative weapon of research, and on that account the underlying theory of those problems is presented in more detail than heretofore.

The boundary condition of a quasi-plane-harmonic problem seldom imposes values on the normal gradient, and accordingly problems of 'Class II' (§ 141) are not exemplified here. They have been treated in Ref. 2, on lines akin to §§ 70–4, Chap. III.

REFERENCES

1. ALLEN, D. N. de G., and SOUTHWELL, R. V. 1944. *Proc. Roy. Soc. A*, **183**, 125–34.
2. ALLEN, D. N. de G., SOUTHWELL, R. V., and VAISEY, G. 1945. *Proc. Roy. Soc. A*, **183**, 258–83.
3. CARSLAW, H. S. 1921. *Mathematical Theory of the Conduction of Heat in Solids* (2nd ed.). Macmillan & Co.
4. CHRISTOPHERSON, D. G. 1941. *Proc. Inst. Mech. Eng.*, **146**, 126–35.
5. EWING, J. A. 1926. *The Steam Engine and other Heat Engines*, 4th ed. Camb. Univ. Press.
6. FOX, L., and SOUTHWELL, R. V. 1944. *Proc. Roy. Soc. A*, **183**, 38–54.
7. GREEN, J. R., and SOUTHWELL, R. V. 1944. *Phil. Trans. Roy. Soc. A*, **239**, 367–86.
8. KARMAN, Th. von. 1941. *Journ. Aero. Sci.* **8**, 337–56.
9. MICHELL, A. G. M. 1905. *Zeitschr. f. Math. u. Phys.* **52**, 123–37.
10. REYNOLDS, OSBORNE. 1886. *Phil. Trans. Roy. Soc. A*, **177** (Part I), 157–234; reprinted in *Collected Papers*, **2**, 228–310.
11. SOUTHWELL, R. V. 1942. *Proc. Roy. Soc. A*, **180**, 367–96.
12. THOM, A., and ORR, J. 1931. *Proc. Roy. Soc. A*, **131**, 30–7.

PROBLEMS INVOLVING BOUNDARIES OR INTERFACES NOT INITIALLY KNOWN

182. In this chapter we extend the relaxation technique to problems in which either (1) different equations govern the wanted function in different parts of the specified domain† or (2) some part of the boundary is not known initially but (like the wanted function) must be determined by computation. Such problems present great if not insuperable difficulties to an orthodox approach.

Prandtl's membrane analogue of plastic torsion

183. Prandtl, who first propounded the membrane analogue of elastic torsion (§ 36), later (Ref. 8) extended it to cases in which the material, over some part of the cross-section, has reached its elastic limit and so no longer obeys Hooke's law. His theory presumes that the relation between shear stress and strain is that presented in Fig. 95. For stresses below some limiting value f_Y (which is specified), the usual (Hooke's law) relation holds and in consequence Ψ, the stress-function, satisfies (17) of § 46, viz.

$$\nabla^2\Psi + 2 = 0; \tag{1}$$

but the stress cannot exceed this limiting value f_Y, with which *any* shear strain in excess of γ_Y can be associated, and in consequence an upper limit is imposed upon the *gradient* of Ψ.

We know from the work of Boussinesq and of Filon that the stress as determined by (1) attains its limiting value on the boundary. Therefore (in Prandtl's argument) knowing Ψ on the boundary we can impose limiting values on Ψ at neighbouring points: we have only to imagine a surface of constant slope to be attached to the boundary in the way that a roof (without eaves) is attached to the wall of a building. This surface is commonly known as the **Prandtl roof**. The term leads us to expect (what is the fact) that its gradient will be discontinuous near a sharp external angle.

The net analogue of plastic torsion

184. Adopting the notion of this 'roof' or rigid surface against which the loaded membrane can press if its elastic deflexion would

† In the 'magnetic line' problems of §§ 87–90 the wanted function was plane-harmonic both in the 'iron' and in the 'air'.

be more than Fig. 95 allows, we may as before regard the finite-difference approximation to (1) as entailing replacement of the membrane by a net of finite mesh. At nodes which have attained their limiting permitted deflexion (i.e. which have come into contact with the roof) residual forces need not be liquidated because the roof,

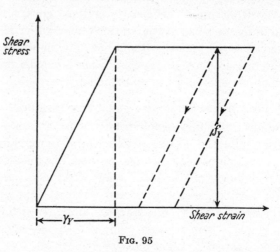

Fig. 95

in virtue of its rigidity, can transmit them to other points; but for any closed contour in that part of the net which does *not* bear against the roof, the total pull of strings which cross the contour must be in equilibrium with the total external load applied to points within it, consequently 'block-relaxation' can be employed as in § 54.

185. Dimensional quantities can be eliminated as in § 46, leaving us with the computational problem of determining nodal values of a numerical quantity χ which

   (i) has a constant value on the boundary (or on every closed boundary, in the case of multiply-connected sections),

  (ii) must not exceed a specified value appropriate to each nodal point (i.e. the value which the 'roof' imposes),

 (iii) subject to the overriding condition (ii), must satisfy the equation

$$\mathbf{F} = \mathbf{F} + F = 0 \qquad\qquad (2)$$

at every internal node, where (cf. § 41)

F, representative of the forces due to external loading,

$$= N\frac{a^2}{4}Z, \qquad\qquad \text{when } N = 3 \text{ or } 4, \qquad\qquad (3)$$

$$= N\left[\frac{a^2}{4}Z + \frac{a^4}{64}\nabla^2 Z\right], \quad \text{when } N = 6, \qquad\qquad (4)$$

(Z having here the value 2); and where F, representative of the forces opposed by tensions in the net,

$$= \sum_{a,N}(\chi) - N\chi, \textit{ for all values of } N. \qquad\qquad (5)$$

When the condition (ii) is overriding, **F** is not required to vanish, therefore (2) is not imposed.

Example XXVIII: Plastic torsion of a bar of equilateral triangular cross-section

186. The significance of §§ 183–5 will be most easily grasped in relation to a simple example: therefore we proceed to investigate the plastic behaviour under torsion of a bar having as its cross-section an equilateral triangle of side D. This shape, as concerns elastic stresses, has been discussed in Chapter II. Its plastic behaviour was first studied by Relaxation Methods in Ref. 4.

187. Let χ be assumed to vanish at every point of the triangular boundary, and let λ be the limiting gradient of χ (i.e. the slope of the 'roof'), expressed 'non-dimensionally'. Clearly, when the substitutions of § 46 are employed, then

$$\lambda = f_Y/\mu D\tau. \qquad\qquad (6)$$

We can at once attach to each nodal point the maximum value which the roof permits χ to attain there. Thus when the net is triangular and of mesh size $a = 1/27$ (Fig. 96), the distance from the boundary of the nearest rows of internal nodes (viz. ab, bc, ca) is

$$\frac{\sqrt{3}}{2}a = \frac{1}{18\sqrt{3}},$$

so the maximum value of χ which is permitted on those rows is

$$\frac{\lambda}{18\sqrt{3}} = 1 \text{ when } \lambda = 18\sqrt{3} = 31{\cdot}177. \qquad\qquad (7)$$

On the next rows (de, ef, fd) the maximum permitted value of χ is twice this figure, and so on.

We multiply χ by 10^4, in computation, with the object of eliminating decimals. Then the 'overriding' values, when λ has the value (7), are

$$\left.\begin{array}{l} \chi \not> 10^4 \text{ in the first rows } ab,\ bc,\ ca, \\ \chi \not> 2\times 10^4 \text{ in the second rows } de,\ ef,\ fd, \\ ...,\ ..., \end{array}\right\} \qquad (8)$$

and so on. Starting from the known 'elastic' solution (§ 47), we now proceed to investigate the modifications which result from the presence of the roof.

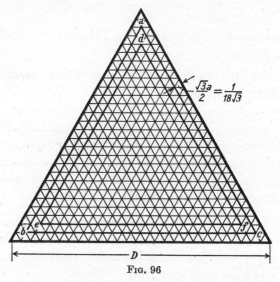

$$\frac{\sqrt{3}a}{2} = \frac{1}{18\sqrt{3}}$$

Fig. 96

188. The work is straightforward and easy. The elastic solution gives values of χ which exceed the overriding values (8) in regions near the centre of each side: we alter them to (8) by suitable (negative) displacements, and we record the effects of those displacements on the residual forces in the usual way. At points thus brought into contact with the roof we neglect residuals of positive sign for the reason that the roof can sustain them, but negative residuals we liquidate in the usual way, by further negative displacements which bring the net out of contact with the roof. The reader should himself work an example. He will meet no difficulty, if he has clearly visualized the 'roof' and its significance in the net analogy.

In Ref. 4, § 30, computations were made in this way by D. G. Christopherson for the following (multiplied) values of λ:

$$(a)\ 3600\sqrt{3}, \quad (b)\ 2700\sqrt{3}, \quad (c)\ 1800\sqrt{3}, \quad (d)\ 900\sqrt{3}. \qquad (9)$$

Fig. 97 exhibits contours of constant χ for these four cases, the extent of the overstrained material being indicated in each instance by a dotted line. Fig. 98 shows how the overstrained region increases

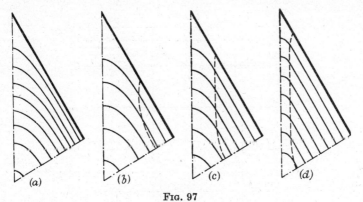

Fig. 97

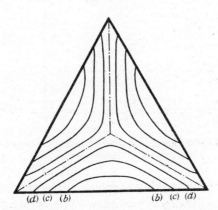

Fig. 98

FIGS. 97 and 98. Plastic torsion of a bar of triangular cross-section.
(D. G. Christopherson)

with increasing torque,† Fig. 99 the relation between torque and twist. It is known (*Elasticity*, §§ 339, 390) that the torque

$$T = \mu\tau H = 2\mu\tau \iint \Psi\, dxdy$$

$$= 2\mu\tau D^4 \iint \chi\, dx'dy', \text{ in the notation of § 46,}$$

$$= \frac{2}{\lambda} D^3 f_Y \iint \chi\, dx'dy', \text{ according to (6),} \qquad (10)$$

† It will eventually occupy the whole triangle with the exception of a small region near each corner, where the membrane *never* comes into contact with the roof.

and with close approximation the surface integral of χ is given by†

$$\iint \chi \, dx'dy' = \frac{\sqrt{3}}{2} a^2 \sum (\chi),$$ (11)

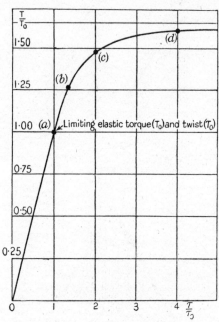

Fig. 99. Plastic torsion of a bar of triangular cross-section.
(D. G. Christopherson)

when the summation extends to every nodal point of a triangular net of mesh-side a. (*Points in contact with the roof must be included in the summation, to take account of the stresses in the plastic region.*) So T/T_0 and τ/τ_0 can be related, T_0 and τ_0 denoting respectively the limiting elastic torque and twist.

Plastic distortion of bars having multiply-connected cross-sections

189. D. G. Christopherson (Ref. 3) has applied these methods (with some modifications of detail) to I-section girders. F. S. Shaw (Ref. 9) has treated a similar example and has also applied the methods to

† A more accurate integration could be effected with a use of the rules explained in §§ 23–5 (Chap. I), but is hardly needed here.

hollow (i.e. multiply-connected) sections, in which plastic strain can start either at the external or at an internal boundary.

The notion of the 'roof' has obvious extension to the case of multiply-connected sections: we have only to imagine the 'light rigid plates' of § 64 replaced by 'saucers' having rims of constant slope (Fig. 100), against which the membrane can press if in their absence its slope would exceed this limiting value. The saucers are to be

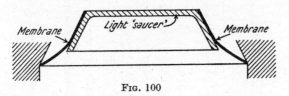

Membrane   Light 'saucer'   Membrane

FIG. 100

pictured as light and as 'floating' under the exactly balancing effects (a) of the tension in the membrane, and (b) of the applied pressure. Replacing the membrane by an 'equivalent' net, we can proceed with computation as before.

Example XXIX: Plastic torsion of a bar of hollow square cross-section

190. Fig. 101, due to F. S. Shaw, shows the effect of thus allowing for plasticity in a case which (for purely elastic stresses) has been treated as Example III, § 58. The limiting stress f_Y (§ 183) is assumed to have the value 23520 when χ is suitably multiplied. Giving this gradient to the roof and to the floating 'saucers', by treatment described above Shaw obtained the recorded χ-values. The reader may either check these values or attack the problem *ab initio* for himself.

The stress-contours shown in Fig. 101 are for our present purpose immaterial, excepting those which define the plastic regions at the four internal corners and in the central parts of the four sides.[†] Shaw went on to compute the residual stresses which would be left after removal of the applied torque,—assuming for this purpose that the stress-strain diagram for unloading from the limiting stress f_Y is a line parallel to the line which represents Hooke's law in Fig. 95. (There, two such 'lines of unloading' are shown in broken line.) His results, as having physical interest, are reproduced in Fig. 102.

---

† On account of symmetry only one-eighth of the complete cross-section needs to be reproduced.

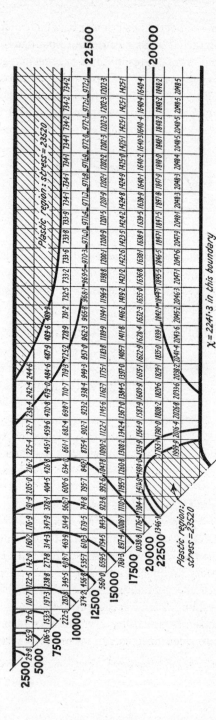

Fig. 101. Plastic stresses induced by torsion in a bar of hollow square section. (F. S. Shaw)

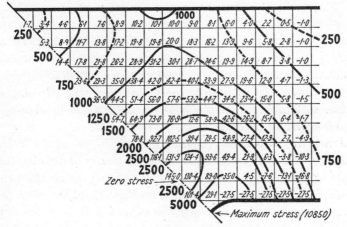

FIG. 102. Residual stresses in an overstrained bar of hollow square cross-section.
(F. S. Shaw)

Free surface conditions in the theory of percolation

191. Another class of problem in which the boundary (or a part of it) is not known at starting is presented in the theory of slow

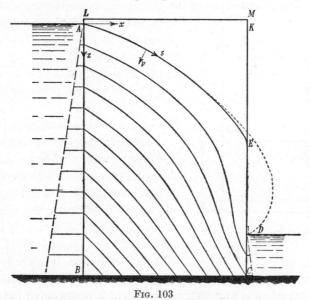

FIG. 103

percolation of fluids through porous materials such as soil or peat. Take, as an example, the problem illustrated in Fig. 103, which concerns the leakage of water through a retaining wall having vertical

O

sides BL, CM. The 'head' of water on each side is specified, and leakage *under* the wall is prevented by an impermeable stratum. If evaporation is sufficient, the free surface inside the wall tends smoothly to the level on the downstream side; but otherwise it reaches this (vertical) side at a point (E) above that level, and fluid seeping through to air drains freely down the wall. In any event the free surface is not known initially and, as will be shown, *on it a double boundary condition is imposed.*

Davison and Rosenhead (Ref. 5), by a skilful use of the 'Schwarz-Christoffel transformation', escaped the necessity of defining the free surface *a priori*; but they did not completely solve the problem indicated in Fig. 103 (which is based on Figs. 1 and 4 of their paper), because except on the assumption of evaporation in excess of a calculable limit they obtained for the free surface a shape of the kind which is indicated by a broken line: the reason being, that their transformation could not allow for the possibility of seepage through the vertical surface ED.

192. The foundations of the theory of percolation appear to have

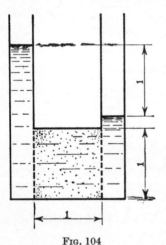

Fig. 104

been laid by Forchheimer and Boussinesq (Refs. 6 and 1). Taking Ox as the horizontal axis and Oy, directed upwards, as the vertical axis, we write p for the average pressure at a point x, y, u and v for the components of 'percolation velocity' along Ox and Oy. The components of frictional force are defined, in agreement with Darcy's law,[†] as $\rho g u/k$ and $\rho g v/k$, ρ denoting the density of the fluid and g the acceleration due to gravity. k is the 'percolation coefficient' or 'coefficient of permeability' (Casagrande, Ref. 2): it measures the flow per unit time through a unit cube of the permeable material (Fig. 104) when a unit difference of head is maintained between two opposite faces and when flow through the other faces is prevented.

---

† Casagrande states (Ref. 2, p. 134): 'The reader may be assured that this law is valid for the study of seepage through dams.'

The equation of continuity is

$$\frac{\partial u}{\partial x} + \frac{\partial v}{\partial y} = 0, \tag{12}$$

and the equations of motion are

$$\left. \begin{aligned} -\frac{\partial p}{\partial x} - \frac{\rho g}{k} u &= 0, \\ -\frac{\partial p}{\partial y} - \frac{\rho g}{k} v - \rho g &= 0, \end{aligned} \right\} \tag{13}$$

showing that u, v have the expressions

$$u = \frac{\partial \phi}{\partial x}, \qquad v = \frac{\partial \phi}{\partial y} \tag{14}$$

in terms of a velocity-potential ϕ defined by

$$\phi = -k\left(\frac{p}{\rho g} + y\right). \tag{15}$$

On substitution from (14) in (12) we find that

$$\nabla^2 \phi = 0,$$

whence $\qquad \nabla^2(p/\rho g) = 0 \quad$ in virtue of (15). $\tag{16}$

193. Again referring to Fig. 103, it is convenient to employ the symbol z for the vertical coordinate measured *downwards* from an origin (A) in the upstream face of the wall and at the level of the water surface. Then along AB (since the fluid is sensibly at rest) we have

$$p/\rho g = z; \tag{17}$$

along AE (the free surface) and ED (the 'seepage face')†

$$p/\rho g = 0; \tag{18}$$

along DC (since the fluid is sensibly at rest)

$$p/\rho g = z - z_D; \tag{19}$$

along the impermeable base BC, $v = \partial\phi/\partial y = 0$, therefore by (15)

$$\frac{\partial}{\partial z}(p/\rho g) = -\frac{\partial y}{\partial z} = 1. \tag{20}$$

We have seen that $(p/\rho g)$ is plane-harmonic, and by definition

---

† We have assumed in (17) that p is measured from atmospheric pressure as datum. In the nature of the case, if another datum were chosen we should have to make a constant addition to $p/\rho g$.

$\partial\phi/\partial\nu = 0$ for all points on AE, ν denoting the normal to this curve. Hence, according to (15),

$$\frac{\partial}{\partial\nu}(p/\rho g) = -\frac{\partial y}{\partial\nu} = \frac{\partial z}{\partial\nu} = \frac{\partial x}{\partial s}, \tag{21}$$

s denoting distance from A along AE. Combined with (18), *which must also be satisfied on AE*, this yields two conditions as under:

$$\left.\begin{aligned} \frac{\partial}{\partial z}(p/\rho g) &= l\frac{\partial}{\partial\nu}(p/\rho g) = l^2, \\[2mm] \frac{\partial}{\partial x}(p/\rho g) &= -m\frac{\partial}{\partial\nu}(p/\rho g) = -lm, \\[2mm] l,\ m \text{ denoting the direction cosines} & \frac{\partial x}{\partial s}, \frac{\partial z}{\partial s}. \end{aligned}\right\} \tag{22}$$

Therefore at A, since $p/\rho g$ must satisfy (17) along AB,

$$l^2 = 1, \quad \text{i.e. the curve } AE \text{ is horizontal}, \tag{i}$$

and at E, since $p/\rho g$ must satisfy (18) along ED,

$$l^2 = 0, \quad \text{i.e. the curve } AE \text{ is tangential to } ED. \tag{ii}$$

At both points (since $l^2+m^2 = 1$) lm will vanish according to (i) and (ii), and so

$$\frac{\partial}{\partial x}(p/\rho g) = 0 \quad \text{according to the second of (22).}$$

We can (initially) make no other assertion about the form of AE, which obviously depends upon the pressure-distribution within the retaining wall, and would be altered (for example) if the wall included an impermeable obstruction.

Introduction of the mechanical (membrane or net) analogue

194. We can, on the other hand, see the nature of the double boundary condition by analogy. Let w stand for the plane-harmonic function $p/\rho g$, and let it be interpreted as the transverse displacement of a uniformly tensioned membrane. Along AB and CD the value of w is determined by (17) and by (19), and it is zero, by (18), at every point in AE and ED. The form of AE (including the position of E) must satisfy the condition

$$\int_0^{\cdot} \frac{\partial w}{\partial\nu}\, ds = x, \tag{23}$$

which results from integration of (21).

When w is thus interpreted, $\partial w/\partial v$ measures the line-intensity of the force exerted, in the direction of w, by the membrane on the boundary. We see from (23) that this line-intensity must be such that the force on any element δs of AE is proportional to the corresponding element δx: in other words, the edge AE of the membrane must be held down (so that $w = 0$) by forces having uniform line-intensity with respect to x. The circumstances are like those of a gas-balloon held down during inflation by 'shot-bags', but with the difference that here the tendency of the membrane to lift comes not directly (from applied pressure) but indirectly by transmission, due to its tension, of the displacements imposed at its edges AB, DC.

195. Substituting the 'net' for the 'membrane analogue', we deduce a process whereby the form of AE can be determined within the accuracy permitted by any particular size of mesh.

Suppose first that p is zero along AK, KE (Fig. 103), and that we solve the potential problem thus presented. It may be expected that w, which vanishes along both arms of the angle AKE, will be small in the region adjacent to this angle; so towards the end K, at any rate, of AK we may expect that $\partial w/\partial v$ (in this instance $\partial w/\partial z$) will have values less than what is required by (22) with $l = 1$. It is certain that we must move the boundary downwards, except at its end A where the relations (22) are already satisfied.

It is also evident on physical grounds (and can be proved mathematically) that depression of any internal point of the membrane will entail depressions everywhere: therefore we may certainly move the boundary downwards so long as the resulting changes in the boundary slopes, *assuming w to remain unchanged at all internal nodes*, are not so great that at any point the analogue of $(\partial w/\partial v)\,ds > dx$. Now the 'net analogue' of this quantity is the pull exerted on an element δs of the boundary by those strings which come to it. If then we accept all consequences of the 'net approximation', we can with certainty depress the boundary through some known distance, after which we must trace the consequence at interior points. These points will also be depressed, reducing the boundary slopes; so now we can depress the boundary further, then recalculate internal values of w, and so on.†

---

† Actually we depress the boundary farther than is immediately justified, anticipating the consequent depression of interior points.

196. Having determined $p/\rho g$ at all internal points of the chosen net, we can estimate the total 'leakage' (i.e. the quantity flowing in unit time through unit thickness of the retaining wall).

In the notation of §§ 192–3, this quantity

$Q = \int u \, dz,$ when the integral extends over any vertical line drawn from AE to the impermeable base BC,

$$= \int \frac{\partial \phi}{\partial x} \, dz = -k \int \frac{\partial}{\partial x}\!\left(\frac{p}{\rho g}\right) dz, \quad \text{by (15).}$$

On the upstream face $(p/\rho g)$ ranges from 0 at the free surface A to $p_0/\rho g = D$, by (17), at B (D denoting the depth below A of the impermeable base). Consequently if $p/\rho g$ at any point be measured as a fraction of D, then

$$Q = -kD \int \frac{\partial P}{\partial x} \, dz, \Bigg\} \tag{24}$$

where P stands for $p/\rho g D$.

The integral in (24) is 'non-dimensional' like P (x and z being measured in the same units); so Q is given by (24) as a fraction of kD—i.e. (cf. § 192) as a fraction of the flow per unit time through the unit cube of Fig. 104, when an excess head D of the fluid is maintained on its left-hand side.

Example XXX: Percolation through a rectangular retaining wall of uniform permeability

197. Fig. 105 exemplifies these methods as applied by F. S. Shaw (Ref. 10). The depths of water on the sides of the wall were taken as in the ratio 6 : 1, and to eliminate decimals a large and arbitrary value 6,000 was given to D (§ 196). Values of $(p/\rho g)$ could then be attached to nodal points on the two sides of the wall, and relaxation started. The condition (20) was satisfied (approximately) along BC by including one horizontal row of fictitious nodal points immediately below that line (exemplified by the point c in Fig. 105), and by identifying, for example, the gradient of $(p/\rho g)$ at d with the gradient of its chord bc.

Fig. 105 shows the last of three successive nets. Except for the determination of the free surface AE, computation might have been ended earlier: even the coarsest net (with mesh-side four times as great) gave a satisfactory picture of the general flow, and on all three the free surface proved stable in the sense that any departure from

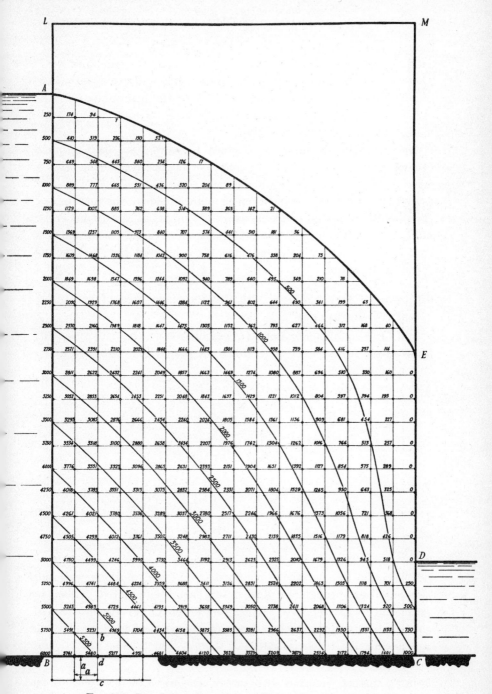

FIG. 105. Percolation through a retaining wall. (F. S. Shaw)

the true form entailed restoring 'forces'. Actually, in the neighbourhood of the boundary, advance was made to two still finer nets.
Thereby confirmation was obtained regarding the rapid curvature
of AE both at A and E, whereby both of the conditions (22) are
in fact satisfied, though the general shape of the free surface approxi-
mates to a line of constant slope.

The contours are lines of constant pressure,—*not lines of flow*,
because the stream-lines cut the ϕ-lines orthogonally, ϕ being related
with $(p/\rho g)$ by (15). It would be easy to deduce values of ϕ, and
the stream-function ψ could then be determined by the methods of
Chapter IV; but what concerns us from a practical standpoint is the
fluid pressures induced in the retaining wall, so Shaw's attention was
concentrated on these throughout. He computed the 'leakage' Q
(§ 196) as $0.729kD$.

Junction of free surface with downstream face of retaining wall. General case

198. In two further examples of percolation which he investigated,
Shaw (Ref. 10) assumed a 'blanket' of permeable rubble to exist,

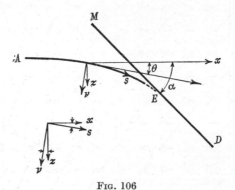

Fig. 106

whereby the free surface is confined within the retaining wall and
so all seepage through the downstream face is eliminated. This is in
accordance with approved engineering practice: nevertheless it is of
interest to consider the general case of seepage through a face having
any inclination to the horizontal, thereby generalizing the conclusions of § 193.

In Fig. 106 AE represents a free surface along which the fluid moves from
A to E, i.e. in the direction of s increasing. Consequently $\partial\phi/\partial s$ is everywhere

positive, and so according to (15), since $(p/\rho g)$ is constant (and k necessarily positive) on AE,

$$\frac{\partial y}{\partial s} < 0, \qquad \text{i.e.} \qquad \frac{\partial z}{\partial s} > 0.$$

This means that AE must everywhere be inclined *downwards* from the horizontal: i.e. θ, in Fig. 106, is everywhere positive.

Again, in that part of the wall which is penetrated by fluid $(p/\rho g)$, being plane-harmonic, can have no minimum value; and on the boundaries of this region it is either zero, or positive, or is required (at the impermeable stratum) to have zero normal gradient. It can be shown that in consequence $\partial/\partial \nu \, (p/\rho g)$ must be positive or zero at every point in AE; and since (§ 193) this normal gradient $\doteq \partial x/\partial s$, it follows that θ cannot exceed $\frac{1}{2}\pi$.

Now on AE, since this is both a stream-line and a line of constant pressure, both of the conditions (22) must be satisfied at every point. Along the face ED (which is also a line of constant pressure, but is *not* a stream-line) we have merely

$$\cos\alpha \frac{\partial p}{\partial x} + \sin\alpha \frac{\partial p}{\partial z} = 0.$$

Therefore at E, *since velocities and therefore pressure-gradients must be single-valued*, we have

$$l(l\sin\alpha - m\cos\alpha) = 0,$$

i.e.

$$\cos\theta \sin(\alpha - \theta) = 0,$$

indicating as alternative possibilities either $\theta = \pm\frac{1}{2}\pi$ or $\theta = \alpha + n\pi$ (n integral or zero).

Because, as we have seen, $0 \leqslant \theta \leqslant \frac{1}{2}\pi$, the second alternative is acceptable only when α lies between 0 and $\frac{1}{2}\pi$—i.e. when the downstream face has positive batter: in that event AE will meet MD tangentially, as in § 193. When α lies between $\frac{1}{2}\pi$ and π (i.e. when the downstream face MD is 'overhung') only the first alternative is acceptable: then AE is vertical at its point of intersection with MD. (In the nature of the case $0 \leqslant \alpha \leqslant \pi$.)

Example XXXI: Earth wall containing a permeable 'blanket' and on subsoil of the same material

199. Shaw's second problem (Fig. 107) related to a wall or 'levee' battered on both sides and assumed to be of the same material as the subsoil, which extends down to an impermeable stratum at a depth below ground-level equal to the depth of the fluid on the upstream side. A 'blanket' of coarse rubble was assumed to maintain atmospheric pressure along the line AB, and Fig. 107 (Shaw's accepted solution) shows that it is effective in preventing seepage through the wall. The free surface OA has a shape which it would have been impossible to predict, but it was determined without difficulty by relaxation methods. The inflexion accords with Casagrande's description (Ref. 2, § F, e).

Example XXXII: Earth wall resting on a subsoil containing two different strata

200. In his last example (Fig. 108, at end of book) Shaw assumed the same depth of subsoil (down to an impermeable stratum) to contain two distinct strata, separated by a horizontal surface, of which the lower offers four times as much resistance as the upper to percolation. The shape of the retaining wall, and the level of the water on its upstream side, were the same as in Example XXXI; consequently the only difference between that problem and this comes from increased resistance to flow in the lower stratum. Example XXXII exemplifies 'refraction' at the common surface of two different materials—a matter discussed in Chapter III, §§ 80–4.

The pressure will be plane-harmonic in each of the two strata, and continuous (i.e. single-valued) at their common surface; also the velocity across this surface must have the same value on either side. The normal velocity is given (§ 192) by

$$\frac{\partial \phi}{\partial \nu} = -\frac{k}{\rho g}\frac{\partial p}{\partial \nu} - k\cos(y, \nu),$$

so at a *horizontal* common surface we have the condition

$$k_{\mathrm{I}}\left\{\left(\frac{\partial w}{\partial y}\right)_{\mathrm{I}} + 1\right\} = k_{\mathrm{II}}\left\{\left(\frac{\partial w}{\partial y}\right)_{\mathrm{II}} + 1\right\}, \tag{25}$$

w standing as in § 194 for $(p/\rho g)$, and suffixes I and II distinguishing values in the two strata. This reduces to

$$\left.\begin{array}{c} 4\left(\dfrac{\partial w}{\partial y}\right)_{\mathrm{I}} + 3 = \left(\dfrac{\partial w}{\partial y}\right)_{\mathrm{II}} \\[2mm] k_{\mathrm{II}} = \tfrac{1}{4}k_{\mathrm{I}}. \end{array}\right\} \tag{26}$$

when (as assumed by Shaw)

It is exactly similar to equation (27) of § 80 (Chap. III), so we have precisely the conditions which were contemplated in §§ 81–4, with $\lambda_{\mathrm{I}} = 4$, $\lambda_{\mathrm{II}} = 1$, $k = -3$. But the circumstances in this example are specially simple in that the net can be so chosen that one row of nodal points lies on the common boundary of the two strata, and on that account we shall reproduce Shaw's treatment (Ref. 10, §§ 14–16).

201. In Fig. 109 this boundary row is denoted by C, rows A and B lying within the medium I, and rows D and E within medium II. The wanted function w is plane-harmonic both within I and II, so at nodal points which lie inside either material (e.g. rows A, B and D, E) we have

$$\mathbf{F} = \sum_{a,4} (w) - 4w = 0 \tag{27}$$

as the finite-difference approximation to $\nabla^2 w = 0$. We now require a corresponding relation to be satisfied at points on the common boundary.

Suppose first that a row of points lies just within the medium I, as indicated by row C in Fig. 109 a; and consider the representative

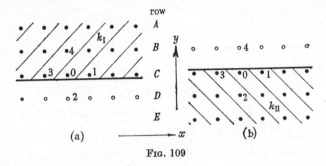

FIG. 109

point 0. Inside the shaded region w may be interpreted as the transverse displacement of a (square-mesh) tensioned net, and if this were extended beyond the common boundary to row D, w would have at the point numbered 2 a value w_2' such that

$$w_1 + w_2' + w_3 + w_4 = 4w_0. \tag{i}$$

Similarly in Fig. 109 b, where row C falls just within the medium II, inside the shaded region w may be interpreted as the transverse displacement of a tensioned net, and if this second net were extended beyond the common boundary to row B, then w would have at the point numbered 4 a value w_4' such that

$$w_1 + w_2 + w_3 + w_4' = 4w_0. \tag{ii}$$

Now let row C, in both diagrams, coincide exactly with the common boundary. Then, in the 'net analogue', this boundary becomes the junction of two nets stretched with different tensions, so w_0, w_1, w_3 have the same significance both in (i) and in (ii); but while w_2 in (ii) and w_4 in (i) have real significance, the quantities w_2' and w_4' (interpreted as above) can have other values. By subtraction we obtain from (i) and (ii)

$$w_2 - w_2' = w_4 - w_4'. \tag{iii}$$

202. We now consider the boundary condition (25) which must hold at all points of the interface, e.g. at point 0, Fig. 109, when the interface contains row C. With neglect of terms of order a^3 we can replace

$$2a\left(\frac{\partial w}{\partial y}\right)_{\mathrm{I}} \text{ at point 0 by } w_4 - w_2',$$

$$2a\left(\frac{\partial w}{\partial y}\right)_{\mathrm{II}} \text{ at point 0 by } w_4' - w_2, \qquad \text{(iv)}$$

when w_2', w_4' have the significance stated in §201; so the finite-difference approximation to (25) is

$$k_{\mathrm{I}}(w_4 - w_2') = k_{\mathrm{II}}(w_4' - w_2) + 2a(k_{\mathrm{II}} - k_{\mathrm{I}}). \qquad \text{(v)}$$

Eliminating w_4' and w_2' in turn between (iii) and (v), we have

$$(k_{\mathrm{I}} + k_{\mathrm{II}})w_2' = 2k_{\mathrm{II}}w_2 + (k_{\mathrm{I}} - k_{\mathrm{II}})w_4 - 2a(k_{\mathrm{II}} - k_{\mathrm{I}}),$$

and $\quad (k_{\mathrm{I}} + k_{\mathrm{II}})w_4' = 2k_{\mathrm{I}}w_4 - (k_{\mathrm{I}} - k_{\mathrm{II}})w_2 - 2a(k_{\mathrm{II}} - k_{\mathrm{I}}). \qquad \text{(vi)}$

Finally, on substituting from (vi) in (i) or (ii) we have

$$(k_{\mathrm{I}} + k_{\mathrm{II}})(w_1 + w_3) + 2(k_{\mathrm{II}}w_2 + k_{\mathrm{I}}w_4) - 2a(k_{\mathrm{II}} - k_{\mathrm{I}}) = 4(k_{\mathrm{I}} + k_{\mathrm{II}})w_0, \quad (28)$$

in place of (27), § 201, at nodal points on the interface.

'Free' stream-lines in hydrodynamic theory

203. Our last examples relate to 'free' stream-lines in the theory of inviscid fluids—a class of problems which is associated with the names of Helmholtz, Kirchhoff, and Rayleigh. They have been selected from a number of solutions computed by Miss G. Vaisey (Ref. 11).

The earlier treatments involved an application of conformal transformation. Writing

$$z = x + iy, \qquad w = \phi + i\psi, \qquad \text{(i)}$$

where ϕ is the velocity-potential and ψ the stream-function of the two-dimensional (laminar) flow, we have

$$\frac{dw}{dz} = \frac{\partial\phi}{\partial x} - i\frac{\partial\phi}{\partial y} = u - iv, \qquad \text{(ii)}$$

u, v standing for the component velocities. Consequently, if

$$q^2 = u^2 + v^2, \qquad \theta = \tan^{-1}(v/u), \qquad \text{(iii)}$$

so that q measures the resultant velocity, θ its inclination to the axis of x, then

$$\zeta = \theta + i\log q = i\log(u - iv) = i\log\frac{dw}{dz}, \qquad \text{(iv)}$$

—i.e. ζ, as well as w, is a function of the complex variable z. If, then, the boundaries can be specified both in the plane of z and of ζ, and if a formula is discoverable whereby either of the regions so delimited can be conformally transformed into the other, we may express (iv) in the form

$$\frac{dw}{dz} = \exp(-i\zeta) = F(z), \qquad (v)$$

and hence, by a single integration, derive w as a function of z. Now the real part of ζ has a known constant value on a boundary which is straight, and *in the absence of gravitational forces* the imaginary part of ζ has a constant value, calculable from Bernoulli's equation, along any 'free' stream-line; so the way is clear to a solution of any problem in which every part of the boundary is either straight or 'free'.

But the form in the ζ-plane is *not* known initially either of a fixed boundary which is curved or of a free stream-line when gravity is operative. As shown by von Karman (Ref. 7, §§ 6–7), we then confront (in an orthodox attack) the difficulty that the boundary conditions are no longer linear. Allowance for gravity seems to have been made in one case only—the problem of 'permanent' waves of finite amplitude.

204. As in the percolation problems of §§ 191–202, the double boundary condition here imposed at a free surface can be interpreted, according to 'Prandtl's membrane analogue', as a specified displacement resulting from a loading of specified line-intensity: on that understanding gravity effects can be included in a relaxation treatment. When gravity effects are negligible or directed along the axis, a like treatment can be applied to problems in which the flow has axial symmetry, whereas the classical method of § 203, being dependent on the theory of a complex variable, is restricted to laminar motion in a plane. In such problems (cf. § 208) the governing equation is of a type (37) which we have described as quasi-plane-harmonic. Its treatment entails no more than a slight alteration of the 'relaxation pattern', discussed in Chapter V; and on that account an axially symmetrical system (flow through an 'orifice plate') has been included (§§ 215–17) in our three examples taken from Ref. 11.

Basic theory. (1) Laminar (two-dimensional) flow

205. We have to determine ϕ and ψ (§ 203) in a field of which the boundaries are not completely specified. Such parts as are specified represent fixed and rigid surfaces on which ψ has to take constant values because the normal component of velocity (measured by $\partial\psi/\partial s$) must vanish; the other parts are not known initially, being lines of constant ψ along which the pressure p is also constant. Such lines, which we call **free stream-lines**, must be determined by calculation.

Assuming the system to be conservative, we have

$$\frac{p}{\rho}+\tfrac{1}{2}q^2+gy = \text{const.} \tag{29}$$

everywhere, by Bernoulli's theorem, when y is measured upwards from some datum level; consequently (ρ being constant) at all points where p has a constant value p_0,

$$q^2+2gy = \text{const.} = 2gy_0, \tag{30}$$

y_0 defining the highest level to which such points can extend (i.e. the 'stagnation level' at which $p = p_0$ and $q = 0$). In (30),

$$q^2 = u^2+v^2 = \left(\frac{\partial\psi}{\partial x}\right)^2+\left(\frac{\partial\psi}{\partial y}\right)^2. \tag{31}$$

206. y being measured as above, x will be measured from left to right. If now (Fig. 110) we reverse the directions of x and y,

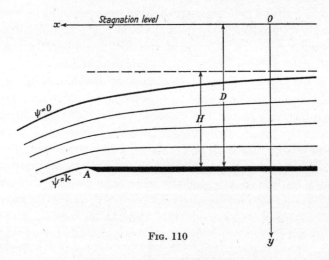

Fig. 110

measuring y downwards from the 'stagnation level' and x from right to left, equation (30) simplifies to

$$q^2 = 2gy, \tag{32}$$

and the form of (31) is unaltered. Along any stream-line ψ is constant, so q is measured by its normal gradient $\partial\psi/\partial v$: consequently on any 'free' stream-line we have the double boundary condition

$$\left.\begin{array}{c} \psi = \text{const.} \\ \left(\dfrac{\partial\psi}{\partial v}\right)^2 = \left(\dfrac{\partial\psi}{\partial x}\right)^2 + \left(\dfrac{\partial\psi}{\partial y}\right)^2 = q^2 = 2gy, \end{array}\right\} \tag{33}$$

according to (31) and (32).

207. In some problems gravity is unimportant, i.e. g may be made zero in (30). Then, in place of (33), we have on a free stream-line

$$\left.\begin{array}{c} \psi = \text{const.} \\ \left(\dfrac{\partial\psi}{\partial v}\right)^2 = \left(\dfrac{\partial\psi}{\partial x}\right)^2 + \left(\dfrac{\partial\psi}{\partial y}\right)^2 = q^2 = \text{const.} = k^2 \quad \text{(say)}, \end{array}\right\} \tag{34}$$

k^2 depending on the pressure and velocity of the fluid at entry; so again a double boundary condition has to be satisfied.

In either class of problem, everywhere, ψ satisfies the equation

$$\nabla^2\psi \equiv \frac{\partial^2\psi}{\partial x^2} + \frac{\partial^2\psi}{\partial y^2} = 0. \tag{35}$$

Basic theory. (2) Flow possessing axial symmetry

208. Here the total flow across a circular area of radius r may be denoted by $2\pi\psi$. Then, *when r is invariant,*

$-2\pi\,\delta\psi = $ *outward* radial flow through an annulus $2\pi r\,\delta z$

$\qquad = u\,.\,2\pi r\,\delta z$,   say, u denoting the radial velocity ;

and *when z is invariant*

$2\pi\,\delta\psi = $ flow *from left to right* through an annulus $2\pi r\,\delta r$

$\qquad = v\,.\,2\pi r\,\delta r$,   say, v denoting the axial velocity.

Accordingly we now have the expressions

$$u = -\frac{1}{r}\frac{\partial\psi}{\partial z}, \qquad v = \frac{1}{r}\frac{\partial\psi}{\partial r}, \tag{36}$$

and so, *if the flow is irrotational*, the governing equation is

$$0 = r\left(\frac{\partial v}{\partial r} - \frac{\partial u}{\partial z}\right) = \frac{\partial^2\psi}{\partial r^2} - \frac{1}{r}\frac{\partial\psi}{\partial r} + \frac{\partial^2\psi}{\partial z^2}. \tag{37}$$

On any stream-line ψ is constant as before, but now the resultant velocity $q\,.\, = \dfrac{1}{r}\dfrac{\partial\psi}{\partial v}$. Consequently on a 'free stream-line' we have the double condition

$$\psi = \text{const.}$$

and $\quad \dfrac{1}{r^2}\left(\dfrac{\partial\psi}{\partial v}\right)^2 = \dfrac{1}{r^2}\left\{\left(\dfrac{\partial\psi}{\partial z}\right)^2 + \left(\dfrac{\partial\psi}{\partial r}\right)^2\right\} = q^2 = \text{const.} = k^2 \text{ (say)}$ $\qquad$ (38)

when gravity is inoperative, or

$$\psi = \text{const.}$$

and $\qquad\qquad \dfrac{1}{r^2}\left(\dfrac{\partial\psi}{\partial v}\right)^2 = q^2 = 2gz + \text{const.}$ $\qquad\qquad$ (39)

when gravity acts in the axial direction Oz.

Implications of the double boundary condition

209. The constant in the first of (33), (34), (38), or (39) is equal or proportional to the total rate of flow, therefore (normally) will not be predictable but must emerge as a result of computation. For example, by attaching a value to k^2 in (34) or (38) we shall specify the total pressure-drop, which is one of the factors on which the rate of flow depends; but it also depends on the resistance offered by the fixed surfaces, and this (initially) is unknown. Equally the resistance is unknown in problems where gravity is operative, e.g. when the double boundary condition is expressed by (33): then, having specified the stagnation level (i.e. the energy of the incoming stream), we again have no initial knowledge of the total rate of flow.

Alternatively we may specify the rate of flow—i.e. impose a value on ψ for the free stream-line; but then the pressure drop is not predictable, so we shall not know what value to attach to k in (34) or (38), or the stagnation level when we are working with equations (33). Only exceptionally (e.g. for the 'Borda mouthpiece' treated in §§ 212–14) shall we be able completely to formulate the computational problem in advance: normally we shall have to proceed by trial and error, giving different values in turn to some parameter and interpolating to obtain the wanted solution.

210. On these and other accounts the relaxational attack entails too many new considerations for detailed explanation here, and interested readers are referred to the original paper (Ref. 11). 'Free stream-line' problems are among the hardest (from a purely computational standpoint) that have yet been confronted, and no routine procedure can be guaranteed to solve every example. Verification, on the other hand, is easy: it is a simple matter (though laborious) to check the solutions which follow and establish that (within reasonable margins of error) the recorded values of the stream-function satisfy both the appropriate governing equation and the double boundary condition.

In their derivation much labour was saved by a use of 'graded' nets (§§ 92–3); the reason being that because the free stream-lines curve sharply where they first leave the rigid boundaries, more intersections (with mesh-sides) are needed in such regions than in others, in order to define their shapes and (more especially) the boundary gradients with precision.

It is a feature of the solutions that they record ψ-values in all parts of the fluid field, thus enabling any required stream-line to be deduced with little additional labour. The same is not true of solutions obtained by the 'orthodox' process which has been outlined in § 203; for even when w has been derived as a function of z, much computation is necessary in order to deduce ψ as a function of x and y in all parts of the field.

Elimination of dimensional factors

211. Actually the recorded values are purely numerical, since 'dimensional' factors were eliminated at the outset. In relation to 'laminar' flow (§§ 205–7), D being a representative dimension of the rigid boundaries, 'non-dimensional' quantities x', y', v', ψ' were obtained by writing

$$x = x'D, \qquad y = y'D, \qquad v = v'D, \qquad \psi = \psi'\sqrt{(2gD^3)}, \quad (40)$$

and thereby (33) and (34) were replaced by

$$\left. \begin{array}{c} \psi' = \text{const.} \\ \left(\dfrac{\partial\psi'}{\partial v'}\right)^2 = q'^2 = y' \end{array} \right\} \qquad (41)$$

and by

$$\left. \begin{array}{c} \psi' = \text{const.} \\ \left(\dfrac{\partial\psi'}{\partial v'}\right)^2 = q'^2 = \text{const.} = k'^2 \quad \text{(say)}, \end{array} \right\} \qquad (42)$$

where $k^2 = 2gDk'^2$. In relation to axially-symmetrical systems (§ 208), D being a representative dimension as before, the substitutions

$$r = r'D, \qquad z = z'D, \qquad v = v'D, \qquad \psi = \psi'\sqrt{(2gD^5)} \quad (43)$$

left the form of (37) unaltered, and gave

$$\psi' = \text{const.}$$
$$\frac{1}{r'^2}\left(\frac{\partial \psi'}{\partial v'}\right)^2 = \frac{1}{r'^2}\left\{\left(\frac{\partial \psi'}{\partial z'}\right)^2 + \left(\frac{\partial \psi'}{\partial r'}\right)^2\right\} = q'^2 = \text{const.} = k'^2 \left.\right\} \quad (44)$$

and
$$\psi' = \text{const.}$$
$$\frac{1}{r'^2}\left(\frac{\partial \psi'}{\partial v'}\right)^2 = q'^2 = z' + \text{const.} \left.\right\} \quad (45)$$

in replacement of (38) and (39).

Equations (41), (42), (44), and (45) were employed in computation *with dashes suppressed for convenience*. Thus x, y, z, r, v, ψ in §§ 212–19 are $x', y', z', r', v', \psi'$ as defined in (40) and (43).

Example XXXIII: Laminar flow through a two-dimensional 'Borda mouthpiece'

212. The nature of the problem is indicated in Fig. 111. Fluid passing down a channel AA' develops a free surface at the edges of a two-dimensional 'Borda mouthpiece' BB'—the whole flow being symmetrical with respect to a centre-line. The (uniform) velocity far upstream of BB' is specified, also the velocity (determined by the pressure) at the boundary of the issuing jet. We have to determine the stream-function ψ, and hence the form of the free stream-line BD, given that $\psi = 0$ at all points on CC, $\psi = \text{const.}$ at all points on $AEFBD$.

This is one of the exceptional problems (cf. § 209) which can be formulated completely at the outset. Let c denote the 'asymptotic breadth' of the free jet far downstream of BB', b the dimension BB' and a the dimension AA' in Fig. 111; and assume that the fluid in contact with the closed end (EF, $F'E'$) is sensibly at rest. Then by elimination of the pressures between Bernoulli's equation and the condition for conservation of momentum (ρ being invariant) we have the relation

$$a(b-2c) + c^2 = 0, \quad (46)$$

whence the 'coefficient of contraction' c/b can be determined when a/b is known. When $a/b = \infty$, then $c/b = \frac{1}{2}$, a known result. Fig. 112 shows the variation of c/b with a/b.

213. In relation to Example XXXIII (Fig. 111), where $a/b = 6$, we have from (46)

$$c/b = 0 \cdot 5228. \quad (47)$$

The values 0 and 6, respectively, were given to ψ on the centre-line

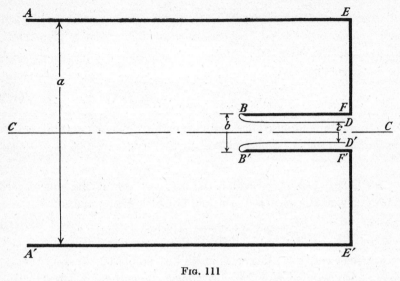

Fig. 111

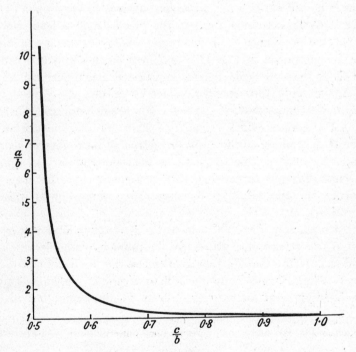

Fig. 112

and on the rigid boundary $AEFB$, and a and b, consistently, were given the values 12 and 2; so the constant in the first of (34) was 6, and ck had the value 12. Consequently k in the second of (34) had to be given the value

$$k = \frac{12}{c} = \frac{12}{b}\left(\frac{b}{c}\right) = \frac{6}{0 \cdot 5228} = 11 \cdot 4772, \tag{48}$$

and thus the computational problem was completely formulated in advance. Actually (to eliminate decimals) values of 100ψ or of 1000ψ were computed.

214. Figs. 113–15 (of which the first two are at the end of this book) present the accepted solution, in which the second of (34), viz.

$$\frac{\partial \psi}{\partial \nu} = k = 11 \cdot 4772, \text{ according to (48),} \tag{49}$$

is satisfied within 0·7 per cent. at all test points on the free stream-line. Accepted values of the boundary gradient (multiplied by 10) are recorded by numerals just outside the stream.

The range of the grading in these diagrams is very wide. Thus in Fig. 113 the mesh-side a is $\frac{1}{2}$ in the regions remote from BB' in Fig. 111, but is reduced to $\frac{1}{16}$ in a region $BabcdefB$ which, to a larger scale, is reproduced in Fig. 114; and here again the net is widely graded, so that $a = 1/64$ in the immediate neighbourhood of B. Fig. 115 exhibits the accepted values of 1000ψ, also contours of 100ψ, in this finest part of the net. The requisite gradient (49) is obtained at points which extend to within one mesh-length of B: nearer B the free stream-line has not (strictly) been determined, so is shown by a broken line. This meets the rigid boundary at a point somewhat different from what was postulated; but the error (of the order of $\frac{1}{2}a = 1/128$) is for practical purposes quite without importance.

For comparison, Fig. 114 also shows (in broken line) the exact shape of free stream-line which can be found by orthodox analysis in the case where outside the mouthpiece the fluid extends to infinity.[†] The difference is appreciable and easy to explain:—In the exact solution fluid approaches B from all directions; but in our

† Cf. Lamb, *Hydrodynamics* (6th ed. 1932), § 74. With origin at B, directions of x and y as in Fig. 110, and b and c carrying the same significance as in Fig. 111,

$$x = \frac{b-c}{\pi}(\sin^2 \tfrac{1}{2}\theta - \text{logsec } \tfrac{1}{2}\theta), \qquad y = \frac{b-c}{2\pi}(\theta - \sin \theta).$$

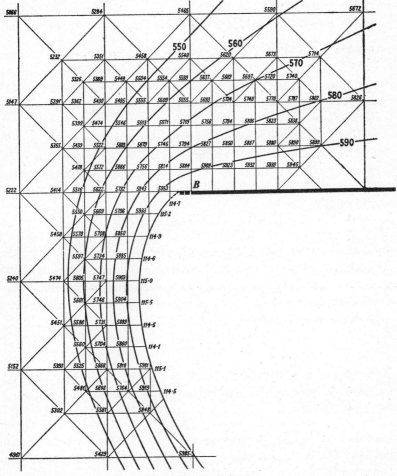

Fig. 115. (G. Vaisey)

solution it is nearly stationary in the closed end which (Fig. 113) lies to the right of B, so the velocities are directed mainly from left to right: consequently we should expect the free stream-line to turn more rapidly, at B, towards the right, and this is what has been found.

Example XXXIV: Orifice plate in a circular tube

215. In Ref. 11 (§§ 23–5) a corresponding treatment was applied to a Borda mouthpiece having the proportions shown in Fig. 111, but *axially-symmetrical with respect to* CC. This problem too could be completely formulated at the outset.

In Example XXXIV such initial formulation is not possible, for the reason that momentum considerations cannot be applied in the manner of § 212. Computation had to proceed by trial and error (cf. § 209), k being varied until a value was found such that the second of (38), viz.

$$\frac{1}{r}\frac{\partial \psi}{\partial v} = k, \qquad (50)$$

could be satisfied at every point of the free stream-line, including the point (B, Fig. 116) at which this leaves the rigid boundary. The procedure (necessarily laborious) was to start from an assumed shape of free stream-line and an assumed value of k, then to compute the 'boundary error' η defined by

$$\eta = \frac{1}{r}\frac{\partial \psi}{\partial v} - k \qquad (51)$$

and reduce it (sensibly) to zero all along the stream-line by systematic modification both of k and of the shape. For every value of k the 'asymptotic solution'

$$\psi = \tfrac{1}{2}kr^2 \qquad (52)$$

was taken as holding far downstream, where the jet becomes parallel so that $\partial \psi/\partial v \equiv \partial \psi/\partial r$: thereby (50) was satisfied downstream, independently of the value of the constant in the first of (38). ψ_B denoting this constant (so that $2\pi\psi_B$ is the total flow through the orifice) and ρ^2 the 'coefficient of contraction' (so that ρ is the 'asymptotic radius' when the radius of the orifice $= 1$), according to (52)

$$k\rho^2 = 2\psi_B, \qquad (53)$$

and hence (knowing ρ approximately from hydraulic experiments) we can, after fixing ψ_B, make a good initial estimate of k.

216. Clearly, in order that η may be given with precision, the gradient of ψ in (51) needs to be estimated closely, so the final net must have small meshes in the neighbourhood of B. In Ref. 11 the accepted solution was presented in three large diagrams, corresponding with Figs. 113–15 for Example XXXIII. Fig. 116 (a folding plate at end of book) relates to a small part of the first diagram (namely, to the region $BCDEFGB$ in the key plan in its right-hand top corner). The third diagram (not reproduced) related, similarly, to a small part $BabcdeB$ of Fig. 116, and defined the shape of the free stream-line near B. In all the mesh-side a (regarded as a fraction of the radius of the orifice) ranged in the graded nets from 1/2 to 1/64.

Along the free stream-line in Fig. 116, numerals just outside the stream record computed values of $\dfrac{1}{r}\dfrac{\partial\psi}{\partial v}$ and of η as defined in (51).

The accepted value of k was 118·34, corresponding with a coefficient of contraction $\rho^2 = (0·78)^2 = 0·61$.

217. Computation was more laborious here than in Example XXXIII, owing to the occurrence of r in equation (37) and therefore in the 'relaxation pattern'. The nature of the requisite modification was never in doubt; for an increase in the assumed value of k, unaccompanied by any change in the assumed shape, decreases η everywhere according to (51), while an increase given at some point to the radius of the jet entails a reduction at that point of $\partial\psi/\partial v$ and therefore of $\dfrac{1}{r}\dfrac{\partial\psi}{\partial v}$ and η. At neighbouring points it increases η by rendering the jet more concave: consequently errors of opposite sign could be eliminated by changing the shape of the free stream-line, errors all of like sign by changing k.

In fact only two changes of k were necessary, since the second (by good fortune) led to negligible errors at all points. Initially ρ was assumed to have the value 0·71, and this was altered later to 0·75 and 0·78 (the accepted figure). The first attempts were made on a net fairly coarse in all parts, since it was apparent that a finer mesh near B would yield for that point an estimate of $\partial\psi/\partial v$ higher by an amount fairly easy to estimate.

Example XXXV: Free jet falling under gravity ('waterfall')

218. In both of Examples XXXIII and XXXIV the jet had only one free surface,—or at least could be treated on that basis, because a line of symmetry could be taken as fixed. In Example XXXV the jet has two free surfaces, fluid being assumed to flow along a horizontal bed to a point A (Fig. 117) at which it springs clear and continues (as a 'waterfall') under the influence of gravity. The governing equations are (35) combined with the double boundary condition (41), which must be satisfied on each of the two free surfaces. On the lower of these, and on the rigid bed from which it springs, the constant in the first of (41) may be given any arbitrary value; on the other the constant must have a value determined by the total rate of flow.

Suppose the stagnation level to be specified, and let D in (40) stand for the distance between this level and the horizontal bed. Far to the right of A (Fig. 117) let $H = hD$ be the depth of the stream, so that y (non-dimensional) has the value $(1-h)$ at the free surface, 1 at the rigid bed; and let the corresponding values of ψ be 0 and C. Then the second of (41), viz.

$$\frac{\partial \psi}{\partial \nu} = \sqrt{y}, \tag{54}$$

gives far upstream of A (where the stream is uniform and horizontal)

$$\frac{C}{h} = \sqrt{(1-h)}. \tag{55}$$

Hence C is known when h is specified. It has its maximum value $(2/3\sqrt{3})$ when $h = 2/3$, and this was the assumption made in Ref. 11 (§ 33), from which Example XXXV has been taken.†

219. In computation (for the avoidance of decimals) ψ was given a value 2000 at the rigid bed and on the lower free stream-line, allowance being made for the multiplying factor when normal gradients were compared with the values required by (54).

Fig. 117 exhibits the accepted solution. The boundary gradient is required by (54) to have different values at different levels: in Fig. 117, at a number of points where the net intersects the free stream-lines, numerals show the computed values of $\sqrt{y}$ (above) and of $\frac{\partial \psi}{\partial \nu}$ (below),—both multiplied by $100\sqrt{3}$. The discrepancies are nowhere large.

† In general, C being given, equation (55) has two real roots (or none) in the range $0 \leqslant h \leqslant 1$. In the case selected these roots are equal.

'Wakes' of constant pressure

220. As has been stated earlier, problems of the types of Examples XXXIII–XXXV present exceptional difficulties to the computer. They are, however, problems which have so far proved intractable by other methods, and the labour that has gone to their solution is not incommensurate to their importance.

Indeed, in Ref. 11 solutions were presented of a *type* which apparently is new: they relate to 'wakes' or regions of approximately constant pressure, formed behind bodies in motion through a fluid which extends to infinity. When the wake is assumed to have a strictly uniform pressure, its boundaries are stream-lines which are also lines of constant pressure, like the 'free stream-lines' of Examples XXXIII–XXXV; and then, if the fluid is taken to be inviscid, the problem is of exactly similar kind. For flow in two dimensions Rayleigh, identifying the wake pressure with the 'pressure at infinity', found by the orthodox method of § 203 that a wake of infinite extent is formed behind a lamina in broad-side presentation: on like assumptions, similar results were obtained in Ref. 11 for cylinders of other shapes, also for bodies characterized by axial symmetry. But the identification of the pressures would appear to be an arbitrary assumption, not always warranted: therefore in Ref. 11 some cases were studied in which the wake pressure exceeded the pressure at infinity. It was anticipated that in these circumstances the wake might no longer extend to infinity, and that its size would contract as the pressure was increased (so as to reduce the normal gradient of ψ).

These expectations were realized, the computed wakes in rear of a circular cylinder being of the type shown in Fig. 118. A wake can have any constant pressure between the 'static pressure' at infinity and the full 'dynamic pressure' at the stagnation point A. At the higher pressure its extent is zero; with falling pressure its extent increases, the second point of bifurcation (B) moving steadily downstream. In each of Figs. 118, (a)–(d), the constant boundary gradient $\partial\psi/\partial\nu$ is stated as a fraction of the 'velocity at infinity'. Where the two symmetrical boundaries coalesce, they meet in a cusp (at B). This could have been anticipated, for if they met at a finite angle, B would be a point of zero velocity.

221. The ability of Relaxation Methods to deal with problems such as these is due to the retention, throughout their development, of a *tentative* quality which orthodox methods do not possess. There is nothing new in the notion of continued approximation to a wanted solution, for this is the basis of all 'iterative' methods of attack.

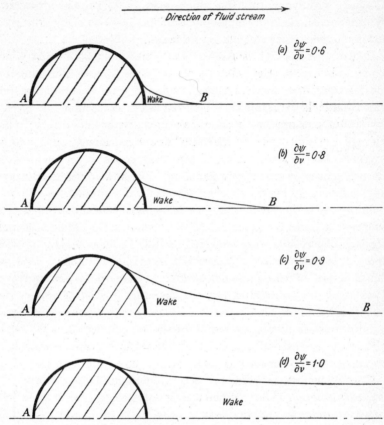

FIG. 118. 'Wakes' formed in rear of a circular cylinder. (G. Vaisey)

What is novel is the freedom that throughout is left to the computer, to decide the nature of his next step.†

† 'In fact, for the computer (as opposed to those who think only about the logic behind the computation methods) the Relaxation Method has a spirit lacking entirely from the iteration process. The former challenges one's intellect at each step to make the best possible guess, while the latter reduces one to the status of an automatic computing machine (without the advantage of no computational errors). It should not be inferred that the Relaxation Method *requires* high intellectual powers. If changes are chosen in a specifiable way, it reduces exactly to the iteration process. The computer can then vary from this completely specified process by whatever amount fits his own skill.' (H. W. Emmons in *Quarterly of Applied Mathematics* (Brown University), October 1944.)

RÉSUMÉ

222. Preceding chapters have shown the power and range of Relaxation Methods regarded as an alternative to orthodox methods of attack. Here they emerge as an essential weapon of research, effective in problems which orthodox analysis cannot even start to solve. Of such problems various examples have been treated in recent papers not yet given open publication. Those included in this chapter are characterized by boundaries or interfaces not initially known.

An interface is a boundary separating regions in which the wanted function has to satisfy different governing equations. It may be known in advance,—e.g. when it separates iron and air in a magnetic problem; but usually it must emerge as a result of computation,— e.g. in a case of plastic straining where the extent of the overstrained region is not predictable. §§ 183–90 deal with the simplest problem of this class—namely, Saint-Venant's torsion problem as modified by the existence of an upper limit to the permissible shear stress (cf. Fig. 95). §§ 191–202 deal with 'free surfaces' in the theory of percolation of fluid through porous material, showing that the essence of the problem is the satisfaction of a double boundary condition on a line initially unknown. The same is true in the (computationally) harder problem of 'free' stream-lines in the hydrodynamics of an inviscid fluid,—more particularly when these are modified by gravity. Here, quite recently, Relaxation Methods have yielded solutions of a *type* which apparently is new.

Abstraction is not feasible. But the chapter will not be read except by workers interested in its special problems, and these would not be helped by briefer summaries.

REFERENCES

1. Boussinesq, J. 1904. *J. Math. pures et appl.* (5), **10**, 11–16, 363–94.
2. Casagrande, A. 1937. *J. New Engl. Wat. Wks. Ass.*, **51**, 131–72.
3. Christopherson, D. G. 1940. *Amer. Journ. of Applied Mechanics*, **7**, A 1–4; reprinted in *Roy. Aero. Soc. Journal*, **44**, 425–32.
4. Christopherson, D. G., and Southwell, R. V. 1938. *Proc. Roy. Soc.* A, **168**, 317–50.
5. Davison, B., and Rosenhead, L. 1940. *Proc. Roy. Soc.* A, **175**, 346–65.
6. Forchheimer, P. 1886. *Z. Arch. Ing. Ver. Hannover*, **32**, 539–64.
7. Karman, Th. von. 1940. *Amer. Math. Soc. Bulletin*, **46**, 615–83.
8. Prandtl, L. 1923. *Z. angew. Math. Mech.*, **3**, No. 6, 442.
9. Shaw, F. S. 1942. *Journ. Inst. Eng. Australia*, **14**, 273–7.
10. Shaw, F. S., and Southwell, R. V. 1941. *Proc. Roy. Soc.* A, **178**, 1–17.
11. Southwell, R. V., and Vaisey, G. 1946. *Phil. Trans. Roy. Soc.* A, **240** (*not yet printed*).

FORMULAE AND TABLES FOR USE IN NUMERICAL COMPUTATION, BASED ON THE CALCULUS OF FINITE DIFFERENCES

(Extracted by permission from papers by W. G. Bickley in *Math. Gazette*, **23** (1939), 352–9, and **25** (1941), 19–27)

TABLE I. *'Three-point' Formula for Differentiation* (*cf.* § 11)

The table gives values of A_0, A_1, A_2 appropriate to the mth differential of y ($m = 1, 2$) at the point $x = ra$ ($r = 0, 1, 2$), for insertion in the formula

$$\frac{a^m}{m!} y_r^{(m)} \approx \frac{1}{2!} (A_0 y_0 + A_1 y_1 + A_2 y_2).$$

m	r	A_0	A_1	A_2	E
1	0	-3	4	-1	$a^3 y^{111} \times +1/3$
	1	-1	0	1	$-1/6$
	2	1	-4	3	$+1/3$
2	0	1	-2	1	$a^3 y^{111} \times -1/2$
	1	1	-2	1	$a^4 y^{1v} \times -1/24$
	2	1	-2	1	$a^3 y^{111} \times +1/2$

TABLE II. *'Four-point' Formula for Differentiation* (*cf.* § 11)

The table gives values of A_0, A_1, A_2, A_3 appropriate to the mth differential of y ($m = 1, 2, 3$) at the point $x = ra$ ($r = 0, 1, 2, 3$), for insertion in the formula

$$\frac{a^m}{m!} y_r^{(m)} \approx \frac{1}{3!} (A_0 y_0 + A_1 y_1 + A_2 y_2 + A_3 y_3).$$

m	r	A_0	A_1	A_2	A_3	E
1	0	-11	18	-9	2	$a^4 y^{1v} \times -1/4$
	1	-2	-3	6	-1	$+1/12$
	2	1	-6	3	2	$-1/12$
	3	-2	9	-18	11	$+1/4$
2	0	6	-15	12	-3	$a^4 y^{1v} \times +11/24$
	1	3	-6	3	0	$-1/24$
	2	0	3	-6	3	$-1/24$
	3	-3	12	-15	6	$+11/24$
3	0	-1	3	-3	1	$a^4 y^{1v} \times -1/4$
	1	-1	3	-3	1	$-1/12$
	2	-1	3	-3	1	$+1/12$
	3	-1	3	-3	1	$+1/4$

TABLE III. 'Five-point' Formula for Differentiation (cf. § 11)

The table gives values of A_0, A_1, A_2, A_3, A_4 appropriate to the mth differential of y ($m = 1, 2, 3, 4$) at the point $x = ra$ ($r = 0, 1, 2, 3, 4$), for insertion in the formula

$$\frac{a^m}{m!} y_r^{(m)} \approx \frac{1}{4!} (A_0 y_0 + A_1 y_1 + A_2 y_2 + A_3 y_3 + A_4 y_4).$$

m	r	A_0	A_1	A_2	A_3	A_4	E
1	0	-50	96	-72	32	-6	$a^5 y^\mathrm{v} \times +1/5$
	1	-6	-20	36	-12	2	$-1/20$
	2	2	-16	0	16	-2	$+1/30$
	3	-2	12	-36	20	6	$-1/20$
	4	6	-32	72	-96	50	$+1/5$
2	0	35	-104	114	-56	11	$a^5 y^\mathrm{v} \times -5/12$
	1	11	-20	6	4	-1	$+1/24$
	2	-1	16	-30	16	-1	$a^6 y^\mathrm{vi} \times +1/180$
	3	-1	4	6	-20	11	$a^5 y^\mathrm{v} \times -1/24$
	4	11	-56	114	-104	35	$+5/12$
3	0	-10	36	-48	28	-6	$a^5 y^\mathrm{v} \times +7/24$
	1	-6	20	-24	12	-2	$+1/24$
	2	-2	4	0	-4	2	$-1/24$
	3	2	-12	24	-20	6	$+1/24$
	4	6	-28	48	-36	10	$+7/24$
4	0	1	-4	6	-4	1	$a^5 y^\mathrm{v} \times -1/12$
	1	1	-4	6	-4	1	$-1/24$
	2	1	-4	6	-4	1	$a^6 y^\mathrm{vi} \times -1/144$
	3	1	-4	6	-4	1	$a^5 y^\mathrm{v} \times +1/24$
	4	1	-4	6	-4	1	$+1/12$

TABLE IV. '*Six-point*' *Formula for Differentiation* (*cf.* §11)

The table gives values of A_0, A_1, A_2, A_3, A_4, A_5 appropriate to the mth differential of y ($m = 1, 2, 3, 4, 5$) at the point $x = ra$ ($r = 0, 1, 2, 3, 4, 5$), for insertion in the formula

$$\frac{a^m}{m!} y_r^{(m)} \approx \frac{1}{5!} \left(A_0 y_0 + A_1 y_1 + A_2 y_2 + A_3 y_3 + A_4 y_4 + A_5 y_5\right).$$

m	r	A_0	A_1	A_2	A_3	A_4	A_5	E
1	0	−274	600	−600	400	−150	24	$a^6 y^{vi} \times -1/6$
	1	−24	−130	240	−120	40	−6	$+1/30$
	2	6	−60	−40	120	−30	4	$-1/60$
	3	−4	30	−120	40	60	−6	$+1/60$
	4	6	−40	120	−240	130	24	$-1/30$
	5	−24	150	−400	600	−600	274	$+1/6$
2	0	225	−770	1070	−780	305	−50	$a^6 y^{vi} \times +137/360$
	1	50	−75	−20	70	−30	5	$-13/360$
	2	−5	80	−150	80	−5	0	$+1/180$
	3	0	−5	80	−150	80	−5	$+1/180$
	4	5	−30	70	−20	−75	50	$-13/360$
	5	−50	305	−780	1070	−770	225	$+137/360$
3	0	−85	355	−590	490	−205	35	$a^6 y^{vi} \times -5/16$
	1	−35	125	−170	110	−35	5	$-1/48$
	2	−5	−5	50	−70	35	−5	$+1/48$
	3	5	−35	70	−50	5	5	$-1/48$
	4	−5	35	−110	170	−125	35	$+1/48$
	5	−35	205	−490	590	−355	85	$+5/16$
4	0	15	−70	130	−120	55	−10	$a^6 y^{vi} \times +17/144$
	1	10	−45	80	−70	30	−5	$+5/144$
	2	5	−20	30	−20	5	0	$-1/144$
	3	0	5	−20	30	−20	5	$-1/144$
	4	−5	30	−70	80	−45	10	$+5/144$
	5	−10	55	−120	130	−70	15	$+17/144$
5	0	−1	5	−10	10	−5	1	$a^6 y^{vi} \times -1/48$
	1	−1	5	−10	10	−5	1	$-1/80$
	2	−1	5	−10	10	−5	1	$-1/240$
	3	−1	5	−10	10	−5	1	$+1/240$
	4	−1	5	−10	10	−5	1	$+1/80$
	5	−1	5	−10	10	−5	1	$+1/48$

TABLE V. 'Seven-point' Formula for Differentiation (cf. §11)

The table gives values of A_0, A_1, A_2, A_3, A_4, A_5, A_6 appropriate to the mth differential of y ($m = 1, 2, 3, 4, 5, 6$) at the point $x = ra$ ($r = 0, 1, 2, 3, 4, 5, 6$), for insertion in the formula

$$\frac{a^m}{m!} y_r^{(m)} \approx \frac{1}{6!}(A_0 y_0 + A_1 y_1 + A_2 y_2 + A_3 y_3 + A_4 y_4 + A_5 y_5 + A_6 y_6).$$

m	r	A_0	A_1	A_2	A_3	A_4	A_5	A_6	E
1	0	−1,764	4,320	−5,400	4,800	−2,700	864	−120	$a^7 y^{\text{vii}} \times$ +1/7
	1	−120	−924	1,800	−1,200	600	−180	24	−1/42
	2	24	−288	−420	960	−360	96	−12	+1/105
	3	−12	108	−540	0	540	−108	12	−1/140
	4	12	−96	360	−960	420	288	−24	+1/105
	5	−24	180	−600	1,200	−1,800	924	120	−1/42
	6	120	−864	2,700	−4,800	5,400	−4,320	1,764	+1/7
2	0	1,624	−6,264	10,530	−10,160	5,940	−1,944	274	$a^7 y^{\text{vii}} \times$ −7/20
	1	274	−294	−510	940	−570	186	−26	+11/360
	2	−26	456	−840	400	30	−24	4	−1/180
	3	4	−54	540	−980	540	−54	4	$a^8 y^{\text{viii}} \times$ −1/1,120
	4	4	−24	30	400	−840	456	−26	$a^7 y^{\text{vii}} \times$ −1/180
	5	−26	186	−570	940	−510	−294	274	−11/360
	6	274	−1,944	5,940	−10,160	10,530	−6,264	1,624	+7/20

3	0	−735	3,480	−6,915	7,440	−4,605	1,560	−225	$a^7 y^{vii} \times +29/90$
	1	−225	840	−1,245	960	−435	120	−15	$+7/720$
	2	−15	−120	525	−720	435	−120	15	$−1/90$
	3	15	−120	195	0	−195	120	−15	$+7/720$
	4	−15	120	−435	720	−525	120	15	$−1/90$
	5	15	−120	435	−960	1,245	−840	225	$+7/720$
	6	225	−1,560	4,605	−7,440	6,915	−3,480	735	$+29/90$
4	0	175	−930	2,055	−2,420	1,605	−570	85	$a^7 y^{vii} \times −7/48$
	1	85	−420	855	−920	555	−180	25	$−1/36$
	2	25	−90	105	−120	−45	30	−5	$+1/144$
	3	−5	60	−195	280	−195	60	−5	$a^8 y^{viii} \times +7/5,760$
	4	−5	30	−45	−20	105	−90	25	$a^7 y^{vii} \times −1/144$
	5	25	−180	555	−920	855	−420	85	$+1/36$
	6	85	−570	1,605	−2,420	2,055	−930	175	$+7/48$
5	0	−21	120	−285	360	−255	96	−15	$a^7 y^{vii} \times +5/144$
	1	−15	84	−195	240	−165	60	−9	$+1/72$
	2	−9	48	−105	120	−75	24	−3	$+1/720$
	3	−3	12	−15	0	15	−12	3	$−1/360$
	4	3	−24	75	−120	105	−48	9	$+1/720$
	5	9	−60	165	−240	195	−84	15	$+1/72$
	6	15	−96	255	−360	285	−120	21	$+5/144$
6	0	1	−6	15	−20	15	−6	1	$a^7 y^{vii} \times −1/240$
	1	1	−6	15	−20	15	−6	1	$−1/360$
	2	1	−6	15	−20	15	−6	1	$−1/720$
	3	1	−6	15	−20	15	−6	1	$a^8 y^{viii} \times −1/2,880$
	4	1	−6	15	−20	15	−6	1	$a^7 y^{vii} \times +1/720$
	5	1	−6	15	−20	15	−6	1	$+1/360$
	6	1	−6	15	−20	15	−6	1	$+1/240$

Q

TABLE VI. *'Nine-point' Formula for Differentiation* (cf. §11)

The table gives values of A_0, A_1, A_2, A_3, A_4, A_5, A_6, A_7, A_8 appropriate to the mth differential of y ($m = 1, 2, 3, 4$) at the point $x = ra$ ($r = 0, 1, 2, 3, 4, 5, 6, 7, 8$), for insertion in the formula

$$\frac{a^m}{m!}\, y_r^{(m)} \approx \frac{1}{8!}\left(A_0 y_0 + A_1 y_1 + A_2 y_2 + A_3 y_3 + A_4 y_4 + A_5 y_5 + A_6 y_6 + A_7 y_7 + A_8 y_8\right).$$

m	r	A_0	A_1	A_2	A_3	A_4		E
1	0	−109,584	322,560	−564,480	752,640	−705,600	8	$a^9 y^{\mathrm{ix}} \times$ +1/9
	1	−5,040	−64,224	141,120	−141,120	117,600	7	−1/72
	2	720	−11,520	−38,304	80,640	−50,400	6	+1/252
	3	−240	2,880	−20,160	−18,144	50,400	5	−1/504
	4	144	−1,536	8,064	−32,256	0	4	+1/630
	5	−144	1,440	−6,720	20,160	−50,400	3	−1/504
	6	240	−2,304	10,080	−26,880	50,400	2	+1/252
	7	−720	6,720	−28,224	70,560	−117,600	1	−1/72
	8	5,040	−46,080	188,160	−451,584	705,600	0	+1/9
		$-A_8$	$-A_7$	$-A_6$	$-A_5$	$-A_4$	r	
3	0	−67,284	390,880	−1,027,768	1,606,752	−1,631,840	8	$a^9 y^{\mathrm{ix}} \times$ +29,531/90,720
	1	−13,132	50,904	−81,872	75,320	−47,880	7	−1/5,670
	2	−140	−11,872	45,864	−70,112	57,680	6	−331/90,720
	3	252	−2,408	−2,800	24,696	−38,360	5	+59/22,680
	4	−196	2,016	−9,464	13,664	0	4	−41/18,144
	5	196	−1,960	9,072	−25,928	38,360	3	+59/22,680
	6	−252	2,464	−11,032	30,240	−57,680	2	−331/90,720
	7	140	−1,512	7,504	−22,792	47,880	1	−1/5,670
	8	13,132	−118,048	471,240	−1,095,584	1,631,840	0	+29,531/90,720
		$-A_8$	$-A_7$	$-A_6$	$-A_5$	$-A_4$	r	

m	r	A_0	A_1	A_2	A_3	A_4	r	E
2	0	118,124	−554,112	1,251,936	−1,794,688	1,741,320	8	$a^9y^{1x} \times$ −761/2,520
	1	13,068	512	−83,664	154,224	−148,120	7	+223/10,080
	2	−1,044	22,464	−37,072	4,032	22,680	6	−19/5,040
	3	188	−2,736	29,232	−52,864	27,720	5	+1/1,120
	4	−36	512	−4,032	32,256	−57,400	4	$a^{10}y^{1x} \times$ +1/6,300
	5	−36	288	−784	−1,008	27,720	3	$a^9y^{1x} \times$ −1/1,120
	6	188	−1,728	7,056	−16,576	22,680	2	+19/5,040
	7	−1,044	9,584	−39,312	94,752	−148,120	1	−223/10,080
	8	13,068	−118,656	480,032	−1,137,024	1,741,320	0	+761/2,520
4	0	22,449	−147,392	428,092	−720,384	769,510	8	$a^9y^{1x} \times$ −89/480
	1	6,769	−38,472	96,292	−140,504	132,510	7	−101/5,760
	2	889	−1,232	−6,468	21,616	−28,490	6	+13/2,880
	3	−231	2,968	−9,548	12,936	−7,490	5	−7/5,760
	4	49	−672	4,732	−13,664	19,110	4	$a^{10}y^{1x} \times$ −41/181,440
	5	49	−392	1,092	616	−7,490	3	$a^9y^{1x} \times$ +7/5,760
	6	−231	2,128	−8,708	20,496	−28,490	2	−13/2,880
	7	889	−8,232	34,132	−83,384	132,510	1	+101/5,760
	8	6,769	−60,032	235,452	−534,464	769,510	0	+89/480
		A_8	A_7	A_6	A_5	A_4	r	

TABLE VII. 'Eleven-point' Formula for Differentiation (cf. §11)

The table gives values of $A_0, A_1, A_2, A_3, A_4, A_5, A_6, A_7, A_8, A_9, A_{10}$ appropriate to the mth differential of y ($m = 1, 2, 3, 4$) at the point $x = ra$ ($r = 0, 1, 2, 3, 4, 5, 6, 7, 8, 9, 10$), for insertion in the formula

$$\frac{a^m}{m!} y_r^{(m)} \simeq \frac{1}{10!} (A_0 y_0 + A_1 y_1 + A_2 y_2 + A_3 y_3 + A_4 y_4 + A_5 y_5 + A_6 y_6 + A_7 y_7 + A_8 y_8 + A_9 y_9 + A_{10} y_{10}).$$

m	r	A_0	A_1	A_2	A_3	A_4	A_5	r	E ($a^{11} y^{x1} \times$)
1	0	-10,628,640	36,288,000	-81,648,000	145,152,000	-190,512,000	182,891,520	10	+1/11
	1	-362,880	-6,636,960	16,329,600	-21,772,800	25,401,600	-22,861,440	9	-1/110
	2	40,320	-806,400	-4,419,360	9,676,800	-8,467,200	6,773,760	8	+1/495
	3	-10,080	151,200	-1,360,800	-2,756,160	6,350,400	-3,810,240	7	-1/1,320
	4	4,320	-57,600	388,800	-2,073,600	-1,330,560	4,354,560	6	+1/2,310
	5	-2,880	36,000	-216,000	864,000	-3,024,000	0	5	-1/2,772
	6	2,880	-34,560	194,400	-691,200	1,814,400	-4,354,560	4	+1/2,310
	7	-4,320	50,400	-272,160	907,200	-2,116,800	3,810,240	3	-1/1,320
	8	10,080	-115,200	604,800	-1,935,360	4,233,600	-6,773,760	2	+1/495
	9	-40,320	453,600	-2,332,800	7,257,600	-15,240,960	22,861,440	1	-1/110
	10	362,880	-4,032,000	20,412,000	-62,208,000	127,008,000	-182,891,520	0	+1/11
		$-A_{10}$	$-A_9$	$-A_8$	$-A_7$	$-A_6$	$-A_5$	r	$a^{11} y^{x1} \times$
3	0	-8,409,500	57,537,360	-187,795,260	384,555,840	-541,968,840	542,959,200	10	+16,103/50,400
	1	-1,172,700	4,490,200	-6,961,140	5,700,240	-2,435,160	-181,440	9	-41/11,200
	2	8,540	-1,266,640	4,959,900	-8,370,240	8,518,440	-6,380,640	8	-593/453,600
	3	7,900	-78,360	-832,140	3,656,400	-5,763,240	4,868,640	7	+263/302,400
	4	-5,340	66,640	-372,060	48,960	1,894,200	-3,296,160	6	-13/21,600
	5	-4,100	-50,440	292,140	-1,048,560	1,401,960	0	5	+479/907,200
	6	4,100	49,200	-275,940	968,640	-2,401,560	3,296,160	4	-13/21,600
	7	5,340	-62,840	342,900	-1,157,040	2,730,840	-4,868,640	3	+263/302,400
	8	-7,900	92,240	-497,340	1,646,400	-3,764,040	6,380,640	2	-593/453,600
	9	-8,540	86,040	-377,460	911,760	-1,171,800	181,440	1	-41/11,200
	10	1,172,700	-12,908,240	64,584,540	-193,872,960	387,902,760	-542,959,200	0	+16,103/50,400
		$-A_{10}$	$-A_9$	$-A_8$	$-A_7$	$-A_6$	$-A_5$	r	

m	r	A_0	A_1	A_2	A_3	A_4	A_5	r	E
2	0	12,753,576	−69,998,400	198,320,400	−376,761,600	510,375,600	−499,105,152	10	$a^{11}y^{x1} \times$ −671/2,520
	1	1,026,576	1,461,240	−13,536,720	28,935,360	−37,991,520	36,097,488	9	+419/25,200
	2	−69,264	1,788,480	−2,348,280	−2,108,160	6,078,240	−5,991,552	8	−31/12,600
	3	11,016	−190,440	2,394,360	−4,165,920	1,527,120	988,848	7	+29/50,400
	4	−2,664	40,320	−336,960	2,833,920	−5,045,040	2,757,888	6	−1/6,300
	5	576	−9,000	72,000	−432,000	3,024,000	−5,311,152	5	$a^{12}y^{x11} \times$ −1/33,264
	6	576	−5,760	22,680	−23,040	−241,920	2,757,888	4	$a^{11}y^{x1} \times$ +1/6,300
	7	−2,664	29,880	−152,280	462,240	−902,160	988,848	3	−29/50,400
	8	11,016	−123,840	635,760	−1,969,920	4,097,520	−5,991,552	2	+31/12,600
	9	−69,264	772,920	−3,933,360	12,064,320	−24,827,040	36,097,488	1	−419/25,200
	10	1,026,576	−11,361,600	57,234,600	−173,318,400	350,834,400	−499,105,152	0	+671/2,520
		A_{10}	A_9	A_8	A_7	A_6	A_5	r	E
4	0	3,416,930	−26,557,640	95,316,120	−208,194,720	306,006,540	−315,246,960	10	$a^{11}y^{x1} \times$ −7,645/36,288
	1	723,680	−4,543,550	13,244,760	−24,091,080	30,619,680	−28,333,620	9	−2,041/181,440
	2	50,840	164,440	−1,747,350	4,856,160	−7,313,880	7,131,600	8	+167/60,480
	3	−12,790	191,530	−539,010	363,000	635,460	−1,404,900	7	−277/362,880
	4	3,590	−52,280	388,980	−1,131,360	1,547,700	−1,023,120	6	+41/181,440
	5	−820	12,610	−97,380	524,280	−1,401,960	1,926,540	5	$a^{12}y^{x11} \times$ +479/10,886,400
	6	−820	8,200	−32,490	37,920	253,680	−1,023,120	4	$a^{11}y^{x1} \times$ −41/181,440
	7	3,590	−40,310	205,650	−624,840	1,222,620	−1,404,900	3	+277/362,880
	8	−12,790	144,280	−743,760	2,316,000	−4,845,540	7,131,600	2	−167/60,480
	9	50,840	−572,030	2,940,480	−9,132,360	19,093,200	−28,333,620	1	+2,041/181,440
	10	723,680	−7,909,640	39,230,370	−116,466,720	229,682,040	−315,246,960	0	+7,645/36,288

TABLE VIII. *Formulae for Numerical Integration (cf. § 23)*

The table gives formulae for $I_n \equiv \int_{x_0}^{x_n} y \, dx$ where $x_n - x_0 = l = na$.

E_n denotes the leading term in the error series; $y^{(m)} \equiv \left[\dfrac{d^m}{dx^m} f(x)\right]_{x=X}$ where $y \equiv f(x)$ and X is some (unspecified) value of x between x_0 and x_n.)

One-strip formula $(n = 1)$

$$I_1 = \frac{a}{2}(y_0 + y_1) + E_1 \qquad [E_1 = -y^{11}a^3/12]$$

(Trapezoidal rule.)

Two-strip formula $(n = 2)$

$$I_2 = \frac{a}{3}(y_0 + 4y_1 + y_2) + E_2 \qquad [E_2 = -y^{1v}a^5/90]$$

(Simpson's first, or One-third, rule.)

Three-strip formula $(n = 3)$

$$I_3 = \frac{3a}{8}(y_0 + 3y_1 + 3y_2 + y_3) + E_3 \qquad [E_3 = -3y^{1v}a^5/80]$$

(Simpson's second, or Three-eighths, rule.)

Four-strip formula $(n = 4)$

$$I_4 = \frac{2a}{45}\{7(y_0 + y_4) + 32(y_1 + y_3) + 12y_2\} + E_4 \qquad [E_4 = -8y^{v1}a^7/945]$$

Five-strip formula $(n = 5)$

$$I_5 = \frac{5a}{288}\{19(y_0 + y_5) + 75(y_1 + y_4) + 50(y_2 + y_3)\} + E_5$$
$$[E_5 = -275y^{v1}a^7/12,096]$$

Six-strip formula $(n = 6)$

$$I_6 = \frac{a}{140}\{41(y_0 + y_6) + 216(y_1 + y_5) + 27(y_2 + y_4) + 272y_3\} + E_6$$
$$[E_6 = -9y^{v111}a^9/1,400]$$

Eight-strip formula $(n = 8)$

$$I_8 = \frac{4a}{14,175}\{989(y_0 + y_8) + 5,888(y_1 + y_7) - 928(y_2 + y_6) +$$
$$+ 10,496(y_3 + y_5) - 4,540y_4\} + E_8 \qquad [E_8 = -2,368y^{x}a^{11}/467,775]$$

Ten-strip formula $(n = 10)$

$$I_{10} = \frac{5a}{299,376}\{16,067(y_0 + y_{10}) + 106,300(y_1 + y_9) - 48,525(y_2 + y_8) +$$
$$+ 272,400(y_3 + y_7) - 260,550(y_4 + y_6) + 427,368y_5\} + E_{10}$$
$$[E_{10} = -134,635y^{x11}a^{13}/326,918,592]$$

PAPERS, ETC., CONCERNED WITH RELAXATION METHODS

Stress Calculation in Frameworks by the Method of Systematic Relaxation of Constraints:

Parts I and II (Southwell 1935*a*): *Proc. Roy. Soc.* A, **151**, 56–95.

Part III (Southwell 1935*b*): *Proc. Roy. Soc.* A, **153**, 41–76.

Relaxation Methods applied to Engineering Problems:

I (Bradfield & Southwell 1937): 'The deflexion of beams under transverse loading.' *Proc. Roy. Soc.* A, **161**, 155–81.

II (Black & Southwell 1938): 'Basic theory, with application to surveying and to electrical networks, and an extension to gyrostatic systems.' *Proc. Roy. Soc.* A, **164**, 447–67.

III (Christopherson & Southwell 1938): 'Problems involving two independent variables.' *Proc. Roy. Soc.* A, **168**, 317–50.

IV (Bradfield, Christopherson & Southwell 1939): 'Problems relating to elastic stability and vibrations.' *Proc. Roy. Soc.* A, **169**, 289–317.

V (Gandy & Southwell 1940): 'Conformal transformation of a region in plane space.' *Phil. Trans. R. S.* A, **238**, 453–75.

VI (Pellew & Southwell 1940): 'The natural frequencies of systems having restricted freedom.' *Proc. Roy. Soc.* A, **175**, 262–90.

VII (Shaw & Southwell 1941): 'Problems relating to the percolation of fluids through porous materials.' *Proc. Roy. Soc.* A, **178**, 1–17.

†VIIA (Fox & Southwell 1941): 'Biharmonic analysis as applied to the flexure and extension of flat elastic plates.' *Phil. Trans. R. S.* C, **1**, 15–56; A, **239** (1945), 419–60.

†VIIB (Christopherson, Fox, Green, Shaw & Southwell 1941): 'The elastic stability of plane frameworks and of flat plating.' *Phil. Trans. R. S.* C, **1**, 57–83; A, **239** (1945), 461–87.

†VIIc (Allen, Fox, Motz & Southwell 1941): 'Free transverse vibrations of membranes, with an application (by analogy) to two-dimensional oscillations in an electro-magnetic system.' *Phil. Trans. R. S.* C, **1**, 85–97; A, **239** (1945), 488–500.

†VIID (Allen, Fox & Southwell 1942): 'Stress distributions in elastic solids of revolution.' *Phil. Trans. R. S.* C, **1**, 99–135; A, **239** (1945), 501–37.

VIII (Southwell & Vaisey 1943): 'Plane-potential problems involving specified normal gradients.' *Proc. Roy. Soc.* A, **182**, 129–51.

†VIIIA (Green & Southwell 1943): 'Problems relating to large transverse displacements of thin elastic plates.' *Phil. Trans. R. S.* C, **1**, 137–76; A, **239** (1945), 539–78.

IX (Green & Southwell 1944): 'High speed flow of compressible fluid through a two-dimensional nozzle.' *Phil. Trans. R. S.* A, **239**, 367–86.

X (Allen & Southwell 1944): 'The graphical representation of stress.' *Proc. Roy. Soc.* A, **183**, 125–34.

XI (Allen, Southwell & Vaisey 1945): 'Problems governed by the quasi-plane-potential equation.' *Proc. Roy. Soc.* A, **183**, 258–83.

XII (Southwell & Vaisey): 'Fluid motions characterized by "free" streamlines.' *Phil. Trans. R. S.* A, **240** (*not yet printed*).

† Treated as a secret paper during the war, but given open publication in the autumn of 1945,—too late to permit detailed reference in this volume.

Relaxation Methods in Engineering Science (Southwell 1940). Oxford Univ. Press.

Dalton, G. C. J. & Shaw, F. S. 1940: 'Note on the calculation of vibration frequencies for an aero-engine installation.' *Aero. Res. Cttee. R. and M.* 1917 (4379). H.M. Stationery Office.

Dalton, G. C. J., Shaw, F. S. & Southwell, R. V. 1940: 'Natural frequencies of vibration for a wing carrying wing engines.' *Aero. Res. Ctee. R. and M.* 1918 (4573 and 4631). H.M. Stationery Office.

Christopherson, D. G. 1941: 'A new mathematical method for the solution of film lubrication problems.' *Proc. Inst. Mech. Eng.* **146**, 126–35.

Southwell, R. V. 1942: 'New pathways in aeronautical theory' (5th Wright Brothers Lecture). *Journ. Inst. Aero. Sci.* (New York), **9**, 77–87.

'On Relaxation Methods: a Mathematics for Engineering Science' (Bakerian Lecture, Southwell 1943). *Proc. Roy. Soc.* A, **184**, 253–88.

INDEX OF PROBLEMS SOLVED

* Figs. 89–94, 108, 113, 114, and 116 are folding plates placed at the end of this book.

NAME INDEX

(The numbers refer to pages, f's indicating footnotes)

INDEX OF MATTERS TREATED

(The numbers refer to pages, f's indicating footnotes. References to definitions are distinguished by heavy type)

PRINTED IN GREAT BRITAIN AT THE UNIVERSITY PRESS, OXFORD
BY CHARLES BATEY, PRINTER TO THE UNIVERSITY